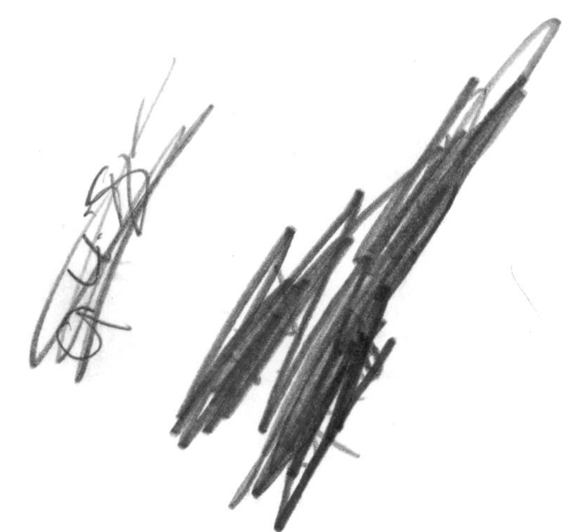

AGS

Consumer Mathematics

by

Kathleen M. Harmeyer

AGS®

American Guidance Service, Inc.

Circle Pines, Minnesota 55014-1796

800-328-2560

About the Author

Kathleen M. Harmeyer, M.S., has taught mathematics for the Baltimore County Public Schools, University of Maryland, General Instrument Corporation, and Computer Entry Systems. As a mathematics specialist for the Maryland State Department of Education, Ms. Harmeyer assisted in the development of the objectives for the Maryland Functional Mathematics Test. She is currently President of ExperTech, a multimedia training company, producing educational programs with the application of appropriate technology.

Photo Credits: pp. x, 48, 70—Jim and Mary Whitmer; p. 11—Mark Joseph/Tony Stone Images; pp. 12, 41, 310—James L. Shaffer; p. 14—Murray and Associates/Tony Stone Images; pp. 26, 66, 124, 152, 239, 297—Patterson Graphics; pp. 29, 154, 246—Comstock; pp. 75, 188, 302—Superstock; p. 76—Michael Krasowitz/FPG International; p. 89—Roger Tully/Tony Stone Images; p. 94—Keith Gunnar/FPG International; p. 98—J. B. Boykin/PhotoEdit; p. 104—Andy Sacks/Tony Stone Images; p. 115—Pete Saloutos/Tony Stone Images; p. 119—Jeff Greenberg/Unicorn Stock Photos; p. 127—Thomas Brase/Tony Stone Images; p. 138—Elizabeth Simpson/FPG International; p. 148—Mike Malyszko/FPG International; p. 165—Richard Gaul/FPG International; p. 167—Steven Gottlieb/FPG International; p. 174—Cathlyn Melloan/Tony Stone Images; p. 179—Dennis Barnes/Tony Stone Images; p. 184—Aneal Vohra/Unicorn Stock Photos; p. 209—Mark Harwood/Tony Stone Images; p. 222—Russ Kinne/Comstock; p. 228—Nancy Brown/The Image Bank; p. 255—Peter Gridley/FPG International; p. 262—Ron Chapple/FPG International; p. 274—Jon Riley/Tony Stone Images; p. 278—J. Pickerell/FPG International; p. 314—Ray Maalce/FPG International

Printed in the United States of America

ISBN 0-7854-2312-5 (Previously ISBN 0-7854-0480-5)

Product Number 91400

A 0 9 8 7 6 5 4 3 2

Contents

Chapter 3

Chapter 4

Chapter 5

Chapter 6

G LIST
SED

Chapter 1

Earning Money

Applying for a new job can be exciting. You probably have a lot of questions. What will I have to do? How much money will I make? How will I spend my paycheck? When you get your paycheck, you will probably find it is smaller than you hoped.

In Chapter 1, you will learn how to determine earnings based on different types of payment. You will also learn about several deductions that may affect the amount of your paycheck.

Goals for Learning

- To compute weekly and annual wages
- To compute wages when overtime is involved
- To determine wages for jobs that involve piecework or tips
- To compute annual salary
- To use rounding to determine salary in a pay period
- To use percents and decimals to compute commissions
- To distinguish between gross pay and net pay

Lesson 1 Wages

Hourly rate
The amount of money paid for each hour of work.

Wages
The number of hours worked multiplied by the hourly rate.

Many people are paid a certain amount of money for each hour they work. This amount of money is called the **hourly rate**. A regular work week is usually 40 hours. The money received on payday is called **wages**.

EXAMPLE Ernie works 40 hours at an hourly rate of $6.89. What are his wages?

Multiply $6.89 by 40.

$	6.89	Hourly rate
×	40	Hours
	$275.60	Wages

Exercise A Find the weekly wages for these people.

	Employee	Hourly Rate	Hours Worked
1)	Inez	$9.00	40
2)	Earl	$7.56	38
3)	Brian	$7.50	40
4)	Edwina	$8.95	40
5)	Corey	$10.57	37
6)	Cathy	$6.13	39
7)	Yoshitaka	$9.22	40
8)	Penny	$9.56	40
9)	Willy	$6.92	35
10)	Woody	$7.87	40

Lesson 2 Annual Wages

Annual wages

Money earned by an employee in one year.

Estimate

To judge the value of something without being exact.

The amount of money earned during a full year is called **annual wages**. To **estimate** an employee's annual wages, first multiply the number of hours worked each week by the number of weeks he or she works in a year. Then multiply the result by the hourly rate.

There are 52 weeks in a year. To allow for unpaid vacations and absences, you can estimate with only 50 weeks. Forty hours multiplied by 50 is 2,000 hours. You multiply the hourly rate by 2,000 hours.

EXAMPLE Estimate the annual wages of Jill Mendoza. She earns $9.00 an hour.

$9.00 × 2,000 = $18,000.00 estimated annual wages.

Exercise A Estimate the annual wages for these people.

	Employee	Hourly Rate
1)	Rod	$6.50
2)	Leroy	$7.50
3)	Tony	$7.15
4)	Mildred	$8.98
5)	Ann	$11.15
6)	Jim	$6.33
7)	Rose	$9.75
8)	Dusty	$10.25
9)	Lily	$6.75
10)	Tim	$9.65

Lesson 3 Time Worked

A.M.

An abbreviation for ante meridiem; *the hours before noon.*

P.M.

An abbreviation for post meridiem; *the hours after noon.*

Employees' wages are based on the time that they spend on the job. In these problems, note that A.M. refers to morning; P.M. refers to afternoon.

EXAMPLE Manny arrived at work at 9:00 A.M. He went out for lunch at 12:00 noon. He returned at 1:00 and worked until 5:00 P.M. How many hours did he work?

Step 1 Find the A.M. time and the P.M. time. Subtract the earlier time from the later time.

12:00	noon (later time)	5:00	P.M. (later time)
− 9:00	A.M. (earlier time)	− 1:00	P.M. (earlier time)
3:00	= 3 hours, 0 minutes	4:00	= 4 hours, 0 minutes

Step 2 Find the total number of hours worked. Add the A.M. time and the P.M. time together.

3 hours and 0 minutes
\+ 4 hours and 0 minutes
7 hours and 0 minutes

Manny worked 7 hours.

Exercise A Find the number of hours worked by each person.

	Employee	A.M. In	A.M. Out	P.M. In	P.M. Out	Total Hours
1)	George	7:00	11:00	1:00	4:00	______
2)	Roberta	9:00	12:00	1:00	5:00	______
3)	Ann	8:00	12:30	1:00	4:30	______
4)	Lee	6:00	11:00	2:00	6:00	______
5)	Kim	10:00	12:00	1:00	5:30	______
6)	Juan	9:00	12:30	2:00	7:30	______
7)	Charles	8:30	12:30	1:30	5:30	______
8)	Richard	7:30	11:30	1:00	6:00	______

The later time might need to be renamed before you can subtract the earlier time from it. Study the following example of **renaming hours**. Notice the abbreviations of **hr.** for **hour** and **min.** for **minute**.

Renaming hours
To express time in a form that is equal to the original; for example, 1 hour = 60 minutes.

Hour (hr.)
A measure of time equal to 60 minutes.

Minute (min.)
A measure of time equal to 60 seconds.

EXAMPLE Keisha began work at 8:30 A.M. She went to lunch at 12:00. How many hours did Keisha work before lunch?

A.M. — Morning

12:00 − 8:30	Rename 1 hour → to 60 minutes. 12:00 = 11 hr. 60 min.	11 60 ~~12:00~~ − 8:30 3:30 = 3 hr. 30 min.

After lunch, Keisha returned to work at 1:45 and worked until 6:15 P.M. How long did Keisha work in the afternoon?

P.M. — Afternoon

6:15 − 1:45	Rename 1 hour to → 60 minutes. Add those 60 minutes to the 15 minutes. 6:15 = 5 hr. 75 min.	5 75 ~~6:15~~ − 1:45 4:30 = 4 hr. 30 min.

Exercise B For each time below, rename one hour to 60 minutes. Add those 60 minutes to the existing minutes.

1) 4:10

2) 11:30

3) 2:45

4) 6:40

5) 2:05

6) 7:25

7) 10:20

8) 1:30

9) 12:15

10) 5:50

11) 3:35

12) 9:55

To find the total hours worked in a day, add the morning hours to the afternoon hours.

EXAMPLE Ralph worked 3 hours and 45 minutes in the morning and 4 hours and 30 minutes in the afternoon. How long did he work?

	3 hours and 45 minutes	
	+ 4 hours and 30 minutes	
	7 hours and 75 minutes	(Rename 75 min.
or	8 hours and 15 minutes	to 1 hr. 15 min.)

Exercise C How long did each person work? Rename 60 minutes to one hour, if necessary.

	Employee	A.M.	P.M.	Total Hours
1)	Thomas	3 hr. 30 min.	4 hr. 30 min.	______
2)	Lucille	4 hr. 15 min.	3 hr. 30 min.	______
3)	Reed	6 hr. 45 min.	1 hr. 30 min.	______
4)	Joan	2 hr. 45 min.	5 hr. 15 min.	______

EXAMPLE Fred worked from 12:15 P.M. to 5:15 P.M. How many hours did he work?

5:15	We cannot subtract.
− 12:15	The 5 must be renamed.

The twelve hours on a clock are used two times during any one 24-hour day. You can add the twelve morning hours to 5:15. (12 + 5:15 = 17:15) Note that 5:15 in the afternoon is the same as 17:15. Now you can subtract.

		17:15	
5:15	Add 12 hours →	~~5:15~~	
− 12:15		− 12:15	
		5:00	= 5 hours and 0 minutes

Exercise D Find the number of hours each employee worked each day. Then find the total hours for the week.

1) Nicole Green

Day	A.M.		P.M.		Daily Hours
	In	Out	In	Out	
Mon.	8:00	11:30	12:30	5:40	______
Tues.	7:45	11:45	12:15	4:30	______
Wed.	8:00	11:30	12:15	5:30	______
Thurs.	7:30	11:00	12:30	4:45	______
Fri.	8:30	12:00	1:30	6:00	______
Total Hours for the Week: ____________					

2) Jerome White

Day	A.M.		P.M.		Daily Hours
	In	Out	In	Out	
Mon.	7:00	11:30	12:30	5:30	______
Tues.	6:45	11:30	12:30	5:15	______
Wed.	6:30	11:00	12:00	4:30	______
Thurs.	7:00	11:45	12:45	5:00	______
Fri.	7:15	12:00	1:15	5:30	______
Total Hours for the Week: ____________					

Lesson 4 Overtime

Overtime

Working time beyond a regular 40-hour week.

Time and a half

Payment of 1.5 times the regular hourly rate.

Double time

Payment of two times the regular hourly rate.

People paid by the hour are paid extra for hours they work in addition to regular hours. **Overtime** is hours worked over 40 hours during a week. Work on Sundays and holidays is usually counted as overtime. **Time and a half** means one and one-half, or 1.5, times the regular hourly rate. **Double time** means two times the regular hourly rate. Time and a half is usually paid for overtime on regular work days, Monday through Saturday. Double time is usually paid for working on Sundays and holidays.

EXAMPLE Lensey earns $6.00 per hour. What are her overtime rates?

Time and a Half	Double Time
\$ 6.00	\$ 6.00
× 1.5	× 2
3000	\$ 12.00
+600	
\$ 9.000	

Lensey's time and a half rate is $9.00.
Her double time rate is $12.00.

Exercise A Complete the chart below. Find the time and a half rate and the double time rate for each hourly rate. Do not round any answers.

	Hourly Rate	Overtime Rates: Time and a Half	Overtime Rates: Double Time
1)	\$ 6.00	______	______
2)	\$ 7.00	______	______
3)	\$ 8.96	______	______
4)	\$10.78	______	______
5)	\$ 6.50	______	______
6)	\$ 8.14	______	______
7)	\$ 9.75	______	______
8)	\$ 7.25	______	______

Exercise B Time card information for twenty workers is given in the chart below. Add to find each person's total hours. Then find the number of regular hours and the number of overtime hours, if any. Remember that overtime hours are those hours worked over 40 hours Monday through Saturday. The first one in each set is done for you.

	Hours Worked Each Day							Total Hours	Regular Hours	Overtime Hours	
	M	T	W	T	F	S	S			Time and a Half	Double Time
								a	b	c	d
1)	8	8	8	9	8	0	0	41	40	1	0
2)	8	8	7	9	8	0	0				
3)	10	8	9	8	0	0	10				
4)	8	9	8	8	8	0	3				
5)	10	9	9	9	9	6	5				
6)	8	9	8	9	8	0	4				
7)	8	8	8	8	8	8	8				
8)	8	9	8	10	0	5	3				
9)	10	10	10	10	0	10	10				
10)	8	8	9	6	9	8	8				
	The following people worked on Monday, July 4. They earned double time for this holiday.										
11)	8	8	8	8	8	0	0	40	32	0	8
12)	8	8	9	8	8	2	0				
13)	10	8	8	8	8	0	0				
14)	8	9	8	9	8	0	0				
15)	8	8	8	8	8	8	8				
16)	8	10	7	8	8	0	0				
17)	10	8	8	8	8	0	0				
18)	8	9	8	8	8	5	0				
19)	8	8	8	8	9	10	5				
20)	8	8	8	8	8	0	6				

Lesson 5 Regular Wages Plus Overtime

Employees who work both regular hours and overtime may compute their total wages by using subtraction, multiplication, and addition.

EXAMPLE Penny worked 43 hours at an hourly rate of $6.24. She was paid time and a half for her overtime. What were her total wages?

Step 1 43 hours − 40 hours = 3 hours overtime

Step 2

$ 6.24	Hourly rate
× 40	Regular hours
$249.60	Regular wages

Step 3

$ 6.24	Hourly rate
× 1.5	Time and a half
3120	
+624	
$9.360	Overtime rate

Step 4

$ 9.36	Overtime rate
× 3	Overtime hours
$28.08	Overtime wages

Step 5

$249.60	Regular wages
+ 28.08	Overtime wages
$277.68	Total wages

Consumer Humor

Did you hear that John got a job at the orange juice plant?

Yes, I guess he concentrates well.

Exercise A Find total wages. Use time and a half to compute overtime wages.

	Hours Worked	Regular Hours	Overtime Hours	Hourly Rate	Total Wages
1)	42	______	______	$ 6.50	______
2)	45	______	______	$ 7.80	______
3)	50	______	______	$ 8.20	______
4)	31	______	______	$ 6.70	______
5)	46	______	______	$10.00	______
6)	55	______	______	$ 8.94	______

PROBLEM SOLVING

Exercise B Compute the total wages for each person described below.

1) Eleanor earns $8.50 per hour. She worked 45 hours from Monday to Friday.

2) Sam earns $6.00 per hour. He worked 40 regular hours and 5 hours on Sunday.

3) Kim earns $9.75 per hour. She worked 32 regular hours and 8 hours on Memorial Day.

4) Keith earns $10.42 per hour. He worked 43 hours from Monday to Friday and 6 hours on Sunday.

5) Bill earns $8 per hour. He worked 40 hours at the regular rate, 2 hours at time and a half, and 3 hours at double time.

6) Roberto earns $6.50 per hour. He worked 32 hours at the regular rate, 8 hours at time and a half, and 8 hours at double time.

7) Larisa earns $7 per hour. She worked 40 hours at the regular rate, 3 hours at time and a half, and 6 hours at double time.

8) Sung Loo worked 54 hours during a special sale at the store. Ten hours were at time and a half, and 4 hours were at double time. Her regular rate is $6.86.

9) After 40 hours of regular time, Rosemary worked 7 hours on a holiday. Her regular rate is $7.98.

10) Ben put in 60 hours at the clock store. The first 40 were paid at $9.55. The remainder was paid at time and a half.

This gas company maintenance worker receives overtime pay plus regular wages when he works late at night.

Lesson 6 Tips

Tip
Extra money given for good service.

Some workers receive extra money from people who appreciate good service. This money is called a **tip**. Examples of workers who are tipped include servers, cab drivers, porters, and hairstylists.

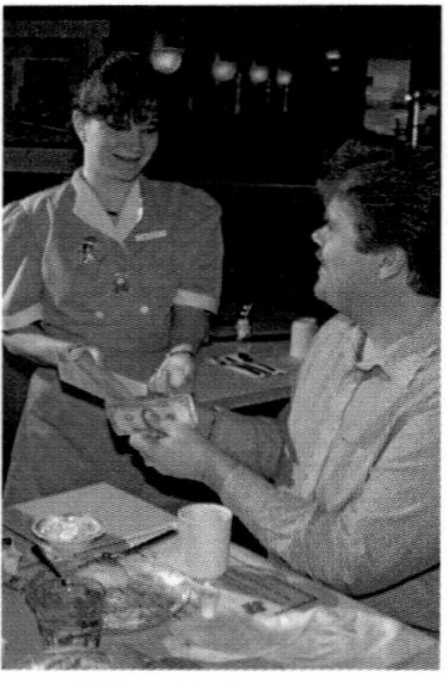
Tips are generally 15% of the total bill.

EXAMPLE Alicia is a server and earns $4.25 an hour. In one week she earned $250 in tips while she worked 40 hours. Find her total income for the week.

$ 4.25	Hourly rate	$170.00	Regular wages
× 40	Hours	+250.00	Tips
$170.00	Regular wages	$420.00	Total income

Alicia's total income for the week was $420.00.

PROBLEM SOLVING

Exercise A Solve these problems.

1) Jon waits on tables and is paid $4.25 an hour. In a 40-hour period, he earned $210.50 in tips. What were his total earnings?

2) Fred, a skycap at the airport, is paid $4.50 per hour. During an 8-hour shift, he averages $40 in tips. About how much does he earn per day?

3) Helene, who drives a cab, is paid $150 per week. She averages $20 per day in tips. About how much does she earn per week?

4) Carla, a hairstylist, received these tips one day: $1.00, $1.50, $2.00, $2.00, $1.50, $1.75, $2.00, $5.00, $1.00, $1.50, $2.00, $1.00, $5.00, and $2.00. What is the total of these tips?

5) Rudy delivers pizzas and earns $4.35 an hour. He averages about $6 per hour in tips. About how much does he earn in a 40-hour week?

Lesson 7 Piecework

Piecework

Work paid according to the number of units completed.

Some people are paid by **piecework**; that is, according to the number of pieces or units of work that they complete. For example, a garment worker may be paid by a rate for the number of collars or cuffs completed in a given day.

EXAMPLE Carl works at a garment factory and sews buttons on shirts. For each shirt he completes that passes inspection, he earns $0.24. How much does he earn for 200 good shirts?

$ .24	Piece rate
× 200	Number of shirts
$48.00	Wages

Carl earns $48.00 for 200 good shirts.

Exercise A Find the wages for each employee.

	Employee	Items Completed	Piece Rate	Wages
1)	Annette	154	$.19	______
2)	Bruce	189	$.09	______
3)	Carlos	217	$.08	______
4)	Diane	179	$.12	______
5)	Eddie	188	$.17	______
6)	Frank	305	$.07	______
7)	Glenn	147	$.26	______
8)	Hai	98	$.37	______
9)	Ingrid	156	$.08	______
10)	Jerome	178	$.13	______
11)	Ken	197	$.16	______
12)	Lisa	139	$.21	______
13)	Michael	197	$.15	______
14)	Nikki	204	$.15	______
15)	Oscar	189	$.27	______

EXAMPLE Virginia stitches complete pants. She made 10 pair on Monday, 12 on Tuesday, 9 on Wednesday, 11 on Thursday, and 15 on Friday. She is paid $5.79 for each completed pair. How much did Virginia earn during this week?

Step 1 Add to find the total number of pairs of pants.

10	Monday
12	Tuesday
9	Wednesday
11	Thursday
+15	Friday
57	Total for week

Step 2 Multiply the piece rate by the total.

$ 5.79	Piece rate
× 57	Total pairs of pants
40 53	
+289 5	
$ 330.03	Total earnings

Several people may work on one garment before it is completed. This garment worker is responsible for finishing the waistband on these pants.

Exercise B Complete the following chart. Find the total items produced and the wages for each employee.

	Employee	Daily Production					Weekly Total	Piece Rate	Wages
		M	T	W	Th	F			
1)	Arthur	8	9	8	7	10	______	$4.25	______
2)	Bernie	6	9	10	12	9	______	$3.20	______
3)	Carol	8	8	8	8	9	______	$6.22	______
4)	David	5	6	5	6	7	______	$8.97	______
5)	Eleni	10	11	9	8	12	______	$4.87	______
6)	Francine	20	20	21	20	23	______	$2.69	______
7)	Geraldo	41	37	48	35	39	______	$.78	______
8)	Hank	65	71	68	73	70	______	$.17	______
9)	Ivan	55	57	58	61	63	______	$.26	______
10)	Joan	95	89	93	87	86	______	$.24	______

Lesson 8 The Key to Rounding Money

When you multiply or divide amounts of money, the answers may have more than two decimal places. Then you usually round the answer to the nearest cent.

Key digit
The number to be rounded.

EXAMPLE Round $92.0769 to the nearest cent.

Step 1 Locate the digit to which the number is to be rounded. In this case, the **key digit** is 7. The key digit is shown in color in the example. $92.0769

Step 2 Check the digit to the right of the key digit. This digit, 6, is boldfaced in the example. $92.07**6**9

Step 3 If that digit is 5 or greater, add 1 to the key digit. $92.0869
7 + 1 = 8 ↕ 7 + 1 = 8

Step 4 Drop all the digits to the right of the key digit. $92.0769 rounded to the nearest cent is $92.08. $92.08

Exercise A Round each amount to the nearest cent.

1) $5.01785
2) $1.333
3) $3.7759
4) $2.065
5) $2.935
6) $1.1966
7) $1.2388
8) $9.8716
9) $8.259
10) $3.204
11) $7.8923
12) $29.9987
13) $2.8135
14) $91.5622
15) $9.4862
16) $3.477
17) $67.723
18) $78.647
19) $8.1672
20) $5.3691
21) $10.4856
22) $16.7203
23) $86.1193
24) $61.825
25) $22.464
26) $1.913
27) $2.0685
28) $1.8946
29) $5.3566
30) $7.345

Amounts of money may also be rounded to the nearest dime or dollar. In some cases, you may replace dropped digits with zeros to hold the places.

EXAMPLE Round \$7.8923 to the nearest dime.

Step 1	Locate the key digit. In this case, the key digit is 8.	\$7.8923
Step 2	Check the digit to the right of the key digit. This digit, 9, is boldfaced in the example.	\$7.8**9**23
Step 3	Because 9 is greater than 5, add 1 to the key digit. 8 + 1 = 9	\$7.9923 ↕ 8 + 1 = 9
Step 4	Drop all of the digits to the right of the key digit. Write a zero in the cents' column to hold the place. \$7.8923 rounded to the nearest dime is \$7.90.	\$7.90

EXAMPLE Round \$10.48 to the nearest dollar.

Step 1	Locate the key digit. In this case, the key digit is 0.	\$10.48
Step 2	Check the digit to the right of the key digit. This digit, 4, is boldfaced in the example.	\$10.**4**8
Step 3	Because 4 is less than 5, do not add to the key digit.	
Step 4	Drop the 4 and the 8. You may replace them with zeros. \$10.48 rounded to the nearest dollar is \$10.00.	\$10.00 *or* \$10

Exercise B Round each amount to the nearest cent, dime, and dollar. Write zeros when necessary to hold the places.

	Cent	Dime	Dollar		Cent	Dime	Dollar
1) \$64.526	______	______	______	**6)** \$302.1723	______	______	______
2) \$404.929	______	______	______	**7)** \$399.802	______	______	______
3) \$77.5674	______	______	______	**8)** \$90.1108	______	______	______
4) \$5.0178	______	______	______	**9)** \$1.833	______	______	______
5) \$29.9987	______	______	______	**10)** \$8.2551	______	______	______

Lesson 9 Salary

Bimonthly
Every two months.

Biweekly
Every two weeks.

Quarterly
Four times a year.

Salary
Payment of a fixed amount of money at regular intervals.

Semiannually
Every six months.

Semimonthly
Twice a month.

Some people are paid a fixed amount of money regularly, no matter how many hours they need to complete their jobs. This money is called a **salary**. People who are paid a salary are usually not paid overtime. Professional workers and supervisors in most businesses are among the employees who are paid a salary.

Salaried workers are paid regularly, but the pay periods may differ from job to job; for example, **biweekly**, **semimonthly**, **bimonthly**, **quarterly**, or **semiannually**.

How often paid	Times per year
Weekly	52 pays per year
Biweekly (every two weeks)	26 pays per year
Semimonthly (twice a month)	24 pays per year
Monthly	12 pays per year
Bimonthly (every two months)	6 pays per year
Quarterly (every three months)	4 pays per year
Semiannually (every six months)	2 pays per year
Annually (every twelve months)	1 pay per year

Exercise A Find each person's earnings per year.

1) Anita is paid a salary of $250 weekly.

2) Eddie's salary is $1,100 per month.

3) Juan is paid a salary of $625 biweekly.

4) Ms. Lisek's salary is $4,500 quarterly.

5) Glenda receives a salary of $4,792 bimonthly.

6) Dr. Lee earns a salary of $2,376 semimonthly.

JANUARY

S	M	T	W	T	F	S
					1	2
3	4	5	6	7	8	9
10	11	12	13	14	15	16
17	18	19	20	21	22	23
24	25	26	27	28	29	30
31						

FEBRUARY

S	M	T	W	T	F	S
	1	2	3	4	5	6
7	8	9	10	11	12	13
14	15	16	17	18	19	20
21	22	23	24	25	26	27
28						

MARCH

S	M	T	W	T	F	S
	1	2	3	4	5	6
7	8	9	10	11	12	13
14	15	16	17	18	19	20
21	22	23	24	25	26	27
28	29	30	31			

APRIL

S	M	T	W	T	F	S
				1	2	3
4	5	6	7	8	9	10
11	12	13	14	15	16	17
18	19	20	21	22	23	24
25	26	27	28	29	30	

Highlighted dates are examples of pay dates for
semi-monthly *bi-monthly* *quarterly*

EXAMPLE Jay makes a salary of $24,000 per year. He gets paid every two weeks, or biweekly. There are 26 pay periods each year. What does Jay earn during each pay period? Round your answer to the nearest cent.

$$26\overline{)\$24{,}000.000} = \$923.076 \approx \$923.08 \text{ (rounded to)}$$

Jay earns a salary of $923.08 each biweekly pay period, or every two weeks.

Exercise B Complete the following chart. Find the number of times per year that each worker is paid. Then find the amount earned during each pay period.

	Worker	Annual Salary	How Often Paid	Times per Year	Amount per Pay Period
1)	Pat	$26,000	Weekly	______	________
2)	Willie	$18,000	Monthly	______	________
3)	Allan	$20,000	Quarterly	______	________
4)	David	$16,000	Semimonthly	______	________
5)	Chong	$15,000	Bimonthly	______	________
6)	Ray	$38,000	Biweekly	______	________
7)	Andrew	$32,000	Semiannually	______	________
8)	Omar	$10,000	Semimonthly	______	________
9)	Wilda	$13,500	Biweekly	______	________
10)	Aaron	$14,750	Weekly	______	________
11)	Sarah	$68,580	Monthly	______	________
12)	Teresa	$29,500	Weekly	______	________

Lesson 10 The Key to Percents and Decimals

Percent (%)
Part per one hundred.

Percent compares a number with 100. **Percent** means part "per 100." There are 100 *cents* per dollar. There are 100 years per *cent*ury.

3% means "3 per 100." 3% of these dots are boxed:

Did you realize that the % symbol is actually made up of the digits in 100, a 1 and two 0s?

75% means "75 per 100." 75% of these squares are shaded:

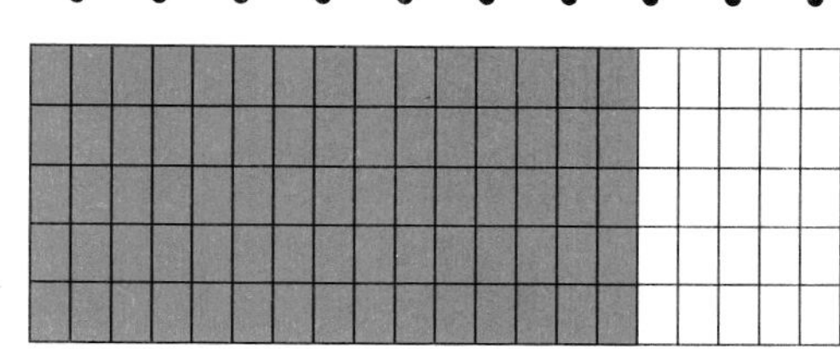

To do a percent problem, you must change the percent to a fraction or to a decimal.

EXAMPLE $3\% = 3 \text{ per } 100 = \frac{3}{100} = .03$

To change any percent to a decimal, locate the decimal point, move it two places to the left, and drop the % sign.

EXAMPLES 4.5% = .04.5 67% = .67.

Exercise A Change these percents to decimals.

1) 6%	**9)** 3.5%
2) 32%	**10)** 1.5%
3) 10%	**11)** 66.6%
4) 15%	**12)** 4.02%
5) 7%	**13)** 9.4%
6) 1%	**14)** 12.5%
7) 50%	**15)** 75%
8) 6.2%	**16)** 23.2%

Lesson 11 Commission

> **Percentage**
> *An amount calculated by multiplying a percent times a number.*

> **Commission**
> *Percentage of total sales.*

> **Rate of commission**
> *The percent used to compute commissions.*

Percentage (an amount, not a percent) is calculated by multiplying a percent by a number. Salespeople generally earn a percentage of their total sales. This payment is called a **commission.** The purpose of a commission is to encourage the salesperson to sell more goods or services.

EXAMPLE Mr. Hwang sells $24,000 worth of computer equipment. His **rate of commission** is 1.3%. What is his commission on that sale?

Commission = Sales × Rate of commission
= $24,000 × 1.3%

Change the percent to a decimal:
1.3% = .013

```
$ 24,000     Sales
×    .013    Rate of commission
   72 000
+240 00
$ 312.000    His commission is $312.00.
```

Exercise A Find the amount of commission earned by each salesperson.

	Salesperson	Amount of Sales	Rate of Commission	Amount of Commission
1)	Voeung	$3,000	3%	______
2)	Nancy	$2,478	4%	______
3)	Norman	$80,000	1.3%	______
4)	Rosa	$30,000	2.7%	______
5)	Willie	$73,989	5.2%	______
6)	Ike	$98,605	1.7%	______
7)	Saritha	$5,098	6.75%	______
8)	Sue	$6,787	1.9%	______
9)	Andy	$5,050	2.2%	______
10)	Carlotta	$36,999	7.8%	______

Lesson 12 Salary Plus Commission

Tenita sells shoes in a department store. She earns a weekly salary of $175 plus a commission of 3% on all her sales. Last week her sales were $2,248. How much did she earn?

$ 2,248	Sales	$ 175.00	Salary
× .03	Rate of commission	+ 67.44	Commission
$ 67.44	Commission	$ 242.44	Total earnings

Exercise A Find the commission and total earnings for the sales listed below.

	Total Sales	Rate of Commission	Salary Earned	Commission	Total Earnings
1)	$30,000	4%	$500	______	______
2)	$120,000	2.5%	$300	______	______
3)	$300,000	4.7%	$250	______	______
4)	$670,985	6.6%	$150	______	______
5)	$90,985	5.4%	$200	______	______

Calculator Practice

Use this method with your calculator to solve Salary Plus Commission problems.

Step 1 Key in the amount of sales
Step 2 Press [×].
Step 3 Key in the number of the commission rate
Step 4 Press [%].
Step 5 Press [+].
Step 6 Key in the amount of the salary
Step 7 Press [=].
Step 8 Round to the nearest cent and affix the dollar sign.

EXAMPLE Let's use the calculator to find the total earnings for Tenita in the last example.
Press 2248 [×] 3 [%] [+] 175 [=]
The display will read 242.44.
Tenita's total earnings were $242.44.

Check your answers for Exercise A by using this method on your calculator.

Lesson 13 Net Pay

Gross pay
Full earnings.

Deductions
Money withheld from gross pay.

Take-home pay or net pay
The amount a worker receives after deductions are subtracted from gross pay.

When employees receive their paychecks, they should know that the check does not include their full earnings or **gross pay**. Some money is withheld or deducted. Employers withhold **deductions** like federal income tax and social security payments. The worker may fill out forms to ask that other deductions be made, such as for health insurance. **Take-home pay**, or **net pay**, is the amount the worker receives after all deductions are subtracted from gross pay.

EXAMPLE Deandra earned $360.56. The following deductions were taken from her paycheck: federal tax, $46.43; state tax, $19.78; social security tax, $22.32; Medicare, $5.22; and dues, $5.00. Find her total deductions and her net pay.

$ 46.43	Federal
19.78	State
22.32	Social security
5.22	Medicare
+ 5.00	Dues
$ 98.75	Total deductions

$360.56	Gross pay
− 98.75	Deductions
$261.81	Net pay

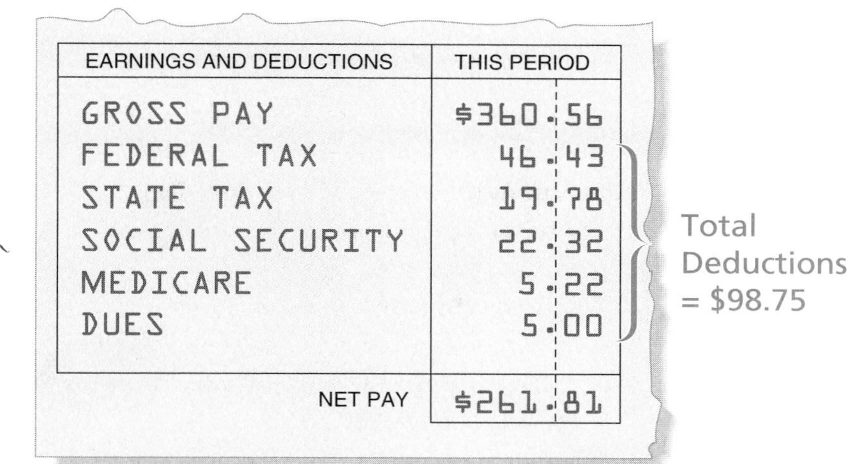

Exercise A The gross pay and deductions are listed below for five workers. Find the total deductions and net pay for each worker.

	Gross Pay	Federal Tax	State Tax	Soc. Sec. Tax	Medicare	Health Insurance	Total Deductions	Net Pay
1)	$600.00	$96.80	$32.97	$37.20	$8.70	$41.63	______	______
2)	$500.00	$60.07	$24.95	$31.00	$7.25	$39.37	______	______
3)	$403.00	$45.52	$19.62	$24.99	$5.84	$26.60	______	______
4)	$776.97	$118.62	$38.95	$48.11	$11.25	$53.88	______	______
5)	$120.75	$10.54	$6.63	$7.49	$1.75	– 0 –	______	______

Chapter 1 Review

Change these percents to decimals.

1) 43% **2)** 13.8% **3)** 9% **4)** 87.5%

Solve these problems.

5) What is the weekly wage for a person who works 40 hours at an hourly rate of $9.75?

6) What are the estimated annual wages for a person who earns $10.25 an hour?

7) A person came to work at 8:30 A.M., went out at 11:45 A.M., had lunch, came in at 12:30 P.M., and left at 5:15 P.M. How many hours did this person work?

8) Find the weekly wages for a person who earns $8 an hour and worked 45 hours from Monday through Friday.

9) A server received these tips in a given week. How much were her total tips?

Monday — $40.50
Tuesday — $32.95
Wednesday — $44.78
Thursday — $56.94
Friday — $80.42

10) A collar maker earns 0.27 per collar. If he sews 55 collars, then how much will he earn?

11) A chef earns $48,000 per year. She is paid every two weeks. There are 26 pay periods per year. How much does the chef earn each pay period? Round to the nearest cent.

12) What is the annual salary for a person who earns a weekly salary of $560.00?

13) What is the weekly income for a person who earns an annual salary of $28,500?

14) A salesperson earns a salary of $12,000 per year plus 5% commission on sales of $300,000. What is his total income?

15) A person has a gross pay of $267.99. Her deductions are $98.65, $14.77, $3.67, $.87, and $2.00. What is her net pay?

Test Taking Tip

Whenever you solve problems that involve money, remember to check the placement of the decimal point in your answer.

$4.99
DELI ITALIAN

Chapter 2 Buying Food

Have you ever thought how important mathematics skills are when you go food shopping? Think about it. You need to know how much money you have to spend. You need to know how much of each item to buy. You need to be able to read the scale at the deli counter. You also need to be able to compare the different prices of similar items. When you think about it, food shopping is a very mathematical experience.

In Chapter 2, you will learn how to apply several different mathematical skills to food shopping. You will also learn how these skills can help you make wise decisions when you shop.

Goals for Learning

- To read and compare prices
- To change prices from cents to dollars and from dollars to cents
- To compute the cost of single items and multiple items
- To compute change
- To use the information on coupons and determine the cost of an item when a coupon is used
- To compute and compare unit prices

Lesson 1 Expressing Prices

Prices may be shown in dollars or in cents. When you compare prices, you must express them the same way. Where is the decimal point in a whole number? You do not always write it, but 89 has a decimal point to the right of the 9. 89.

EXAMPLES Change cents to dollars: 49¢ = $ .49

Move the decimal point two places to the left. Remove the ¢ sign and write a $ sign to the left of the price.

Change dollars to cents: $1.19 = 119¢

Move the decimal point two places to the right. Remove the $ sign and write a ¢ sign to the right of the price.

Exercise A Express these prices as dollars.

1) 45¢

2) 25.5¢

3) 25¢

4) 139¢

5) 5¢

6) 36¢

Exercise B Express these prices as cents.

1) $ .75

2) $3.45

3) $ .80

4) $1.299

5) $ .09

6) $4.89

Lesson 2 Reading Prices

Prices under a dollar can be shown in different ways.

EXAMPLES **A)** 59¢ **B)** $ .59 **C)** .59

Price A has a cent sign. Price B has a dollar sign and a decimal point. Price C uses only a decimal point. These three prices all mean fifty-nine cents.

Produce prices are often written several different ways.

Exercise A Copy the three equal prices in each row. Do not copy the price that shows a different value.

1) 17¢	$ .17	.17	$17
2) $ .99	$99.	99¢	.99
3) .68	68¢	6.8¢	$ .68
4) $25	.25	$ .25	25¢
5) 89¢	8.9¢	.89	$ .89

Prices over a dollar are sometimes shown in different ways.

EXAMPLES $2.39 2.39 $\$2^{39}$ 2^{39}

Exercise B Copy the four equal prices in each row. Do not copy the price that shows a different value.

1) $1.09	$109	1.09	1^{09}	$\$1^{09}$
2) 4^{39}	$4.39	$.439	4.39	$\$4^{39}$
3) 3.99	$\$3^{99}$	$39	$3.99	3^{99}
4) $\$1^{69}$	1.69	$1.69	$169.	1^{69}
5) 2^{98}	$\$2^{98}$	$298	2.98	$2.98

Lesson 3 Adding Prices

Pound (lb.)
A unit of weight equal to 16 ounces.

Ounce (oz.)
A unit of weight equal to one-sixteenth of a pound.

Pkg.
An abbreviation for package.

Grocery store ads list the prices of foods. Prices may be shown in different ways. Notice the abbreviations **lb.** and **oz.** (for **pound** and **ounce**) used in the sample ad shown below. **Pkg.** is an abbreviation for package.

opened with a win, the Spring Valley Tigers squandered a 14-6 lead.

election, Smith has not visited Maine once. He plans a trip in October.

SAVE This Week at

Friendly Foods

Grapes	lb.	\$ 1.99
Dill Pickles	32-oz. jar	\$ 4.39
Corn Flakes	18-oz. pkg.	\$ 3.57
Rye Bread	16-oz. loaf	\$ 2.49
Boneless Ham	lb.	\$ 5.09
Swiss Cheese	lb.	\$ 6.39

Prices good through week ending 8/5

EXAMPLE Suki wants to buy a pound of Swiss cheese and a loaf of rye bread. How much will these two items cost together?

Step 1 Write a decimal in each price.
Swiss cheese, 6^{39} → $6.39
Rye bread, 2^{49} → $2.49

Step 2 Line up the decimal points.
$6.39
2.49

Step 3 Add the two prices.

$ 6.39	Price of Swiss cheese
+2.49	Price of rye bread
$ 8.88	Total cost

Exercise A From the ad, find the price for each food item listed below. Then find the total cost of each group of items.

1) 1 lb. grapes
1 lb. ham

2) 1 loaf rye bread
1 lb. ham
1 pkg. corn flakes

3) 1 pkg. corn flakes
1 jar pickles

4) 2 lb. grapes
2 jars pickles
2 lb. Swiss cheese

5) 1 lb. ham
1 lb. Swiss cheese

6) 1 lb. grapes
1 jar pickles
1 pkg. corn flakes
1 loaf rye bread
2 lb. ham
2 lb. Swiss cheese

Lesson 4 Computing Change

Read the following sample ad from a food store.

GOOD FOOD STORE

Rice	24-oz. pkg.	$\$2^{39}$
Wheat Bread	16-oz. loaf	89¢
English Muffins	pkg. of 6	99¢
	pkg. of 12	$\$1^{69}$
Waffles	10-oz. pkg.	$\$1^{15}$

Item	Size	Price	Item	Size	Price
Eggs	doz.	$\$1^{39}$	**Mustard**	6-oz. jar	55¢
Milk	gal.	$\$2^{37}$	**Chicken**	lb.	$\$2^{19}$
Lunch Meat	8-oz. pkg.	$\$3^{79}$	**Bean Soup**	8 10-oz. cans	$\$4^{49}$
Ravioli	13-oz. pkg.	$\$2^{49}$	**Apples**	lb.	$\$1^{79}$

EXAMPLES

John goes to the Good Food Store and buys one dozen eggs and one pound of apples. What is the total cost?

Add.	$ 1.39	Eggs
	+1.79	Apples
	$ 3.18	Total cost

John gives the cashier a $10.00 bill. How much change should the cashier give John?

Subtract.	$10.00	Given to cashier
	− 3.18	Cost of groceries
	$ 6.82	Change

Exercise A Check the correct prices from the ad for the Good Food Store. Find the total cost of each list of groceries. Then find the change that each shopper should get from a $20.00 bill. Notice the abbreviations **gal.** and **doz.** (for **gallon** and **dozen**) used in these lists.

Gallon (gal.)
A unit of capacity equal to four quarts.

Dozen (doz.)
A group of 12.

1) 1 pkg. ravioli
8 cans soup
1 lb. apples
1 loaf bread
1 doz. eggs

2) 2 gal. milk
16 cans soup
2 loaves of bread

3) 2 pkg. rice
2 gal. milk

4) 1 pkg. 6 muffins
2 jars mustard
1 loaf bread

5) 16 cans soup
1 pkg. waffles
1 gal. milk

6) 2 lb. apples
1 pkg. ravioli
2 doz. eggs
1 pkg. rice

7) 1 jar mustard
1 pkg. 12 muffins
1 pkg. lunch meat
1 gal. milk
2 doz. eggs

8) 2 lb. apples
1 gal. milk
1 pkg. rice

9) 1 pkg. 6 muffins
1 pkg. ravioli
1 lb. chicken

10) 1 pkg. lunch meat
1 doz. eggs
1 lb. apples

11) 2 loaves of bread
2 pkg. waffles
1 pkg. rice

12) 1 pkg. 12 muffins
8 cans soup
2 lb. chicken
2 pkg. lunch meat

Lesson 5 Coupons

Food companies and stores often offer money-off coupons to encourage sales. Study the following example.

EXAMPLE The price of Granny's Pancake Mix is $2.29. Sarah has a coupon worth 25¢. How much will she pay for the pancake mix?

Subtract.	$2.29	Price marked
	− .25	Coupon
	$2.04	Cost with coupon

Exercise A For each item below, find the cost if a coupon is used.

	Item	Price Marked	Coupon Value
1)	Cereal	$3.49	15¢
2)	Margarine	$1.29	40¢
3)	Popcorn	$2.75	13¢
4)	Frozen vegetables	$1.99	10¢
5)	Frozen yogurt	$3.79	25¢
6)	Mayonnaise	$1.65	20¢
7)	Crackers	$1.95	12¢
8)	Spaghetti sauce	$2.09	40¢
9)	Orange juice	$2.19	25¢
10)	Cheese	$1.79	15¢

Lesson 6 Coupons for More Than One

Several different types of coupons are offered. Some coupons are good only when the shopper buys more than one item.

EXAMPLE Mike has a coupon that offers a savings of 80¢ on any two Hearty Frozen Dinners. Each dinner is marked \$3.89. How much will the two dinners cost with the coupon?

Step 1 Multiply

\$3.89	Price of 1 dinner
× 2	
\$7.78	Price of 2 dinners

Step 2 Subtract

\$7.78	Price of 2 dinners
− .80	Value of coupon
\$6.98	Cost when coupon is used

Exercise A For each set of items, find the cost when a coupon is used.

	Item	Price for 1 Item	Coupon Value
1)	Canned fruit	\$2.29	25¢ on 2 cans
2)	Tuna fish	\$1.29	25¢ on 3 cans
3)	Evaporated milk	\$ .69	35¢ on 4 cans
4)	Grape juice	\$ .89	20¢ on 2 bottles
5)	Soup mix	\$1.19	40¢ on 6 boxes
6)	Stuffing mix	\$2.09	30¢ on 3 boxes
7)	Instant coffee	\$4.19	80¢ on 2 jars
8)	Jelly	\$2.79	35¢ on 2 jars
9)	Peanut butter	\$4.15	80¢ on 2 jars
10)	Salad dressing	\$1.59	12¢ on 2 bottles

Lesson 7 Coupons With Conditions

Some coupons can only be used when certain conditions are met. Here is a sample of this type of coupon. Read the conditions.

Exercise A Answer these questions about the coupon for Cruncho Pickles.

1) What is the value of the coupon?

2) What product is the coupon good for?

3) How many items must you buy to use the coupon?

4) What size must the items be?

5) May the customer use two coupons to buy four items?

6) What is the last day that this coupon may be used?

Exercise B Now answer the six questions above for this mayonnaise coupon.

Lesson 8 Expiration Dates

Expiration date
The point at which something ends.

Expires
Comes to an end.

Many store coupons can be used for only a limited time. The **expiration date** shows when the coupon offer **expires**, or comes to an end.

EXAMPLE Heather cut from the newspaper a Cruncho coupon like the one shown on page 36. If the date is October 2, 1998, how much longer may she use the coupon? Since October has just begun, count October as one month. Count one month each for November, December, and January. Heather has 4 months in which to use the coupon: October 2, 1998, to January 31, 1999.

JANUARY

S	M	T	W	T	F	S
				1	2	3
4	5	6	7	8	9	10
11	12	13	14	15	16	17
18	19	20	21	22	23	24
25	26	27	28	29	30	31

FEBRUARY

S	M	T	W	T	F	S
1	2	3	4	5	6	7
8	9	10	11	12	13	14
15	16	17	18	19	20	21
22	23	24	25	26	27	28

MARCH

S	M	T	W	T	F	S
1	2	3	4	5	6	7
8	9	10	11	12	13	14
15	16	17	18	19	20	21
22	23	24	25	26	27	28
29	30	31				

APRIL

S	M	T	W	T	F	S
			1	2	3	4
5	6	7	8	9	10	11
12	13	14	15	16	17	18
19	20	21	22	23	24	25
26	27	28	29	30		

MAY

S	M	T	W	T	F	S
					1	2
3	4	5	6	7	8	9
10	11	12	13	14	15	16
17	18	19	20	21	22	23
24	25	26	27	28	29	30
31						

JUNE

S	M	T	W	T	F	S
	1	2	3	4	5	6
7	8	9	10	11	12	13
14	15	16	17	18	19	20
21	22	23	24	25	26	27
28	29	30				

JULY

S	M	T	W	T	F	S
			1	2	3	4
5	6	7	8	9	10	11
12	13	14	15	16	17	18
19	20	21	22	23	24	25
26	27	28	29	30	31	

AUGUST

S	M	T	W	T	F	S
						1
2	3	4	5	6	7	8
9	10	11	12	13	14	15
16	17	18	19	20	21	22
23	24	25	26	27	28	29
30	31					

SEPTEMBER

S	M	T	W	T	F	S
		1	2	3	4	5
6	7	8	9	10	11	12
13	14	15	16	17	18	19
20	21	22	23	24	25	26
27	28	29	30			

OCTOBER

S	M	T	W	T	F	S
				1	2	3
4	5	6	7	8	9	10
11	12	13	14	15	16	17
18	19	20	21	22	23	24
25	26	27	28	29	30	31

NOVEMBER

S	M	T	W	T	F	S
1	2	3	4	5	6	7
8	9	10	11	12	13	14
15	16	17	18	19	20	21
22	23	24	25	26	27	28
29	30					

DECEMBER

S	M	T	W	T	F	S
		1	2	3	4	5
6	7	8	9	10	11	12
13	14	15	16	17	18	19
20	21	22	23	24	25	26
27	28	29	30	31		

Exercise A How much longer may each coupon be used?

	Current Date	Expiration Date on Coupon
1)	September 15, 1999	July 31, 2000
2)	January 1, 2000	May 31, 2000
3)	February 6, 1997	April 30, 1997
4)	April 10, 1998	September 15, 1998
5)	August 15, 1997	August 30, 1997
6)	December 1, 1998	February 28, 1999
7)	November 2, 1999	March 10, 2000
8)	June 30, 1997	December 31, 1997

Lesson 9 Finding the Cost of One

To encourage shoppers to buy more items, food stores often mark a single price for two items. Study the following example.

EXAMPLE Jim wants one box of pudding. How much will it cost?

Divide.

$$
\begin{array}{r}
49\tfrac{1}{2}¢ \\
2\,\overline{)\,99¢} \\
\underline{-8} \\
19 \\
\underline{-18} \\
1
\end{array}
$$

The store charges a full penny for any fraction of a cent. One single box of pudding will cost Jim 50¢.

What is the benefit of buying two boxes of pudding at the same time? Compare the following two ways of buying this product.

EXAMPLE Which price gives Jim a savings?

$ .50	One single box	$1.00	Two single boxes
× 2		− .99	Two boxes together
$1.00	Two single boxes	$ .01	Savings

When stores mark a single price for the purchase of two items, it is often helpful to compare prices. If Jim buys two single boxes of pudding at different times, he will pay 50¢ each, or a total of $1.00. If he buys two boxes of pudding at the same time, he will pay only 99¢, a savings of 1¢.

Any number of items may be offered for one price. Study the following example. How does the cost of buying one item compare to the cost of buying three items at the same time?

EXAMPLE

Kelly wants only one green pepper. The price is 3 for $1.48. How much will one pepper cost?

Divide. $3 \overline{)\$1.48}$ = $ $.49\frac{1}{3}$ or $49\frac{1}{3}$¢

One pepper will cost 50¢.

How much will three peppers cost if they are bought at different times?

Multiply. $ .50 One single pepper
× 3
$1.50 Three single peppers

How much do you save by buying the three peppers at the same time?

Subtract. $1.50 − $1.48 = $ .02 or 2¢ Savings

Exercise A Copy this chart. Fill in the missing information.

	Price	Cost of One Item	Total Cost of Single Items	Savings by Buying Items at the Same Time
1)	2/49¢	______	______	______
2)	2/99¢	______	______	______
3)	5/99¢	______	______	______
4)	3/$1.29	______	______	______
5)	7/89¢	______	______	______
6)	12/$1.00	______	______	______
7)	5/$1.00	______	______	______
8)	6/99¢	______	______	______
9)	8/$1.39	______	______	______

Lesson 10 The Key to Using the Word "Per"

Per

For each or for one; for example, miles per gallon.

The word **per** means "for each" or "for one." When used in an expression *per* means division. You can always replace the word *per* with the words "divided by." Study the following examples.

EXAMPLES

A. miles per gallon =
miles divided by gallons = $\text{gallons}\overline{)\text{miles}}$

B. cost per ounce =
cost divided by ounces = $\text{ounces}\overline{)\text{cost}}$

C. 5 percent = $\quad .05$
5 divided by 100 = $100\overline{)5.00}$

(Remember that percent means "per hundred.")

Exercise A Rewrite each of the following expressions. Use the words "divided by." Then set up the division problem. Look at the examples on the top of this page.

1) miles per hour
2) 6 percent
3) feet per minute
4) cost per dozen
5) 15%
6) 17%
7) miles per minute
8) cost per inch
9) attendance per game
10) miles per trip
11) newspapers per day
12) inches per second
13) cost per pound
14) gallons per week

Exercise B Follow the same directions as in Exercise A.

1) cost per liter

2) kilometers per liter

3) cost per kilogram

4) meters per second

5) liters per week

6) kilometers per year

Consumer Humor

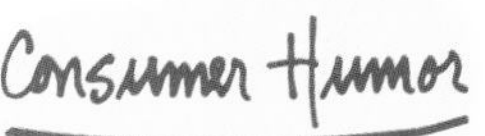

Millie is truly dedicated to thinking metric.

She even eats graham crackers.

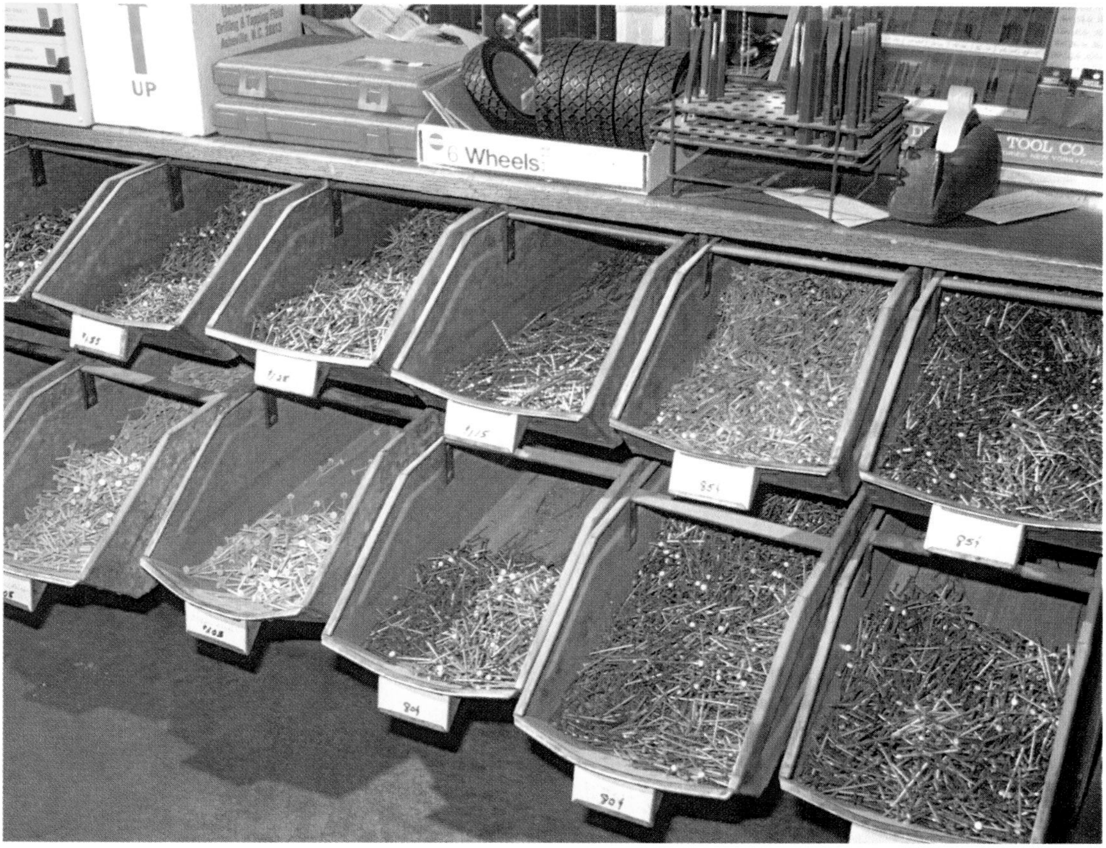

Nails and other loose hardware are sold at a price per pound.

Lesson 11 Unit Price

Unit price
The cost of one unit of something.

The **unit price** is the cost of one unit of something. The unit price may be the cost per ounce, cost per pound, cost per item, or any other unit. The word *per* tells us to divide.

EXAMPLE A package of ground beef weighs 0.85 lb. The price marked is \$2.69. What is the unit price or the cost per pound?

pounds) cost

Note that you must move the decimal point so that you can divide by a whole number.

```
        3.164 ≈ 3.16
.85. ) 2.69.000
      -2 55
        14 0
        -8 5
         5 50
        -5 10
          400
         -340
```

Round your answer to the nearest cent.
$3.164 \approx 3.16$

The unit price is \$3.16 per pound.

Exercise A Find the unit price for each item listed. Round your answer to the nearest cent.

	Price	Item	Unit	Unit Price
1)	\$25.00	24 doz. eggs	dozen	____
2)	\$2.29	6 bagels	bagel	____
3)	\$3.09	8 oz. granola bars	ounce	____
4)	\$3.79	1.5 lb. cat food	pound	____
5)	\$2.85	5 oz. cheese	ounce	____
6)	\$2.43	1 gal. milk	gallon	____
7)	\$1.79	3 lb. apples	pound	____
8)	\$2.29	12 oz. crackers	ounce	____

Calculator Practice Use this method with your calculator to solve Unit Price problems.

Step 1 Key in the cost of the package.

Step 2 Press ÷.

Step 3 Key in the number of units.

Step 4 Press =.

Step 5 Round the answer to the nearest cent and affix the dollar sign or the cents sign.

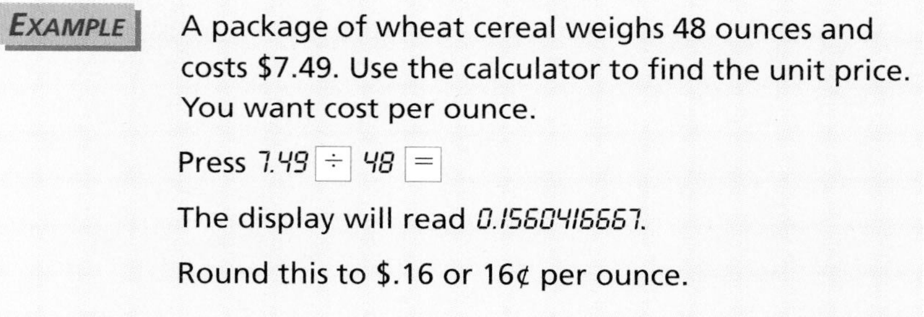

EXAMPLE A package of wheat cereal weighs 48 ounces and costs \$7.49. Use the calculator to find the unit price. You want cost per ounce.

Press 7.49 ÷ 48 =

The display will read 0.1560416667.

Round this to \$.16 or 16¢ per ounce.

Use this method to check your work in Exercise A.

Lesson 12 Comparing Unit Prices

Sometimes shoppers compare different products to decide the best buy. For example, some items may be different in size:

Brand A weighs 6.5 oz.	It sells for 98¢.
Brand B weighs 12.5 oz.	It sells for $2.19.

Which size has the lower unit price? Study the example shown below.

EXAMPLE Divide the cost by the number of ounces in each brand to find the unit price of both Brand A and Brand B. You can then compare these unit prices to determine which brand has the lower unit price.

Brand	Size	Cost	Unit Price
A	6.5 oz.	$ .98	6.5.) $.9.800 = $.150 per oz.
B	12.5 oz.	$2.19	12.5.) $2.1.900 = $.175 per oz.

Brand A, the 6.5 oz. size, has the lower unit price.

Brand name

A characteristic or distinctive kind.

You may compare different brand names and sizes. A **brand name** identifies a product as being made by a single company or manufacturer. Compare the unit prices of Brands A, B, and C.

EXAMPLE

Brand	Size	Cost	Unit Price
A	12.5 oz.	$2.19	12.5.) $2.1.900 = $.175 per oz.
B	9.25 oz.	$1.49	9.25.) $1.49.000 = $.161 per oz.
C	9.25 oz.	$1.89	9.25.) $1.89.000 = $.204 per oz.

The 9.25 oz. size of Brand B has the lowest unit price.

Remember that sometimes you must consider quality when deciding on the best buy. Paying less money for food that you do not like is not a bargain.

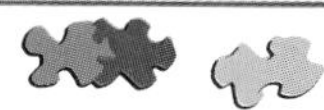

Exercise A Find the lowest unit price for each set of items.

1)	Rice cereals: Size: Price: Cost per ounce:	A 17 oz. $3.89 ________	B 16 oz. $3.29 ________	C 13 oz. $3.59 ________	
2)	Lemonade: Size: Price: Cost per quart:	A 2 qt. $1.53 ________	B 2 qt. $1.03 ________	C 2.5 qt. $2.01 ________	D 2.75 qt. $2.71 ________
3)	Tortilla chips: Size: Price: Unit price:	A 7 oz. $1.29 ________	B 18 oz. $2.09 ________	C 11 oz. $1.59 ________	D 4 oz. $ .99 ________
4)	Cheese pizzas: Size: Price: Unit price:	A 6.5 oz. $1.99 ________	B 7 oz. $2.49 ________	C 8 oz. $3.29 ________	D 19 oz. $4.39 ________

Chapter 2 Review

Review your ability to read and express prices.

1) Express this price in dollars: 7¢

2) Express this price in cents: $.89

Solve these problems.

3) In the newspaper ad for a local food store, oranges are marked 4/99. What is the price of one orange? What is the price of 8 oranges?

4) You want to buy a stuffing mix. You have a $5 bill. There are three brands of stuffing mix available:

   a) Cook Top Stuffing Mix
   6 oz. for $1.49 or 12 oz. for $2.99

   b) Saltridge Farms Stuffing Mix
   6 oz. for $1.79

   c) Cousin Ben's Stuffing Mix
   6 oz. for $1.29

   You like the flavor of all three brands. However, you have a 10¢ off coupon for Cook Top Stuffing Mix.

   Find the best buy. Then compute your change.

5) You need some peanut butter.

You have a 40¢ off coupon for Creemy Peanut Butter. This coupon is good for one 40 oz. jar, or one 28 oz. jar, or two 18 oz. jars, or two 12 oz. jars.

The prices for Creemy Peanut Butter are:

12 oz. jar $2.85
18 oz. jar $3.49
28 oz. jar.................$5.15
40 oz. jar.................$6.29

What is the best buy? It may help to organize your work this way:

Size	Jars Needed	Cost per Jar	Total Cost	Cost with Coupon	Total Ounces	Cost per Ounce

Test Taking Tip Check the reasonableness of your answers by rounding and estimating.

SALE
50%OFF

Chapter 3 Shopping for Clothes

There are many different ways to shop for clothes. You can buy them in a small shop or in a huge department store. You can use a mail order catalog or make a telephone call to a home shopping television channel. You may even buy materials to make your own clothes. Regardless of how you buy your clothes, you always try to find the best items for the best possible price.

In Chapter 3, you will learn about several different ways to purchase clothing. You also learn how you can save money through sales and discounts.

Goals for Learning

- To compute the cost of clothing, including sales tax
- To determine the amount of money saved due to sale prices and discounts
- To read catalog descriptions and order from a catalog
- To find the amount of fabric needed to make clothing
- To compute the balance of a charge account
- To determine a payment schedule for a layaway plan

Lesson 1 Ready-to-Wear

Shirt	$21.95
Vest	$35
Socks	$1.79 pair
Jeans	$31.95

These clothing items are on sale at a department store. Read the price for each item. Then study the example.

EXAMPLE Jack needs clothes for school. He plans to buy 5 pairs of socks, 2 pairs of jeans, 2 shirts, and 1 vest. Look at the prices for these items. What is the total cost?

To find the total, make a list like the one shown below. The symbol @ means **at** and indicates unit price (the cost of one unit of something; for example, one sweater or one pair of socks). Multiply the number of items by the unit price. Line up the decimal points. Add to find the total cost.

At (@)

A term and symbol used to indicate unit price.

socks	5	@	$ 1.79	=	$ 8.95	
jeans	2	@	$31.95	=	63.90	
shirts	2	@	$21.95	=	43.90	
vest	1	@	$35.00	=	+ 35.00	
					$151.75	Cost of clothes

In many states, a **sales tax** is computed on the sale of goods and services. Jack has to pay a sales tax of 5%. How much is the tax? What is the total amount that Jack will pay?

Sales tax

A tax figured as a percentage of the purchase price and collected by the seller.

EXAMPLE To compute sales tax, multiply the cost by the rate. Round to the nearest cent.

$151.75 × 5%
(Remember that 5% = .05)

$151.75	Cost of clothes
× .05	Tax rate
$7.5875	≈ $7.59 Sales tax (nearest cent)

Add the sales tax to the cost to find the total amount Jack will pay.

$151.75	Cost of clothes
+ 7.59	Sales tax
$159.34	Total amount

Exercise A Find the cost of each set of purchases. Find the sales tax. Then add the sales tax to the cost to find the total amount paid.

	Consumer	Purchases	Cost	Sales Tax		Total Amount Paid
1)	Cyrus	Shirt, $19.95 Jeans, $39.99	_____	5%	_____	_____
2)	Pedro	3 pr. socks @ $1.99 pr. Jacket, $64.59	_____	6%	_____	_____
3)	Alma	Shoes, $47.99 3 pr. stockings @ $3.59	_____	4%	_____	_____
4)	Huijing	Dress, $25.99 2 sweaters @ $20.90 ea.	_____	5%	_____	_____
5)	Zoe	Suit, $84.90 2 shirts @ $21.95	_____	7%	_____	_____
6)	Delia	Down-filled vest, $95.00 Flannel shirt, $24.99	_____	5%	_____	_____
7)	Katarina	Nightgown, $29.50 Slippers, $22.90 Robe, $49.80	_____	3%	_____	_____
8)	Felix	Boots, $67.00 Overcoat, $139.99	_____	None	_____	_____
9)	Roy	2 pr. pajamas @ $29.99 Robe, $75.00	_____	8%	_____	_____
10)	Andrea	Cashmere coat, $359.99 Calfskin boots, $175.00	_____	7%	_____	_____

Lesson 2 Sale Prices

Merchants often sell items at reduced prices. A careful shopper watches for these sales because they could provide good bargains.

EXAMPLE A pair of jeans regularly sells for $54.99. They are now on sale for $46.75. How much is saved by buying the jeans on sale?

To find the amount saved, subtract the sale price from the regular price. The regular price is the original or usual price of the item.

$$\begin{array}{rl} \$\ 54.99 & \text{Regular price} \\ -\ 46.75 & \text{Sale price} \\ \hline \$\ \ 8.24 & \text{Amount saved} \end{array}$$

Exercise A Find the amount saved on each item by using the sale price. Subtract to find the answer in each case.

	Item	Regular Price	Sale Price	Amount Saved
1)	Dress	$60.00	$52.99	______
2)	Belt	$17.50	$15.99	______
3)	Coat	$125.00	$95.90	______
4)	Shoes	$35.80	$29.95	______
5)	Gloves	$15.00	$12.59	______
6)	Socks	$3.29	$1.79	______
7)	Sweater	$65.90	$56.95	______
8)	Shirt	$25.00	$19.65	______
9)	Pants	$41.00	$35.89	______
10)	Suit	$200.00	$179.98	______

Lesson 3 Percent Saved

Sometimes you may want to know what percent of the regular price is saved on a sale item. To find the percent saved, divide the amount saved by the regular price. Then change the decimal to a percent.

EXAMPLE A pair of jeans regularly sells for $54.99. $8.24 is saved by using the sale price. To find the percent saved, divide the amount saved, $8.24, by the regular price, $54.99.

regular price $\overline{)\text{amount saved}}$ 54.99 $\overline{)8.24}$

$.1498 \approx .15$ or 15%

54.99. $\overline{)8.24.0000}$

The sale price is 15% off the regular price.

Exercise A Find the percent saved for each of the purchases listed in Exercise A on page 52.

Calculator Practice Use a calculator to find the percent saved on a sale purchase.

Step 1 Key in the amount saved.

Step 2 Press ÷.

Step 3 Key in the amount of the regular price.

Step 4 Press =. This answer is the decimal that you want.

Step 5 To change the decimal to the percent saved, press ×. Key in 100. Press =.

EXAMPLE Use the calculator to find the percent saved in the last example.

Press 8.24 ÷ 54.99 =

The display will read 0.1498454.

Press × 100 =. Round to the nearest percent.

The percent saved is 15%.

Check your answers for Exercise A by using this method on your calculator.

Lesson 4 Discounts

Discount

An amount subtracted from the regular price.

A **discount** indicates an amount subtracted from the regular price. Stores may give discounts to reduce prices for a sale. Occasionally a store offers a percent off every item in the store. Sometimes this discount is given at the checkout counter and is not marked on the price tag. Before you check out of the store, you will need to compute the sale price to decide if it is a good bargain.

EXAMPLE A shirt is marked 20% off. What is the sale price if the regular price of the shirt is $49.99?

Step 1 Subtract the discount from 100%.

100%	
− 20%	Discount rate
80%	Difference

Step 2 Multiply the difference times the regular price.

$ 49.99	Regular price
× .80	Difference from Step 1
$39.9920 ≈	$39.99 Sale price

How much is saved?

$ 49.99	Regular price
−39.99	Sale price
$ 10.00	Amount saved

Buying the shirt at 20% off the regular price of $49.99 gives a sale price of $39.99 and a savings of $10.00.

Exercise A Use the discount. Find the sale price of each item and the amount saved.

	Item	Regular Price	Discount	Sale Price	Amount Saved
1)	Sweater	$39.99	10%	______	______
2)	Jeans	$44.99	15%	______	______
3)	Shirt	$24.99	10%	______	______
4)	Blouse	$49.95	20%	______	______
5)	Shoes	$34.99	25%	______	______
6)	Coat	$179.99	15%	______	______
7)	Dress	$64.00	10%	______	______
8)	Suit	$210.00	50%	______	______
9)	Vest	$27.99	12%	______	______
10)	Pants	$39.99	40%	______	______

Lesson 5 Buying From a Catalog

Catalog
An organized listing of items for purchase.

A **catalog** lists items in an organized way; for example, toys or household supplies. Descriptions are often included. Many companies send catalogs of their goods to people throughout the country. Customers look at the catalogs and decide what, if anything, they wish to buy. They may mail, fax, or phone their orders to the store. Catalog buyers usually pay the cost of shipping and handling in addition to the cost of the goods.

EXAMPLE Ray wants two of the shirts advertised in a catalog. Read the following ad. Then notice the way Ray fills out his order form.

Men's Shirt

Fine, lightweight cotton knit shirt for sports and casual wear. Washable. 3-button opening. Short sleeves. White collar. Three colors: Navy, Green, Red. Men's sizes S, M, L, XL.
A4610 . . . . Men's shirt, $35.00 postpaid

Perkins & Dodge
CATALOG SALES
456 PERKINS AVE.· SPRINGFIELD, NY 23453

ORDER FORM

Ordered by:
Name ______
Address ______
City ______ State ______ Zip ______

Ship to:
Name ______
Address ______
City ______ State ______ Zip ______

Item No.	How Many?	Color	Size	Description	Amount
A4610	1	Navy	M	Men's Shirt	35 00
A4610	1	Red	M	Men's Shirt	35 00
				Total of merchandise	70 00
				Add 6% state sales tax	4 20
				TOTAL AMOUNT	74 20

Thank you!

Exercise A Compute the following answers. Include 6% sales tax.

1) What is the total amount for three of these shirts?

2) What is the total amount for one shirt?

Some mail order companies require the customer to pay shipping and handling charges based on the total of the order. Here is a table of these charges from a catalog.

Shipping Charges	
Total	
Up to $115.99	$4.90
$116.00 to $130.99	$5.90
$131.00 to $140.99	$6.90
$141.00 to $150.99	$7.90
Over $151.00	$9.90
Next Day Delivery	+ $2.50

EXAMPLE Terry ordered a sweatshirt. It costs $34.50. How much is the shipping charge?

The shipping charge is $4.90.

Exercise B Find the cost and shipping charge for each order.

1) 2 pair gloves
2 sweaters

2) 2 sweatshirts
1 pair gloves

3) 3 belts
1 sweatshirt

4) 1 belt
1 pair gloves
1 sweater

Exercise C Find the cost of each order. Add 5% sales tax and shipping charges from page 56 to find the total amount due.

1) 1 sweater
   1 belt

2) 2 sweatshirts
   2 sweaters

3) 1 sweater
   2 belts

4) 2 pair gloves
   1 sweatshirt

5) 3 belts
   1 sweatshirt

6) 3 sweatshirts
   1 sweater

A person ordering clothes from a catalog must write the correct sizes on the order form. Some catalogs give directions for finding proper measurements and sizes. Read the following example.

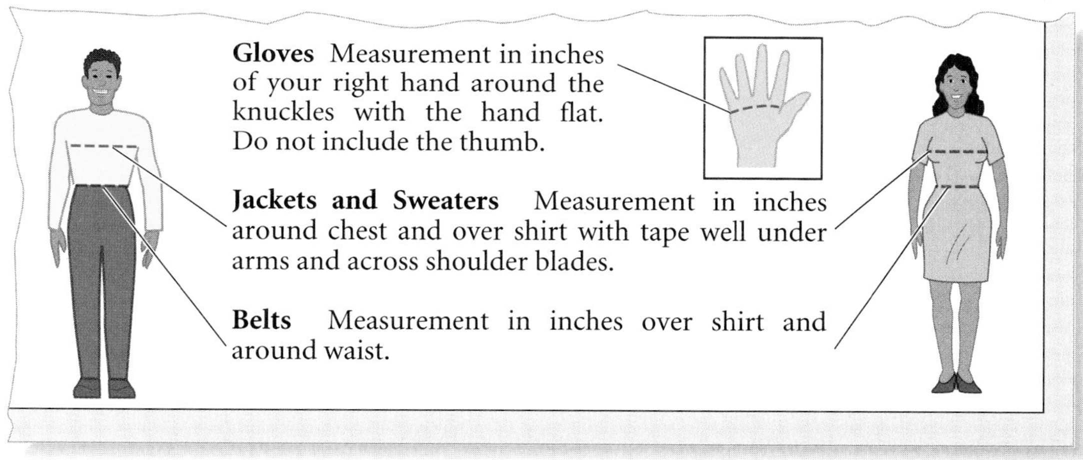

Exercise D Determine the correct size for each item described in these problems. Use information from the catalog ads on page 56.

1) Gary's chest measurement is 39″. His hand measurement is $9\frac{1}{2}$″. He is ordering a sweatshirt and gloves.

2) Meg's waist measurement is 30″. She usually wears a size 10. She is ordering a belt and a sweatshirt.

3) Brad's waist measurement is 40″. His chest measurement is 44″. He wants a belt and a sweater.

Lesson 6 The Key to Simplifying Fractions

Numerator

The part of a fraction that is above the line and that tells how many parts are used.

Denominator

The part of a fraction that is below the line and that tells the number of parts in the whole.

Greatest common factor

The largest factor of two numbers.

A fraction is made up of a **numerator** and a **denominator.** To simplify fractions, divide the numerator and the denominator by the **greatest common factor**.

EXAMPLE $\frac{2}{8} = \frac{2 \div 2}{8 \div 2} = \frac{1}{4}$ $\frac{6}{9} = \frac{6 \div 3}{9 \div 3} = \frac{2}{3}$

Exercise A Write each fraction in simplest form.

1) $\frac{2}{4}$ **5)** $\frac{8}{10}$ **9)** $\frac{14}{16}$ **13)** $\frac{9}{15}$

2) $\frac{6}{8}$ **6)** $\frac{3}{9}$ **10)** $\frac{6}{9}$ **14)** $\frac{6}{16}$

3) $\frac{5}{10}$ **7)** $\frac{12}{15}$ **11)** $\frac{12}{32}$ **15)** $\frac{8}{24}$

4) $\frac{13}{39}$ **8)** $\frac{12}{16}$ **12)** $\frac{14}{21}$ **16)** $\frac{10}{45}$

EXAMPLE If the numerator of a fraction is larger than the denominator, then divide the numerator by the denominator. Write any remainder as a fraction.

$$\frac{11}{8} = 8\overline{)11} \quad 1 = 1\frac{3}{8}; \quad 11 - 8 = 3$$

$$\frac{20}{8} = 8\overline{)20} \quad 2 = 2\frac{4}{8} = 2\frac{1}{2}; \quad 20 - 16 = 4$$

Exercise B Write each fraction in simplest form.

1) $\frac{5}{4}$ **5)** $\frac{11}{7}$ **9)** $\frac{12}{5}$ **13)** $\frac{15}{8}$

2) $\frac{3}{2}$ **6)** $\frac{13}{8}$ **10)** $\frac{20}{9}$ **14)** $\frac{10}{8}$

3) $\frac{7}{5}$ **7)** $\frac{9}{5}$ **11)** $\frac{19}{9}$ **15)** $\frac{9}{4}$

4) $\frac{9}{2}$ **8)** $\frac{17}{4}$ **12)** $\frac{17}{3}$ **16)** $\frac{27}{5}$

Lesson 7 The Key to Common Denominators

Factor

The number being multiplied.

The number being multiplied is called a **factor**. To change the denominator of a fraction, multiply the numerator and the denominator by the same factor.

EXAMPLE Change the denominator of $\frac{1}{4}$ to 8. $\frac{1}{4} = \frac{■}{8}$

Think: $4 \times 2 = 8$

$\frac{1}{4} = \frac{1 \times 2}{4 \times 2} = \frac{2}{8}$

Exercise A Change each numerator so the fractions are equal.

1) $\frac{2}{3} = \frac{■}{9}$ **4)** $\frac{1}{2} = \frac{■}{8}$ **7)** $\frac{3}{8} = \frac{■}{16}$

2) $\frac{3}{4} = \frac{■}{8}$ **5)** $\frac{3}{5} = \frac{■}{10}$ **8)** $\frac{1}{2} = \frac{■}{4}$

3) $\frac{1}{8} = \frac{■}{16}$ **6)** $\frac{7}{8} = \frac{■}{32}$ **9)** $\frac{3}{4} = \frac{■}{16}$

To find the common denominator, find the smallest number that has both denominators as a factor.

EXAMPLE Find the common denominator of $\frac{3}{4}$ and $\frac{5}{6}$.

Think: $4 \times 3 = 12$ $6 \times 2 = 12$

$\frac{3}{4} = \frac{3 \times 3}{4 \times 3} = \frac{9}{12}$ $\frac{5}{6} = \frac{5 \times 2}{6 \times 2} = \frac{10}{12}$

Exercise B Write these pairs of fractions with common denominators.

1) $\frac{5}{8}$ and $\frac{1}{2}$ **4)** $\frac{1}{2}$ and $\frac{3}{8}$ **7)** $\frac{1}{3}$ and $\frac{1}{5}$

2) $\frac{3}{4}$ and $\frac{1}{8}$ **5)** $\frac{3}{4}$ and $\frac{5}{8}$ **8)** $\frac{3}{4}$ and $\frac{2}{3}$

3) $\frac{1}{4}$ and $\frac{1}{2}$ **6)** $\frac{7}{8}$ and $\frac{1}{4}$ **9)** $\frac{3}{10}$ and $\frac{4}{15}$

Lesson 8 Making Your Own Clothes

Some people sew their own clothes in order to match the right fabric with the right style. Others sew for enjoyment or as a hobby. Besides saving money, sewing your own clothes can make them fit better. Buying fabric requires a knowledge of mathematics.

Pattern

A sewer's pattern pieces and directions for making clothes.

EXAMPLE Sergio is making a costume which includes a pair of pants, vest, hat, and cummerbund. He selects a **pattern**. On the back of the pattern envelope, he finds a chart that shows how much fabric to use. He wants to make the entire outfit from the same fabric. Sergio is a size medium. The fabric he wants to use is 60 inches wide.

	Size	XS	S	M	L	
VEST C (Men's) 60″		$1\frac{1}{4}$	$1\frac{1}{4}$	$1\frac{1}{4}$	$1\frac{3}{8}$	Yd.
PANTS C (Men's) 60″		$2\frac{7}{8}$	$2\frac{7}{8}$	$2\frac{7}{8}$	$2\frac{7}{8}$	Yd.
CONTRAST C #1 (Hat, Cummerbund) 60″		$\frac{7}{8}$	$\frac{7}{8}$	$\frac{7}{8}$	$\frac{7}{8}$	Yd.

Yard (yd.)

A measure of length equal to three feet.

Patterns indicate fabric requirements in **yards**. From the chart, Sergio finds that he needs $\frac{7}{8}$ of a yard for the hat and cummerbund, $1\frac{1}{4}$ yards for the vest and $2\frac{7}{8}$ yards for the pants. How much fabric does he need altogether?

Add the three numbers. The common denominator is 8.

$$\begin{aligned} \frac{7}{8} &= \frac{7}{8} \\ 1\frac{1}{4} &= 1\frac{2}{8} \\ +\,2\frac{7}{8} &= 2\frac{7}{8} \\ \hline & \quad 3\frac{16}{8} \end{aligned}$$

$$3\frac{16}{8} = 3 + \frac{16}{8} = 3 + 2 = 5$$

Sergio needs 5 yards of fabric to make the hat, cummerbund, vest, and pants.

This chart appears inside of Sergio's pattern envelope. It includes types of fabrics, **notions**, and amounts of fabric needed to make various costumes for men and women in different sizes.

> **Notions**
> *Small items needed to complete a sewing project.*

3048 Arabian Costume and Accessories **18 PIECES**

Size	XS	S	M	L
SHIRT A, PANTS A, & CAPE A (Men's)	Number of yards needed			
45″	$9\frac{3}{8}$	$9\frac{1}{2}$	$9\frac{1}{8}$	$10\frac{1}{4}$
60″	$8\frac{1}{8}$	$8\frac{1}{4}$	$8\frac{1}{2}$	$8\frac{5}{8}$
CONTRAST A #1 (Flap, Cummerbund)				
45″,60″	$1\frac{1}{4}$	$1\frac{1}{4}$	$1\frac{1}{4}$	$1\frac{1}{4}$
CONTRAST A #2 (Boots)				
35″	$\frac{1}{4}$	$\frac{1}{4}$	$\frac{1}{4}$	$\frac{1}{4}$
72″	$\frac{1}{2}$	$\frac{1}{2}$	$\frac{1}{2}$	$\frac{1}{2}$
CONTRAST A #3 (Top—Turban)				
35″, 45″, 60″....	$\frac{1}{4}$	$\frac{1}{4}$	$\frac{1}{4}$	$\frac{1}{4}$
TOP B, PANTS B & HEADBAND B (Misses)				
45″	$3\frac{1}{2}$	$3\frac{5}{8}$	$3\frac{7}{8}$	$4\frac{1}{8}$
60″	$2\frac{7}{8}$	$2\frac{7}{8}$	3	$3\frac{1}{4}$
72″	$2\frac{3}{8}$	$2\frac{1}{2}$	$2\frac{1}{2}$	$2\frac{3}{4}$
VEST C (Men's)				
35″	$2\frac{3}{8}$	$2\frac{3}{8}$	$2\frac{1}{2}$	$2\frac{1}{2}$
45″	$1\frac{1}{4}$	2	$2\frac{1}{2}$	$2\frac{1}{2}$
60″	$1\frac{1}{4}$	$1\frac{1}{4}$	$1\frac{1}{4}$	$1\frac{3}{8}$
PANTS C (Men's)				
45″, 60″	$2\frac{7}{8}$	$2\frac{7}{8}$	$2\frac{7}{8}$	$2\frac{7}{8}$
72″	$2\frac{3}{4}$	$2\frac{3}{4}$	$2\frac{3}{4}$	$2\frac{3}{4}$
CONTRAST C #1 (Hat, Cummerbund)				
45″	1	1	1	1
60″	$\frac{7}{8}$	$\frac{7}{8}$	$\frac{7}{8}$	$\frac{7}{8}$
CONTRAST C #2 (Patch)—$6\frac{1}{2}$″ × $6\frac{1}{2}$″ **FUSIBLE INTERFACING** (Heavy Weight—Hat)				
18″, 24″	$\frac{3}{4}$	$\frac{3}{4}$	$\frac{7}{8}$	$\frac{7}{8}$

FABRICS: A, B, C: Satin, Gauze, Tricot
Contrast A #2: Felt
Contrast A #3: Knits only

NOTIONS: $\frac{5}{9}$″ Sequin trim, seam binding, $\frac{5}{8}$″ grosgrain ribbon, 1″ elastic, feather, jewel stone.

Use this chart to answer the problems in Exercise A on page 62 and Exercise B on page 63.

PROBLEM SOLVING

Exercise A Use the pattern chart on page 61 to solve these problems. Follow the example on page 60.

1) How much 60″ fabric is needed to make a men's size medium style A shirt, pants, and cape?

2) How much 60″ fabric is needed to make a men's size large style A shirt, pants, and cape?

3) How much 45″ fabric is required to make two medium misses' outfits (top, pants, and headband)?

4) How much 72″ fabric is required to make two pairs of size medium boots?

5) How much 60″ fabric is needed to make a top turban style A?

6) How much 45″ fabric is needed to make two pairs of men's size medium style C pants? Add to find your answer.

7) How much 45″ fabric is needed to make a misses' size large style B outfit (top, pants, and headband)?

8) How much 45″ fabric is needed to make both a misses' medium style B outfit and a men's large style A outfit (shirt, pants, and cape)?

9) How much 60″ fabric is needed to make both a misses' size large style B outfit and a men's size small style A outfit?

10) A man decides to make a size medium boots, top turban, and style C vest using 35″ fabric. How much fabric will he need? Add the three numbers.

11) Two women are planning matching style B outfits. One woman is size large; the other is medium. They will use 45″ fabric for the tops, pants, and headbands. How much fabric must they buy?

EXAMPLE How much more 45″ fabric will be required to make a size medium men's vest (C) than an extra small vest?

Size	XS	S	M	L
VEST C (Men's)	Number of yards needed			
45″	$1\frac{1}{4}$	2	$2\frac{1}{2}$	$2\frac{1}{2}$

Step 1 Read the chart. Size medium .... $2\frac{1}{2}$ yards

Size extra small....... $1\frac{1}{4}$ yards

Step 2 Subtract.

$$\begin{array}{rcr} 2\frac{1}{2} & = & 2\frac{2}{4} \\ -\,1\frac{1}{4} & = & -\,1\frac{1}{4} \\ \hline & & 1\frac{1}{4} \end{array}$$

The common denominator is 4.

The size medium vest requires $1\frac{1}{4}$ yard more fabric than the size extra small vest.

PROBLEM SOLVING

Exercise B Use the pattern chart on page 61 to solve these problems.

1) How much more 60″ fabric is required to make a men's size large than a size medium shirt, pants, and cape?

2) How much more 45″ fabric is required to make a men's size large vest (style C) than a men's small vest?

3) How much more 45″ fabric is needed than 60″ fabric for a misses' size medium style B outfit? Subtract to find your answer.

4) How much more 60″ fabric is needed to make a men's size medium style A outfit than a misses' size small style B outfit?

5) How much more 45″ fabric than 60″ fabric is needed to make a size medium style C hat and cummerbund?

6) How much more 45″ fabric is needed than 60″ fabric for a misses' size medium style B top, pants, and headband?

Lesson 9 Finding the Cost of Fabric

To find the cost of fabric, multiply the price per yard by the number of yards needed.

EXAMPLE What is the cost of $3\frac{1}{8}$ yards of fabric at $6.99 per yard?

Step 1 Write $3\frac{1}{8}$ as a decimal.

$$\frac{1}{8} = 8\overline{)1.000} = .125$$

$$3\frac{1}{8} = 3.125$$

Step 2 Multiply 3.125 by $6.99

3.125	Amount of fabric
× $6.99	Price per yard
$21.84375 ≈	$21.84 Cost

The cost of $3\frac{1}{8}$ yards of fabric is $21.84.

Exercise A Write the decimal equivalent for each fraction.

1) $\frac{1}{8}$ **3)** $\frac{1}{4}$ **5)** $\frac{3}{8}$ **7)** $\frac{1}{2}$

2) $\frac{5}{8}$ **4)** $\frac{3}{4}$ **6)** $\frac{7}{8}$ **8)** $\frac{8}{8}$

Exercise B Find the total cost of each fabric purchase.

	Length	Cost per Yard		Length	Cost per Yard
1)	2 yd.	$9.00	**7)**	$5\frac{1}{4}$ yd.	$7.99
2)	$4\frac{1}{2}$ yd.	$12.00	**8)**	$6\frac{1}{8}$ yd.	$8.00
3)	$5\frac{3}{8}$ yd.	$5.49	**9)**	$9\frac{7}{8}$ yd.	$16.00
4)	$1\frac{7}{8}$ yd.	$15.00	**10)**	$8\frac{5}{8}$ yd.	$4.00
5)	$3\frac{3}{4}$ yd.	$8.99	**11)**	$7\frac{7}{8}$ yd.	$8.99
6)	$10\frac{1}{2}$ yd.	$4.99	**12)**	$24\frac{1}{4}$ yd.	$34.59

Lesson 10 Using a Charge Account

Charge account
An account with a store or company to which the purchase of goods is charged and paid for at a later date.

Interest
A fee charged on the unpaid balance of a charge account.

Minimum payment
The smallest amount due to be paid on a charge account.

Statement
A monthly record sent to charge account customers.

Many consumers find it convenient to charge their purchases with a credit card and pay for them at a later date. People who use a **charge account** are expected to make a **minimum payment** each month. **Interest** is a fee charged on any unpaid balance.

EXAMPLES Adam Lee owes $126.60 on his charge account. The minimum payment due is $10.00. Part of his monthly record or **statement** is shown below. It indicates all payments and charges to date. Adam will mail a portion of this statement with his payment of $10.00.

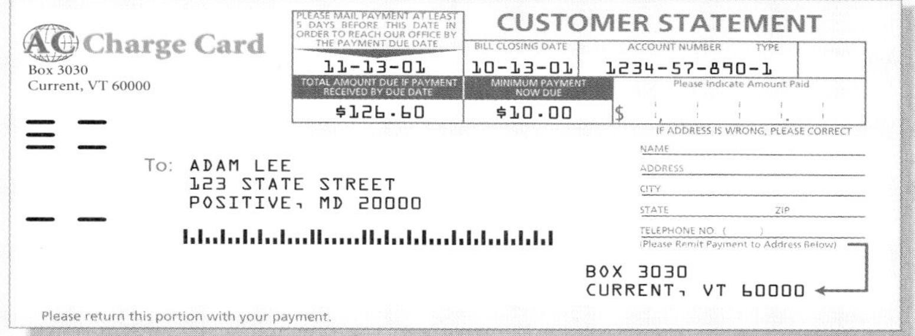
AC Charge Card
Box 3030
Current, VT 60000

CUSTOMER STATEMENT

PLEASE MAIL PAYMENT AT LEAST 5 DAYS BEFORE THIS DATE IN ORDER TO REACH OUR OFFICE BY THE PAYMENT DUE DATE	BILL CLOSING DATE	ACCOUNT NUMBER	TYPE
11-13-01	10-13-01	1234-57-890-1	
TOTAL AMOUNT DUE IF PAYMENT RECEIVED BY DUE DATE	**MINIMUM PAYMENT NOW DUE**	Please Indicate Amount Paid	
$126.60	$10.00	$	

To: ADAM LEE
123 STATE STREET
POSITIVE, MD 20000

IF ADDRESS IS WRONG, PLEASE CORRECT
NAME
ADDRESS
CITY
STATE ZIP
TELEPHONE NO. ( )
(Please Remit Payment to Address Below)

BOX 3030
CURRENT, VT 60000

Please return this portion with your payment.

Adam's interest charge is 1.8% of the unpaid balance. How much will he owe next month if he makes no new purchases?

Step 1 Subtract his payment from the current balance.

$126.60	Current balance
− 10.00	Payment
$116.60	Unpaid balance, or amount owed

Step 2 Find and add the interest.

Interest = Rate × Amount Owed

$ 116.60	Amount owed
× .018	Rate (1.8% = .018)
$2.09880	Interest

$116.60	Amount owed
+ 2.10	Interest
$118.70	New balance / Amount owed

Adam will owe $118.70 next month.

Exercise A For each cardholder below, find the unpaid balance after the minimum payment is made. Then find the interest charge and the new balance in each case. Follow the example on page 65.

	Cardholder	Current Balance	Minimum Payment	Interest Rate	Unpaid Balance	Interest Charge	New Balance
1)	Electra	$245.78	$10.00	1.5%	______	______	______
2)	Stefan	$101.98	$15.00	1.6%	______	______	______
3)	Colleen	$78.69	$10.00	1.9%	______	______	______
4)	Ben	$2,889.76	$50.00	2.0%	______	______	______
5)	Tim	$99.87	$5.00	1.8%	______	______	______
6)	Jiang	$100.00	$7.00	1.3%	______	______	______
7)	Anna	$105.05	$10.00	1.7%	______	______	______
8)	José	$88.88	$9.00	1.5%	______	______	______
9)	Laurie	$755.34	$6.00	1.75%	______	______	______
10)	Vanessa	$162.54	$10.00	1.50%	______	______	______

You can use a charge card to purchase items such as shirts.

Lesson 11 Using a Layaway Plan

Layaway

A plan under which customers can buy something, pay part of the price as a deposit, and receive the items when the remainder of the price is paid.

Some customers prefer to buy their clothes by using a **layaway** plan. They pay part of the price as a deposit. The store keeps the item until the customer pays the remainder of the price. There are no interest charges. However, there is usually a limit to the time that the item may be laid away.

EXAMPLE Shateel put a $250 suit on layaway. He made a 10% deposit. How much does he owe?

$ 250	Cost
× .10	Rate of deposit (10% = .10)
$25.00	Deposit

$250.00	Cost
− 25.00	Deposit
$225.00	Remainder due

Shateel will need $225.00 to get his suit out of layaway.

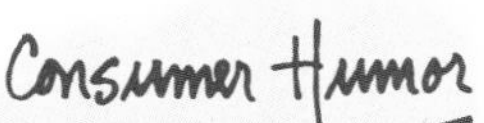

Did you see that customer taking a nap on the hide-a-bed in the furniture department?

Yes, I guess he decided to use the layaway plan!

Some stores allow the customer to pay one third of the cost as a deposit and one third each month until the item is paid for. Under this plan, how much will Shateel pay each month on the suit?

EXAMPLE To find one third of a price, divide the price by 3. Round to the nearest cent.

$\$250.00 \div 3 = \$83.333 = \$83.33$

Notice that: $83.33 × 3 is only $249.99

For the last payment, Shateel will pay $83.34.
$83.33 + $83.33 + 83.34 = $250.00, the total amount owed.

Exercise A Find the amount of deposit and the remainder due for each layaway item.

	Item	Cost	Deposit	Amount of Deposit	Remainder Due
1)	Dress	$85.00	10%	______	______
2)	Shoes	$48.00	1/3	______	______
3)	Hat	$24.00	15%	______	______
4)	Coat	$125.00	$10.00	______	______
5)	Jacket	$65.99	20%	______	______

Chapter 3 Review

Solve these problems.

1) What is the total cost of three shirts @ $22.50 and two ties @ $14.90 with a 5% sales tax?

2) What is the amount saved on a coat that was regularly $199.00 and is now on sale for $149.99?

3) What percent is saved when a $129.99 dress is bought on sale for $84.49?

4) What is the amount saved on a dress that was regularly $69.99 and now has a 20% discount?

5) Look at the catalog page shown above. Find the cost for a belt and pair of gloves. Calculate 6% sales tax and shipping charges. Find the total amount due.

Shipping Charges	
Total	
Up to $115.99	$4.90
$116.00 to $130.99	$5.90
$131.00 to $140.99	$6.90
$141.00 to $150.99	$7.90
Over $151.00	$9.90
Next Day Delivery	+ $2.50

6) Look at the chart. How much fabric is required for a turban and cummerbund?

Size	XS	S	M	L
SHIRT A, PANTS A, & CAPE A (Men's)	Number of yards needed			
45″	$9\frac{3}{8}$	$9\frac{1}{2}$	$9\frac{1}{8}$	$10\frac{1}{4}$
60″	$8\frac{1}{8}$	$8\frac{1}{4}$	$8\frac{1}{2}$	$8\frac{5}{8}$
CONTRAST A #1 (Flap, Cummerbund)				
45″, 60″	$1\frac{1}{4}$	$1\frac{1}{4}$	$1\frac{1}{4}$	$1\frac{1}{4}$
CONTRAST A #2 (Boots)				
35″	$\frac{1}{4}$	$\frac{1}{4}$	$\frac{1}{4}$	$\frac{1}{4}$
72″	$\frac{1}{2}$	$\frac{1}{2}$	$\frac{1}{2}$	$\frac{1}{2}$
CONTRAST A #3 (Top—Turban)				
35″, 45″, 60″. . . .	$\frac{1}{4}$	$\frac{1}{4}$	$\frac{1}{4}$	$\frac{1}{4}$

7) How much will $5\frac{3}{8}$ yards of fabric cost at $10.99 a yard?

8) What is the interest charge on $45.75 at 1.8% interest?

9) A person owes $252.00 on his charge card. If he pays a minimum payment of $15.00, what will the unpaid balance be? If the interest rate is 1.5%, what will the interest charge and the new balance be?

10) If a layaway plan requires a 20% deposit, then how much will the deposit be for a $158.90 dress? What is the remainder due to get the dress out of layaway?

Test Taking Tip Before you answer any question on an exam, skim through the whole test to find out what is expected of you.

SOLD
For Sale
Financing Available
Bauer Realty
653-1900

Chapter 4

Managing a Household

Buying a home or renting an apartment is an exciting event. But it also involves a great deal of responsibility. In addition to the monthly house payments or rent, there are a number of other expenses. These include things such as utilities and insurance. All of these expenses need to be considered when you plan a monthly budget you can afford.

In Chapter 4, you will learn how to determine housing costs and monthly expenses. You will see the type of information that is needed to manage a household effectively.

Goals for Learning

- To state and apply the renter's rule and the banker's rule to plan monthly rent or mortgage payments
- To compute the cost of rent for one year
- To solve problems related to down payments, monthly payments, and total amounts paid for mortgages
- To read utility meters and compute monthly utility expenses
- To solve word problems related to utility expenses
- To compute expenses related to mortgage insurance and homeowners insurance

Lesson 1 Renting a Home

Landlord

The person who owns and rents property to another.

Lease

A contract to rent property.

Many people rent their homes. They pay a monthly or weekly fee to the **landlord**, the owner of the property rented to another person. Renters also sign a **lease**. This contract or agreement states the amount of rent and the length of time that the property will be rented.

Renter's Rule You should spend no more than one week's income for a month's rent.

Applying this renter's rule helps the renter to have enough money for other needs, such as food, clothing, utilities, transportation, and entertainment.

EXAMPLE Lisa earns \$1,165 per month. What is the maximum amount that she should pay for rent?

There are about 4.3 weeks in each month. To estimate Lisa's weekly income, divide her monthly income by 4.3.

$$4.3.\overline{)\$1{,}165.0.0} \quad 27\,0.93 \text{ One week's income}$$

Lisa can afford to spend about \$270.00 per month for rent.

Exercise A Use the renter's rule to find the maximum amount that should be spent for rent with each of these incomes. Remember that 1 year equals 12 months or 52 weeks.

1) \$1,300 per month

2) \$566 every 2 weeks

3) \$1,604 per month

4) \$14,000 per year

5) \$24,575 per year

6) \$1,420 per month

7) \$610 every 2 weeks

8) \$16,000 per year

9) \$19,000 per year

10) \$800 twice a month

Hourly Income A 40-hour work week is considered typical for employees who earn hourly wages.

Exercise B Multiply by 40 to find the maximum amount that should be spent for rent from each of these incomes.

1) $6.90 per hour
2) $8.85 per hour
3) $14.00 per hour
4) $8.39 per hour
5) $9.80 per hour
6) $16.00 per hour

Exercise C Divide by 40 to find how much a person must earn per hour to be able to afford each of these monthly rents.

1) $400.00
2) $564.50
3) $800.00
4) $442.90
5) $278.90
6) $325.00

Annual Renting Costs To find **annual**, or yearly, renting costs, multiply the monthly rent by 12, the number of months in a year.

Annual

Yearly; relating to a period of 12 months.

EXAMPLE Lisa's four aunts share a large townhouse. How much do they pay in rent per year if the monthly rent is $1,255.00?

$ 1,255.00	Rent per month
× 12	Months per year
$15,060.00	Rent per year

Exercise D Find the total rent paid in a year for each monthly rent.

1) $640.00
2) $256.50
3) $488.88
4) $248.90
5) $307.00
6) $456.36
7) $367.89
8) $1,275.00
9) $495.95
10) $578.50
11) $821.50
12) $380.00

Exercise E Look in the local newspaper. Find three homes or apartments listed for rent. How much is the monthly rent? How much is the total rent for one year?

Lesson 2 Buying a Home

Down payment
Part of the price paid when something is purchased.

Financed
Borrowed.

Interest
A payment charged to the borrower for the use of money.

Mortgage
A property loan.

Principal
The amount of money loaned to a creditor.

Many people wish to buy a home. Houses cost so much money that most people cannot pay the full price at the time of purchase. They borrow money from a bank or another financial institution.

Lenders require a certain percent of the price of the house to be paid in cash at the time of purchase. That amount is called a **down payment**. The remainder of the cost of the house is borrowed or **financed**. This financed loan on property is called a **mortgage**. The amount of money borrowed is called **principal**. The owner repays the principal plus interest in monthly payments. The **interest** is a fee charged for borrowing money.

The following banker's rule is used to help determine how much money a person can borrow to buy a house.

Banker's Rule You may borrow up to 2.5 times your annual income.

EXAMPLE How much can Ms. Moore borrow if her income is $20,000 per year?

$20,000	Annual income
× 2.5	Banker's rule
$50,000	Amount that may be borrowed

Exercise A Use the banker's rule to find the amount that may be borrowed for each annual income.

1) $26,000
2) $32,870
3) $63,560
4) $26,750
5) $18,440
6) $24,390
7) $48,290
8) $22,500
9) $20,570
10) $85,720
11) $50,500
12) $76,900

Exercise B Look in the local newspaper. Find three homes listed for sale. What is the price of each home?

Hourly Income Some people wanting to buy a house earn an hourly wage. Their annual income is estimated to find out how much money they may borrow. There are about 2,080 paid working hours in a year, so you can multiply the hourly rate by 2,080.

When you borrow money to buy a home, your income is one factor used to decide if you qualify for a loan.

EXAMPLE William earns $6.58 per hour. How much money may he borrow for a home?

$ 6.58	Hourly rate
× 2,080	Hours per year
$13,686.40	Annual income

$13,686.40	Annual income
× 2.5	Banker's rule
$34,216.00	May be borrowed

Exercise C Find the amount that may be borrowed for each of these hourly wages.

1) $6.00
2) $6.49
3) $14.75
4) $8.50
5) $8.00
6) $8.32
7) $9.15
8) $9.60
9) $7.50
10) $16.00
11) $6.15
12) $17.35

Minimum Annual Income You can estimate the amount a person should earn to qualify for a mortgage. Divide the amount of the mortgage by 2.5.

EXAMPLE Ann McCarthy wants to borrow $125,000. What should her minimum annual income be?

$5 0,00 0	Minimum annual income
2.5.) $125,0 00.0.	Mortgage

Ann should have a minimum annual income of $50,000 to borrow $125,000.

Exercise D Find the minimum annual income for each mortgage.

1) $35,000
2) $40,000
3) $55,000
4) $80,000
5) $45,000
6) $60,000
7) $150,000
8) $50,000
9) $65,000

Lesson 3 Computing the Down Payment

To find the down payment, multiply the cost of the home by the rate of the down payment.

EXAMPLE Anita Perez found the house of her dreams. The price is $159,900. What is her 20% down payment?

$ 159,900	Cost of the house
× .20	Rate of down payment (20% = .20)
$31,980.00	Down payment

How much remains to be financed? That is, what will the amount of the mortgage be? Subtract the down payment from the cost of the house.

$159,900	Cost of the house
− 31,980	Down payment
$127,920	Amount of mortgage

Consumer Humor

Did you hear the poultry farm was sold?

Yes, they used feathers as a down payment.

Oh, boy! That really quacks me up!

You will work with a loan officer to decide how much money you need for a down payment.

Exercise A Find the amount of the down payment and the amount of the mortgage for each house.

	Cost of House	Rate of Down Payment	Down Payment	Mortgage
1)	$125,900	15%	________	________
2)	$125,900	10%	________	________
3)	$125,900	25%	________	________
4)	$159,900	30%	________	________
5)	$45,750	20%	________	________
6)	$138,990	17%	________	________
7)	$64,500	30%	________	________
8)	$72,950	18%	________	________
9)	$87,400	19%	________	________
10)	$149,900	23%	________	________

Lesson 4 Paying the Mortgage

Fixed-rate mortgage
A loan in which the interest rate and payments remain the same.

Monthly payment
The amount of money paid every month.

Variable-rate mortgage
A loan in which the interest rate and payments change over time.

Several kinds of mortgage loans exist. The most common loan is called a **fixed-rate mortgage**. The interest rate and the **monthly payment** on principal and interest remain the same until the loan is paid. On a **variable-rate mortgage**, the interest rate and the monthly payments may change periodically.

EXAMPLE Joseph Gould wants to buy a home. He has enough money for a large down payment. He took out a fixed-rate mortgage for $50,000, to be paid in 30 years. The bank charges him 8% interest. What is his monthly payment? Joseph finds the answer quickly by using the following table. He looks down the column for 8%. He looks across the row for $50,000. Where these two lines meet, he reads, "367." His monthly payment will be $367.00.

Monthly Principal and Interest Payments for 30 Years

Mortgage Amount	7%	7.5%	8%	8.5%	9%	9.5%	10%	10.5%	11%	11.5%	12%	12.5%	13%
$40,000	$266	$280	$294	$308	$322	$336	$351	$366	$381	$396	$411	$427	$442
$50,000	333	350	367	384	402	420	439	457	476	495	514	534	553
$60,000	399	420	440	461	483	505	527	549	571	594	617	640	664
$70,000	466	489	514	538	563	589	614	640	667	693	720	747	774
$80,000	532	559	587	615	644	673	702	732	762	792	823	854	885
$90,000	599	629	660	692	724	757	790	823	857	891	926	961	996
$100,000	665	699	734	769	805	841	878	915	952	990	1,029	1,067	1,106
$110,000	732	769	807	846	885	925	965	1,006	1,048	1,089	1,131	1,174	1,217

Exercise A Find these monthly payments. Use the table to help you.

	Mortgage	Interest Rate		Mortgage	Interest Rate
1)	$40,000	9%	**6)**	$50,000	9.5%
2)	$70,000	12%	**7)**	$60,000	13%
3)	$90,000	8.5%	**8)**	$60,000	11.5%
4)	$70,000	12.5%	**9)**	$80,000	7%
5)	$100,000	10%	**10)**	$110,000	7.5%

EXAMPLES How much will Joseph Gould pay the bank over 30 years?

Step 1 To find out how much he pays in one year, multiply the monthly payment by 12.

$ 367	Monthly payment (see table)
× 12	Months in a year
$4,404	Amount paid in 1 year

Step 2 Multiply the result by 30, the term of the mortgage.

$ 4,404	Amount paid in 1 year
× 30	Number of years
$132,120	Amount paid over 30 years

How much of this money is **total interest** paid to the bank? Subtract the amount borrowed from the total amount paid to the bank over the term of the mortgage.

$132,120	Amount paid to the bank
− 50,000	Amount borrowed
$ 82,120	Total interest paid

Total interest
A total fee for borrowing money.

Exercise B Find the amount paid in 30 years and the total interest paid for each of these mortgages. Use the table on page 78 to help you.

	Amount of Mortgage	Rate of Interest	Amount Paid	Total Interest
1)	$40,000	10%	________	________
2)	$70,000	12%	________	________
3)	$40,000	7%	________	________
4)	$60,000	13%	________	________
5)	$80,000	9.0%	________	________
6)	$50,000	11%	________	________
7)	$60,000	10.5%	________	________
8)	$90,000	11.5%	________	________
9)	$100,000	9.5%	________	________
10)	$60,000	8.5%	________	________

Lesson 5 Terms of Mortgages Differ

Term
The period of time for which money is loaned.

Not all mortgages are for a **term** of 30 years. Mortgages may be taken out for any term, or number of years.

EXAMPLE Alma Wallace took out a 25-year mortgage for \$35,000 at an interest rate of 11%. What is the monthly payment for this loan? The table below shows the monthly payment (principal and interest) per \$1,000 of mortgage.

Monthly Payments per \$1,000

Years	7%	8%	9%	10%	11%	12%	13%
15	\$8.99	\$9.56	\$10.14	\$10.75	\$11.37	\$12.00	\$12.65
20	7.75	8.36	9.00	9.65	10.32	11.01	11.72
25	7.07	7.72	8.39	9.09	9.80	10.53	11.28
30	6.65	7.34	8.05	8.78	9.52	10.29	11.06
35	6.39	7.10	7.84	8.60	9.37	10.16	10.95
40	6.21	6.95	7.71	8.49	9.28	10.08	10.90

Step 1 Look down the column for 11%. Look across the row for 25 years. Read the amount where the two lines meet. This number, 9.80, means that \$9.80 must be paid for every \$1,000 of principal.

Step 2 Divide the principal by \$1,000.

$$\$1{,}000 \overline{)\ \$35{,}000}\quad \text{quotient } 35 \qquad \text{Principal}$$

There are 35 \$1,000's in the principal.

Step 3 Multiply \$9.80 by 35.

\$ 9.80	Payment per \$1,000
× 35	Number of \$1,000's in principal
\$343.00	Monthly payment

Alma's monthly payment (principal and interest) is \$343.00.

Exercise A Find the monthly payment for each of these mortgages. Use the table on page 80 to help you.

	Interest Rate	Term	Principal	Payment
1)	10%	15 years	$10,000	________
2)	9%	25 years	$30,000	________
3)	7%	30 years	$45,000	________
4)	11%	40 years	$50,000	________
5)	8%	20 years	$35,900	________
6)	12%	35 years	$45,900	________
7)	10%	15 years	$57,890	________
8)	8%	20 years	$100,000	________
9)	7%	40 years	$95,900	________
10)	9%	30 years	$85,900	________

Exercise B Compute the total amount to be repaid on a mortgage for $90,000 under each of the following conditions.

	Interest Rate	Term	To Be Repaid
1)	8%	15 years	________
2)	8%	20 years	________
3)	8%	25 years	________
4)	8%	30 years	________
5)	8%	35 years	________
6)	8%	40 years	________
7)	7%	15 years	________
8)	7%	30 years	________
9)	9%	20 years	________
10)	9%	40 years	________

Calculator Practice

Use this method with your calculator to find the total amount repaid on a mortgage.

Step 1 Key in the principal.

Step 2 Press ÷ .

Step 3 Key in *1,000*.

Step 4 Press × .

Step 5 Key in the monthly payment per $1,000.

Step 6 Press × .

Step 7 Key in the number of years for the mortgage.

Step 8 Press × .

Step 9 Key in *12*.

Step 10 Press = .

Step 11 Round to the nearest cent, affix the dollar sign, and insert commas into the number.

EXAMPLE Compute the total amount to be repaid on a 25-year mortgage for $35,000 at an interest rate of 11%.

35,000 ÷ *1,000* × *9.80* × *25* × *12* =

The display will read *102900*.

The amount to be repaid on the mortgage is $102,900.00.

Exercise C Use a calculator to help you find the total amount to be repaid on a mortgage under each of the following conditions.

	Interest Rate	Term	Principle	To Be Repaid
1)	8%	40 years	$45,000	________
2)	13%	15 years	$90,000	________
3)	7%	30 years	$30,000	________
4)	10%	20 years	$85,900	________
5)	9%	40 years	$50,000	________
6)	11%	30 years	$56,000	________
7)	9%	25 years	$63,000	________
8)	12%	20 years	$78,800	________
9)	8%	35 years	$102,500	________
10)	10%	15 years	$98,300	________

Lesson 6 Reading Utility Meters

Utilities
Household services.

Meters
Devices that measure gas, electricity, or water.

Dials
The parts of a meter that show units.

Services for your home—such as gas, electricity, water, and telephone—are called **utilities**. The word utility comes from the word "use." Only one gas and electric company and one water company provide services to everyone living in a given community. The amount of gas, electricity, and water that a customer uses is measured with devices called **meters**. The **dials** or numbers on the meter show how many units of the product have been consumed, or used, since the meter was installed.

Reading a Meter Sample dials from a gas meter are shown below. Each dial is divided into ten units. The numbers go in opposite directions because of the special gears that turn the pointers.

EXAMPLE

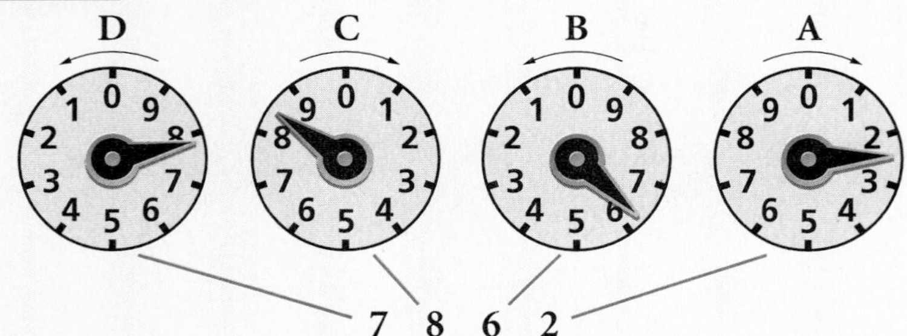

Begin with dial A. Read the number that the pointer has just passed. Take the lower number.

Then read dial B. If the pointer is between numbers, read the lower number. Even though the pointer appears to be exactly on a number, read the next lower number—unless the pointer to its right has passed zero. Dials C and D are read in the same way as dial B. The dials here read 7862.

Some utility meters show digits instead of a dial for each number. Read each digit as it appears on the meter. If a digit is between numbers, read the lower number.

EXAMPLE 7862 The meter reads 7862.

Consumer Humor

"Did you know that John got a new job at the electric company?"

"Yes, they heard that he was a real live wire."

Exercise A Record the readings on these sample utility meters.

1) 

2) 

3) 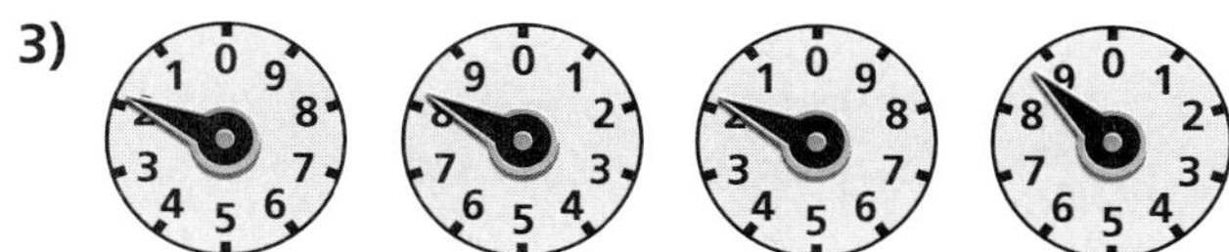

4) 

5) 

6) 7065

7) 6826

8) 5310

9) 5916/7

10) 4994

Lesson 7 Utility Consumption

Units

Single quantities.

How do utility companies know how many **units** customers consume, or use? The companies send meter readers regularly to determine consumption of utilities.

Rule The amount of water, gas, or electricity consumed is the difference between meter readings.

EXAMPLE These water meter readings were taken quarterly, or every 3 months.

	Year 1	Year 2
January	391	506
April	445	542
July	462	570
October	488	584

How many units were used from January to April in the first year? Subtract the earlier reading from the later reading.

445	Later reading	(April of year 1)
− 391	Earlier reading	(January of year 1)
54	Units used	

Cubic feet

Units used to measure volume.

A water unit equals a volume of 100 **cubic feet**. How many cubic feet of water were used from January to April in the first year?

Number of units $\times$ 100 = number of cubic feet.

$54 \times 100 = 5{,}400$ cubic feet.

Exercise A For each billing period, find the amount of water consumed in units and in cubic feet. Use the example readings shown above.

1) From April to July in year 1
2) From July to October in year 1
3) From October, year 1, to January, year 2
4) From January to April in year 2
5) From April to July in year 2
6) From July to October in year 2

Customers are billed for the number of units of water, gas, and electricity that they use.

EXAMPLE The Great Gas Company's rate is $.75 per unit. A customer uses 200 units. How much is the bill?

Multiply.	$ .75	Charge per unit
	× 2 00	Units used
	$150.00	Total bill

Exercise B Find how many units of gas were used each month. Subtract consecutive meter readings listed below. Then find the total bill for each month. Multiply by a rate of $.75 per unit.

			Units Used	Total
	December	8917		
1)	January	9265	______	______
2)	February	9402	______	______
3)	March	0054	______	______
4)	April	0195	______	______
5)	May	0316	______	______
6)	June	0451	______	______
7)	July	0465	______	______
8)	August	0499	______	______
9)	September	0528	______	______
10)	October	0571	______	______

Exercise C Subtract consecutive electric meter readings to find the number of units of electricity used each month. Then find the total bill for each month. Multiply by a rate of $.09 per unit.

			Units Used	Total
	December	65183		
1)	January	65836	______	______
2)	February	66433	______	______
3)	March	66995	______	______
4)	April	67611	______	______
5)	May	68184	______	______
6)	June	68700	______	______
7)	July	69336	______	______
8)	August	70202	______	______
9)	September	71875	______	______
10)	October	73245		

Consumers may also be interested in finding out the **average** use of utilities per month.

Rule To find an average:

1. Find the total of the items to be averaged.
2. Divide the total by the number of items.

EXAMPLE Karen's family uses the following units of electricity over four months. These units of electricity are measured by the **kilowatt hour,** or **kwh**. A **watt** is a unit of electrical power named after James Watt, a Scottish inventor. A **kilowatt** is 1,000 watts. What is the average number of units used per month?

December	323 kwh
January	561 kwh
February	272 kwh
March	311 kwh

Step 1 Find the total.

$$\begin{array}{r} 323 \text{ kwh} \\ 561 \\ 272 \\ +311 \\ \hline 1467 \text{ kwh} \end{array}$$

Step 2 Divide by 4.

$$4\overline{)1467.0} = 366.8 \approx 367 \text{ kwh}$$

Karen's family uses an average of 367 kwh per month.

Average
The middle point in a group of numbers; a common or usual number.

Kilowatt
A unit of electricity equal to 1,000 watts.

Kilowatt hour (kwh)
The energy used by one kilowatt in one hour.

Watt
A unit of electricity.

Exercise D Find the average number of units consumed for the following sets. Round each answer to a whole number.

1) 653, 597, 562, 616

2) 542, 506, 488, 445, 391, 366

3) 36, 18, 26, 17, 54, 25, 19

4) 29, 29, 46, 348, 137, 652, 262, 135, 14

5) 1267, 573, 555, 558, 670, 532, 552, 480, 509, 747

6) 566, 653, 597, 562, 616, 572

Lesson 8 Telephone, Gas, and Electric Bills

Flat rate
A base amount charged for monthly telephone service.

Optional
Involving a choice.

Telephone customers receive a bill every month. It shows basic telephone service, or the **flat rate**, plus additional charges for **optional** services and long distance calls.

EXAMPLE The Browns' telephone bill usually has these two charges.

Flat rate . . . $17.19 Call waiting . . . $3.15

Exercise A Find the charge for the Brown's local telephone service.

Exercise B Find the monthly bill when these long distance charges and taxes are added to the Browns' usual charges

	Long Distance	Taxes	Monthly Bill
1)	$11.21	$1.44	______
2)	$22.31	$2.48	______
3)	$12.57	$1.31	______
4)	$8.57	$1.09	______
5)	0.00	$0.69	______
6)	$14.98	$1.68	______
7)	$5.78	$0.61	______
8)	$4.94	$0.98	______
9)	$5.66	$0.64	______
10)	$11.99	$1.59	______

Part of your monthly telephone bill goes toward the maintenance of the telephone poles and lines.

Exercise C Following are summaries of a family's gas, electric, and telephone bills for one year. Find the total expenses for these utilities for each month.

	Month	Gas	Electricity	Telephone
1)	January	$60.32	$31.44	$18.90
2)	February	$135.73	$30.95	$18.65
3)	March	$113.39	$33.23	$23.89
4)	April	$71.72	$31.69	$30.18
5)	May	$48.12	$31.05	$26.85
6)	June	$24.67	$38.57	$19.05
7)	July	$17.05	$55.74	$24.69
8)	August	$14.68	$102.83	$27.36
9)	September	$14.61	$84.93	$27.09
10)	October	$18.31	$35.45	$29.00
11)	November	$65.03	$21.61	$40.99
12)	December	$93.27	$21.97	$28.36

PROBLEM SOLVING

Exercise D Answer the following questions. Use the information given in Exercise C to help you.

1) How much more did the family spend for gas in February than in March?

2) How much more did the family spend for electricity in August than in December?

3) How much more did the family spend for the telephone in November than in February?

4) Did the family use the same amount of gas each month? Why or why not?

5) What could account for the different charges for electricity in various months?

With an Equal Monthly Payment plan, the customer pays the same amount each month for a utility. This amount is the average of the payments from the previous year.

6) What is the family's average gas payment?

7) What is the family's average electricity payment?

8) What is the family's average telephone payment?

Long distance companies give discounts for calls made outside business hours.

EXAMPLE The Long Distance Telephone Company offers a 35% discount on evening calls (5 P.M. to 11 P.M.). For late night calls (11 P.M. to 8 A.M.) and weekend calls, it gives a 60% discount.

Toshika makes a call at 8 P.M. that would have cost $5.25 during business hours. How much does she save by calling during the evening?

$ 5.25	Cost of call	$ 5.25	Cost of call
× .35	Discount	− 1.84	Savings
$1.83 75	Savings	$ 3.41	Discounted cost

Toshika saves $1.84 by calling during the evening. Her call costs $3.41.

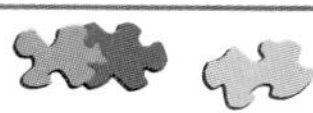

PROBLEM SOLVING

Exercise E Answer these questions based on the example shown above.

1) Antonio makes a call on Saturday that would have cost $6.00 during business hours. How much does he save?

2) How much does Antonio's call cost?

3) Pam calls her sister at 10 P.M. Friday. If the call costs $8.36 during business hours, how much does this call cost?

4) Pam calls her sister again at 10 P.M. on Saturday. If the call costs $8.36 during business hours, how much does this call cost?

5) How much does Pam save on these two calls?

Lesson 9 Mortgage Insurance

> ***Mortgage insurance***
>
> *A policy that pays all or part of the balance owed on a house.*

Homeowners can purchase insurance to protect their home. **Mortgage insurance** is a policy that can be purchased by owners of mortgaged property. It covers one or both owners of a house. If an insured owner dies, then the insurance company pays the balance owed on the house to the beneficiary.

The following table shows the percent of mortgage covered at different times for different mortgages.

Percent of Mortgage Covered					
Policy Year in Which Death Occurs	**30 Year Mort.**	**25 Year Mort.**	**20 Year Mort.**	**15 Year Mort.**	**10 Year Mort.**
1	100%	100%	100%	100%	100%
5	94%	92%	88%	80%	66%
10	84%	77%	67%	49%	12%
15	71%	59%	41%	9%	
20	55%	36%	8%		
25	34%	7%			
30	7%				

EXAMPLE Jack Benson had a $37,000 mortgage for a term of 25 years. He died in the fifteenth year. How much should the insurance company pay?

Step 1 Using the table on page 92, look in the first column, "Policy Year in Which Death Occurs," for 15. The percentage to be paid will be found in this row.

Step 2 Find the column for "25 Year Mort." Go down this column to row 15. Read "59%."

Step 3 Multiply the mortgage by 59%, or .59.

$ 37,000	Amount of mortgage
× .59	Percent covered by insurance
$21,830.00	Amount to be paid by insurance company

Exercise A Find the amount to be paid by the insurance company in each of these situations. Use the table to help you.

	Policy Year in Which Death Occurs	Years of Mortgage	Amount of Mortgage
1)	10	15	$40,000
2)	5	25	$33,500
3)	25	30	$25,700
4)	15	15	$10,000
5)	30	30	$95,800
6)	20	25	$88,000
7)	15	20	$64,500
8)	1	25	$32,700
9)	5	15	$46,800
10)	10	25	$39,900

Homeowners Insurance

Homeowners insurance

A policy that pays for loss from fire or other reasons.

Coverage rate

The percent paid for homeowners insurance protection.

A **homeowners insurance** policy covers the home and its contents. The coverage is for damage or loss caused by such things as fire, smoke, theft, or severe weather. Some policies also cover injuries people incur on the property.

The amount that a person pays for protection differs from home to home. Some factors that affect the **coverage rate** are:

- construction of brick or wood;
- location in a high or low crime area;
- distance from a fire hydrant or source of water;
- types of violent weather that occur in the area.

Sample Homeowners Rate Chart

Area	Construction	Coverage Rate
A	Brick Wood Frame	0.36% 0.46%
B	Brick Wood Frame	0.42% 0.54%
C	Brick Wood Frame	0.325% 0.444%
D	Brick Wood Frame	0.395% 0.518%

If you live near a body of water that could flood, you will need to purchase flood insurance.

EXAMPLE Felipe Peña owns a $65,000 brick home in Area A. How much will it cost him to insure the home each year with a homeowners insurance policy?

Step 1 Look at the chart on page 94.

Step 2 Find the coverage rate for a brick home in Area A. Read "0.36%."

Step 3 Multiply the value of the dwelling by 0.36%, or .0036.

$ 65,000	Value of dwelling
× .0036	Coverage rate
$234.0000	Annual insurance payment

His annual homeowners insurance payment will be $234.00.

Exercise A Find the annual payment for homeowners insurance on the following homes. Use the information given in the chart to help you.

	Area	Construction	Value of Dwelling
1)	A	Brick	$67,000
2)	C	Wood	$64,470
3)	B	Brick	$101,000
4)	D	Brick	$150,000
5)	C	Brick	$99,900
6)	A	Wood	$75,000
7)	B	Wood	$150,000
8)	D	Wood	$75,980
9)	C	Brick	$125,690
10)	D	Brick	$202,709

Review

Solve these problems.

1) Brad pays $346.50 per month for his rent. How much does he pay in a year? If Brad earns $1,586 per month, then does he pay rent according to the renter's rule? Remember, use 4.3 weeks per month when you apply the renter's rule.

2) Use the banker's rule, which states you may borrow up to 2.5 times your annual income. Calculate the minimum annual income needed to borrow $75,000.

3) A house is purchased for $87,000 with a down payment of $17,000. What is the monthly payment on a 9.5% mortgage? How much will be repaid in 30 years? Use the table to help you.

Monthly Principal and Interest Payments for 30 Years

Mortgage Amount	7%	7.5%	8%	8.5%	9%	9.5%	10%	10.5%	11%	11.5%	12%	12.5%	13%
$40,000	$266	$280	$294	$308	$322	$336	$351	$366	$381	$396	$411	$427	$442
$50,000	333	350	367	384	402	420	439	457	476	495	514	534	553
$60,000	399	420	440	461	483	505	527	549	571	594	617	640	664
$70,000	466	489	514	538	563	589	614	640	667	693	720	747	774
$80,000	532	559	587	615	644	673	702	732	762	792	823	854	885
$90,000	599	629	660	692	724	757	790	823	857	891	926	961	996
$100,000	665	699	734	769	805	841	878	915	952	990	1,029	1,067	1,106
$110,000	732	769	807	846	885	925	965	1,006	1,048	1,089	1,131	1,174	1,217

4) How much will homeowners insurance cost if the full value of a brick house in Area C is $97,000?

Sample Homeowners Rate Chart

Area	Construction	Coverage Rate
A	Brick	0.36%
	Wood Frame	0.46%
B	Brick	0.42%
	Wood Frame	0.54%
C	Brick	0.325%
	Wood Frame	0.444%

5) Which is more—the amount repaid on a mortgage for $67,900 for 15 years at 9%, or the amount repaid on a mortgage for $67,900 for 40 years at 7%? Use the table to help you.

Monthly Payments per $1,000

Years	7%	8%	9%	10%	11%	12%	13%
15	$8.99	$9.56	$10.14	$10.75	$11.37	$12.00	$12.65
20	7.75	8.36	9.00	9.65	10.32	11.01	11.72
25	7.07	7.72	8.39	9.09	9.80	10.53	11.28
30	6.65	7.34	8.05	8.78	9.52	10.29	11.06
35	6.39	7.10	7.84	8.60	9.37	10.16	10.95
40	6.21	6.95	7.71	8.49	9.28	10.08	10.90

6) What is this meter reading?

7) How many kilowatt hours were used between these meter readings: March meter reading—2750; April meter reading—3049? If the unit cost per kilowatt hour is $0.11, then how much is the bill for this month?

8) Compute the average number of units consumed: 504, 519, 576, 321, 256, 101, 76, 75, 127, 289, 367, and 511.

9) What is the total amount due for these utility bills? Electric—$156.19; Telephone—25.16; Gas—32.78

10) Find the amount to be paid by the mortgage insurance company for a claim on an $89,000 mortgage. The company will pay 37%.

Test Taking Tip

Try using a straightedge when you read tables that contain many numbers.

Chapter 5 Buying and Maintaining a Car

When people approach age sixteen, they look forward to getting their driver's licenses. If they have saved some money, then they also begin to look forward to their first major purchase—their own car. For most people their first purchase is a used car. A first car may require new tires, lots of repairs, and a good cleaning. Even though you may purchase dozens of cars during your lifetime, your first car will probably be the one you remember best.

In Chapter 5, you will learn about the expenses related to purchasing and maintaining a car. You will also learn about the expenses involved when insuring a car.

Goals for Learning

- To compute the price of a car when financing arrangements are made
- To determine the cost of an automobile when trade-ins or rebates are involved
- To compute insurance premiums
- To solve problems related to average speed and driving time
- To compute fuel costs
- To compute costs associated with car repairs

Lesson 1 Buying a New Car

Base price

The first amount listed on a car's price.

Options

Extra items added to a car.

Transportation/ Handling

A delivery fee charged to the buyer of a car.

Each new car has a **base price** charged for standard equipment. Any extra items that the customer wants to add to the car—such as an AM/FM stereo radio or air conditioning or radial tires—increase this price. These extra items are called **options**.

Following are several examples of sticker prices on new cars. Notice the base price, the costs of various options, and the fee for **transportation and handling** in each case.

EXAMPLE Here is a sticker from a car that Gene wants. The first amount is the base price. Then the options are listed. The last fee, transportation and handling, must be paid by the buyer. Gene finds that, with all the options, the car's total sticker price is $20,542.

$16,796	Base price
2,868	Options
+ 878	Trans./Hand.
$20,542	Total price

Sedan	**$16,796**
Anti-theft alarm	190
6-cylinder engine	313
Remote keyless entry	135
Automatic transmission	570
4 radial tires	195
Factory air conditioner	950
Anti-lock brakes	450
Spare tire	65
Transportation/Handling	878

Exercise A Find the total sticker price for each of these new cars.

1)

Hatchback 3-door	**$8,869**
Metallic paint	100
Console	178
Automatic transmission	550
Radial tires upgrade	59
Power steering	176
Rear window defroster	115
Factory A/C	950
AM/FM stereo radio	188
Mirrors	75
Tinted glass	82
Transportation/Handling	445

2)

Station Wagon	**$12,216**
Luggage rack	195
Remote control mirror	115
Power steering	195
6-cylinder engine	170
2-way liftgate	105
Rear window defroster	124
Air conditioning	900
Radio: AM/FM stereo with cassette	172
Tinted glass	88
Power windows and door locks	570
Transportation/Handling	508

3)

4-door Liftgate	**$16,719**
Power steering	176
Luggage rack	195
Rear window defroster	111
Air conditioning	963
AM/FM stereo radio	150
Dual remote-control sports mirrors	210
Tinted glass	76
Cruise control	270
Transportation/Handling	559

4)

Hatchback	**$10,988**
Automatic transmission	411
Clock	57
Power steering	190
Bucket seats	253
Anti-lock brakes	450
Rear defroster	120
AM/FM stereo radio	106
Dual sports mirrors	66
CFC-free air conditioning	1,000
Transportation/Handling	445

5)

Luxury Sedan	**$33,985**
Anti-theft alarm	190
Anti-lock brakes	450
Keyless entry system	141
Leather seats	854
License plate frames	20
Power windows and door locks	570
Head lamp package	175
AM/FM stereo w/CD	150
Dual remote-control mirrors	210
Power sunroof	981
Computer command ride	380
Defroster group	151
Transportation/Handling	976

Lesson 2 Buying a Used Car

Depreciate
To decrease in value.

New cars **depreciate** or lose value after they are bought. Many people buy used cars because of their lower prices. Sometimes used car dealers offer special sale prices to encourage people to buy these cars.

EXAMPLE The "Used But Not Abused" car lot is having a big sale. A two-year-old car that had been $9,200 is now sale priced at $8,750. How much money can be saved by buying this car on sale?

To find the savings, subtract the sale price from the original price.

$9,200	Price before sale
−8,750	Sale price
$ 450	Savings

Exercise A Find the amount that can be saved on each of these sales.

	Car	Years Old	Price Before Sale	Sale Price
1)	King	3	$8,889	$8,489
2)	Iguana	3	$9,389	$8,650
3)	Cat	4	$9,989	$9,589
4)	Mastery	1	$8,664	$6,894
5)	Windsprite	2	$9,689	$9,179
6)	Gazelle	4	$8,839	$7,959
7)	Checkmate	3	$10,199	$9,659
8)	Mirage	1	$10,323	$8,895
9)	Fox	3	$10,783	$9,295
10)	Cheetah	5	$11,097	$9,495
11)	Traveler	2	$12,998	$10,295
12)	Destiny	1	$13,000	$10,495

Exercise B Some buyers trade in their old car as part of the payment on a newer car. Find the cash price in each case. Subtract the trade-in value from the list price to find the cash price.

	List Price	Trade-in Value		List Price	Trade-in Value
1)	$16,895	$900	**6)**	$27,344	$3,795
2)	$15,595	$1,200	**7)**	$15,238	$8,770
3)	$14,908	$2,456	**8)**	$16,767	$869
4)	$10,345	$1,845	**9)**	$13,456	$1,457
5)	$10,449	$3,300	**10)**	$16,000	$4,879

The used-car dealership, Sue's Used Cars, offers this special:

Rebate
A return of part of a payment to a buyer.

Exercise C Find the sale price of each of these used cars from Sue's Used Cars. For a trade-in, subtract $750 from the original price. For a cash rebate, subtract $500 from the original price. The first answer is provided for you.

	Price of Car	With Trade-in	With Rebate
1)	$6,395	$5,645	$5,895
2)	$8,195	______	______
3)	$5,595	______	______
4)	$5,395	______	______
5)	$6,295	______	______
6)	$8,095	______	______
7)	$9,895	______	______
8)	$7,995	______	______

Lesson 3 Financing a Car

Few people pay cash for a car since cars are such expensive items. Financing terms vary with car dealers, banks, or other lenders. Most finance plans require a down payment. The remainder is paid in monthly installments.

Deferred price

The total amount paid, including interest on monthly payments.

The total amount paid in down payment and monthly payments is called the **deferred price**. The amount of the down payment, the number of months to pay, and the amount of the monthly payment may all differ with each sale. Study the example on the following page.

When you buy a new or used car, you may choose to finance your purchase with the car dealer, a bank, or some other lender.

EXAMPLE Manny's Used Cars makes the following offer on one of its cars: $499.00 down payment and $138.00 per month for 48 months. The cash price is $6,454. What is the total amount paid for the deferred price?

Step 1 Multiply.

$ 138	Monthly payment
× 48	Months
$6,624	Monthly payment total

Step 2 Add.

$6,624	Monthly payment total
+ 499	Down payment
$7,123	Deferred price

Exercise A Find the deferred price of each of these cars sold at Manny's Used Cars.

	Cash Price	Down Payment	Monthly Payment	Months to Pay
1)	$3,197	$99	$70	48
2)	$5,379	$299	$115	48
3)	$7,984	$499	$170	48
4)	$9,849	$999	$202	48
5)	$6,983	$299	$155	48
6)	$7,391	$299	$160	48
7)	$9,970	$599	$212	48

People who finance a car pay more than the cash price. They also must pay an interest charge, which is included in their monthly payments.

EXAMPLE Look at the example on page 105. What is the total interest paid on this car loan?

Step 1 Subtract.

$6,454	Cash price
− 499	Down payment
$5,955	Amount financed

Step 2 Multiply.

$ 138	Monthly payment
× 48	Months
$6,624	Monthly payment total

Step 3 Subtract.

$6,624	Monthly payment total
−5,955	Amount financed
$ 669	Interest paid

Exercise B Find the total interest paid for each purchase.

	Cash Price	Down Payment	Monthly Payment	Months to Pay
1)	$3,989	$89.00	$106.78	40
2)	$6,989	$1,307.00	$152.87	40
3)	$7,789	$289.00	$205.35	40
4)	$4,798	$198.00	$111.16	46
5)	$4,798	$1,461.82	$79.94	46
6)	$5,601	$89.00	$152.23	40
7)	$5,398	None	$128.20	46
8)	$8,798	$99.00	$185.25	52

Calculator Practice

Use this method to calculate the deferred price, the amount repaid, on a car loan.

Step 1 Key in the monthly payment.

Step 2 Press ×.

Step 3 Key in the number of months to pay.

Step 4 Press +.

Step 5 Key in the down payment.

Step 6 Press =.

Step 7 Affix the dollar sign and insert commas.

Did you hear that Jiang left his job in the loan department at the bank?

Yes, I understand that he lost interest in the job.

Find the deferred cost of a car with $199.00 down payment and $76 per month for 48 months.

76 × 48 + 199 =

The display will read 3847. The deferred price is $3,847.00.

Check your answers to Exercise A.

To find the amount of interest paid, start with the deferred price.

Press − and key in the cash price. Then press = again.

Check your answers to Exercise B by subtracting the cash price from the deferred price.

Lesson 4 Automobile Insurance

Liable

Forced by law to make good for damages done.

Liability insurance

A policy that pays for damages in an accident.

Premium

The amount paid for insurance.

The owner of a car is **liable**, or legally responsible, for any damage done by the car to persons or property. **Liability insurance** protects the owner against claims resulting from an accident that is his or her fault. It covers personal injuries and property damage. The cost of the policy, or the **premium**, is usually affected by the age and gender of the driver and the garaging location of the car.

Liability Insurance

10/20/15

Personal Injury	Personal Injury	Property Damage
A maximum of $10,000 for injury per person	A maximum of $20,000 for injuries per accident	A maximum of $15,000 for damage to property per accident

	Liability Insurance Premiums							
	Personal Injury				Property Damage			
Area	10/20	20/40	40/80	75/150	5	10	25	50
High risk	$210	$470	$610	$835	$72	$84	$99	$148
Average	$167	$339	$470	$620	$56	$69	$77	$98
Low risk	$140	$229	$340	$489	$48	$52	$61	$73

PROBLEM SOLVING

Exercise A Use this table to help you find the total premiums due in each case.

1) What is the premium for the 40/80/25 coverage for a car garaged in a high risk area? ($610 + $99 = ■)

2) Find the premium for a 10/20/25 policy in an average risk area.

3) What is the premium for a 75/150/50 policy in a low risk area?

4) Find the premium for a 20/40/5 policy in a high risk area.

EXAMPLE Because Shirin has a good driving record, she earns a "Good Driver Discount." After finding her premium, the insurance agent multiplies her premium by the good driver factor, .86, to find her actual cost. Shirin buys 40/80/25 coverage in a high risk area.

$610	For the 40/80
+ 99	For the 25
$709	Regular premium

$ 709	Regular premium
× .86	Good driver factor
$609.74	Shirin's premium

PROBLEM SOLVING

Exercise B Find these premiums. Use the table on page 108 to help you. Remember to multiply the factor times the regular premium.

1) Roland is 18 years old, lives in an average risk area, and wants 10/20/10 coverage. Because young males have the highest rate of accidents, he will be charged a 1.77 factor on his policy. Find his premium.

2) Lindsay lives in a high risk area and wants 40/80/50 coverage. Because she also uses her car for business, she is charged a 1.29 factor on her policy. Find her premium.

3) Because Woody has a poor driving record, he must pay a 1.48 factor on his policy for 20/40/25 coverage in a low risk area. What is his premium?

4) After six years of careful driving, Sanjiv marries. With the double discount of reaching age 25 and being married, he gets a .78 factor on his premium for 10/20/5 coverage in an average risk area. What is his premium?

5) Susan has a terrible driving record, drives 30 miles to work every day, and lives in a high risk area. She needs 75/150/50 coverage. Her factor is 2.08. What is Susan's premium?

Lesson 5 Reading an Odometer

Odometer

A measuring device that counts the miles a car travels.

Operating a car involves working with distance. The **odometer** on a car's dashboard counts the number of miles that the car has traveled. There are usually six digits of one color and a seventh digit of another color. Imagine a decimal point between the last two digits.

EXAMPLE

Whole miles Tenths of a mile

This odometer reads, "64,143.6 miles."
The reading in words is: "Sixty-four thousand, one hundred forty-three and six tenths miles."
Notice that the word "and" stands for the decimal point. It is never used in any other part of the number.

Spelling Review of Some Number Names

28	twenty-eight
30	thirty
44	forty-four
55	fifty-five
60	sixty
70	seventy
80	eighty
90	ninety
100	one hundred
1,000	one thousand
120,000	one hundred twenty thousand

Exercise A Copy these odometer readings. Then write each reading in words.

1) 0 0 0 3 0 4 6
2) 0 0 7 1 2 3 5
3) 1 1 2 8 9 0 5
4) 0 5 0 0 7 0 1
5) 0 9 9 9 9 9 9
6) 0 1 2 3 4 5 6
7) 0 3 0 0 5 6 7
8) 0 7 4 5 8 2 0
9) 0 6 0 0 0 6 2
10) 1 0 5 4 1 7 3

Lesson 6 Average Miles Driven Per Year

To find the average miles driven per year, divide the odometer reading by the age of the car.

EXAMPLE Charlotte's odometer reads 64,143.6 miles. Her car is six years old. On the average, how many miles does Charlotte drive each year?

$$6\overline{)64143.6} = 10690.6 \approx 10{,}691 \text{ Miles per year}$$

Exercise A Find the average number of miles driven per year for each car. Round your answer to the nearest mile.

	Odometer Reading	Age of Car in Years
1)	0303657	3
2)	0160606	2
3)	0497567	5
4)	0367558	4
5)	0124895	5
6)	1536259	12
7)	0958976	10
8)	0880459	9
9)	0702070	6
10)	0924881	7
11)	1263942	9
12)	1395273	4

Lesson 7 Number of Miles Traveled

To find the number of miles traveled, or trip distance, subtract the beginning odometer reading from the ending odometer reading.

EXAMPLES At the beginning of a trip, the odometer reading is 64,143.6. At the end of the trip, the odometer reading is 64,507.2. How many miles are traveled?

Subtract.	64,507.2	Reading at end of trip
	− 64,143.6	Reading at beginning of trip
	363.6	Miles traveled

Odometers in older cars show only six digits. If an odometer starts all over again, what number follows this reading?

99999|9

Counting, we would go to 100,000.0. However, since the odometer has only six digits, the next number it shows is 00000|0 . To find the distance traveled, use the 1 that you know should be the seventh digit.

Beginning of trip 99304|7

End of trip 00006|9

100,006.9	End of trip
−99,304.7	Beginning of trip
702.2	Miles traveled

Exercise A Find the miles traveled for each trip. Remember that decimal points indicate tenths of a mile.

	Beginning	End		Beginning	End
1)	12345.6	12489.0	**6)**	10101.1	10192.6
2)	00370.9	01000.8	**7)**	76842.3	76951.2
3)	36875.8	36879.2	**8)**	30306.7	31765.6
4)	99375.8	00305.9	**9)**	58410.4	58901.7
5)	00856.3	01746.5	**10)**	62307.6	63205.0

Lesson 8 Computing Gas Mileage

Gas mileage

The average number of miles a car will travel on a gallon of gas.

The farther a driver can go on a unit of gasoline, the better. One measure of how well a car operates is the miles per gallon (mpg) the car can get. This figure is called the **gas mileage** or the mileage rating.

"Miles per gallon" means $\text{gallons}\overline{)\text{miles}}$

EXAMPLE Alex travels 274 miles on 15 gallons of gas. What is his mileage?

$$15\overline{)274.0} = 18.3 \approx 18 \text{ miles per gallon}$$

Alex's gas mileage is 18 miles per gallon.

Exercise A Find the gas mileage for each trip. Round your answer to the nearest whole number.

	Distance	Gas Used
1)	400 miles	20 gallons
2)	1,200 miles	70 gallons
3)	356 miles	15 gallons
4)	489 miles	12 gallons
5)	25 miles	1.2 gallons
6)	565 miles	23 gallons
7)	256 miles	12 gallons
8)	1,024 miles	46 gallons
9)	245 miles	10 gallons
10)	779 miles	64 gallons

Lesson 9 Computing the Range of a Car

EPA rating

Estimate of how far a car can travel on one gallon of gas.

Range

How far a car can travel on a given number of gallons of gas.

How far can a car travel on a tank of gas? The Environmental Protection Agency (EPA) rates gas consumption for all cars and vans. The **EPA rating** is given for stop-and-start city driving as well as for highway driving on the open road.

To find the **range** of a car, multiply the miles per gallon rating by the capacity of the tank.

EXAMPLE Sun Lee's compact car has an EPA rating of 35 mpg in the city and 40 mpg on the highway. Her tank holds 12 gallons. What is the range of her car?

City:
$$\begin{array}{rl} 35 & \text{mpg} \\ \times 12 & \text{Gallons} \\ \hline 420 & \text{Miles range} \end{array}$$

Highway:
$$\begin{array}{rl} 40 & \text{mpg} \\ \times 12 & \text{Gallons} \\ \hline 480 & \text{Miles range} \end{array}$$

Exercise A Find the range for each car in the city and on the highway.

	EPA Rating		Tank	Range	
	City	Highway	Capacity	City	Highway
1)	40 mpg	50 mpg	10 gal.	______	______
2)	6 mpg	8 mpg	20 gal.	______	______
3)	20 mpg	30 mpg	19 gal.	______	______
4)	7 mpg	9 mpg	16 gal.	______	______
5)	21 mpg	29 mpg	17 gal.	______	______
6)	8 mpg	12 mpg	10 gal.	______	______
7)	27 mpg	38 mpg	19 gal.	______	______
8)	9 mpg	30 mpg	9 gal.	______	______
9)	29 mpg	37 mpg	18 gal.	______	______
10)	5 mpg	9 mpg	11 gal.	______	______

Lesson 10 Computing the Fuel Needed

It is often helpful to estimate how many gallons of gasoline will be needed for a trip. To find out how much fuel is needed for a trip, divide the distance by the mileage rating.

EXAMPLE Richard is planning a 390-mile trip. His car's EPA rating is 25 mpg on the highway. How many gallons of gas will he require for this trip?

$$25 \overline{)390.0} = 15.6 \approx 16$$

15.6 ≈ 16 gallons needed for the trip
25) 390.0 Miles

Among the factors that affect the mpg on your car are the engine's size, whether you drive more in the city or on a highway, and your personal driving habits.

Exercise A Find the amount of fuel needed for each trip. Round your answer to the nearest whole number.

	Distance	Mileage Rating	Amount of Fuel
1)	150 miles	20 mpg	________
2)	370 miles	27 mpg	________
3)	896 miles	35 mpg	________
4)	1,040 miles	40 mpg	________
5)	4,488 miles	44 mpg	________
6)	204 miles	60 mpg	________
7)	168 miles	48 mpg	________
8)	542 miles	68 mpg	________
9)	1,503 miles	44 mpg	________
10)	5,887 miles	36 mpg	________

Lesson 11 Computing Average Speed

Miles per hour (mph)

A customary measurement of speed.

Speed is measured in **miles per hour** (mph). To find the average rate of speed on a trip, divide the distance by the time.

EXAMPLE Carlotta drives 360 miles in 8 hours and 36 minutes. What is her average rate of speed?

Step 1 Convert minutes to a decimal part of an hour by dividing by 60.

$$60\overline{)36.0} = 0.6$$ (0.6 Hour; 36.0 Minutes)

Step 2 Write the hours as a decimal number.
8 hours and 36 minutes
8 hours + 0.6 hour = 8.6 hours

Step 3 Divide the miles by the hours.

$$8.6.\overline{)360.0.0} = 41.9 \approx 42 \text{ mph}$$

Carlotta's average rate of speed is 42 miles per hour (mph).

Exercise A Find the average rate of speed for each trip. Round your answer to the nearest whole number.

	Distance	Time
1)	180 miles	4 hours, 30 minutes
2)	340 miles	6 hours, 12 minutes
3)	1,100 miles	21 hours, 24 minutes
4)	65 miles	3 hours, 15 minutes
5)	385 miles	7 hours, 48 minutes
6)	203 miles	8 hours, 18 minutes
7)	46 miles	1 hour, 15 minutes
8)	205 miles	3 hours, 42 minutes
9)	233 miles	3 hours, 54 minutes
10)	261 miles	5 hours, 6 minutes

Lesson 12 Computing Travel Time

To find the time it should take for a trip, divide the distance by the speed.

EXAMPLE Chong plans a 418-mile trip to Virginia. Because he and his family will travel on the interstate highways for most of the trip, they hope to average 50 mph. How long should they expect the trip to take?

Step 1 Divide the distance by the average speed.

$$\begin{array}{r l} 8.36 & \text{Hours} \\ 50\overline{)418.00} & \text{Miles} \end{array}$$

Step 2 Convert the decimal part of the quotient to minutes by multiplying it by 60.

$$\begin{array}{r l} .36 & \text{Hours} \\ \underline{\times\ 60} & \text{Minutes per hour} \\ 21.60 \approx & 22 \text{ minutes} \end{array}$$

Step 3 Write the hours and minutes. 8 hours, 22 minutes

Exercise A Find the travel time for each of these trips. Round your answer to the nearest minute.

	Distance	Average Speed
1)	180 miles	45 mph
2)	91 miles	35 mph
3)	56 miles	42 mph
4)	360 miles	50 mph
5)	143 miles	37 mph
6)	285 miles	47 mph
7)	708 miles	50 mph
8)	163 miles	40 mph
9)	664 miles	55 mph
10)	25 miles	48 mph

Lesson 13 Buying Gasoline

Operating a car involves buying gasoline. Gasoline prices are quoted per gallon. Each price has three decimal places because gasoline is priced to the nearest tenth of a cent.

EXAMPLE Suppose premium unleaded gasoline costs $1.459 per gallon. It is customary to read that price as "one dollar forty-five and 9/10 cents." If we write that price in cents, it looks like this: 145.9¢. This number, 145.9¢, is read as "one hundred forty-five and nine-tenths cents."

To find the cost of gasoline, multiply the number of gallons purchased times the cost per gallon. Round to the nearest cent.

EXAMPLE Suppose regular unleaded gasoline costs 138.9¢ per gallon. Find the cost of 18 gallons.

138.9¢ = $1.389

$ 1.389		Cost per gallon
× 18		Number of gallons purchased
$25.002	≈	$25.00 for 18 gallons

Exercise A Find the cost for each of these gasoline purchases.

1) 17 gal. at $1.379 per gallon
2) 17 gal. at $1.489 per gallon
3) 17 gal. at $1.569 per gallon
4) 17 gal. at $1.299 per gallon
5) 17 gal. at $1.439 per gallon
6) 19 gal. at 137.9¢ per gallon
7) 19 gal. at 142.9¢ per gallon
8) 19 gal. at $1.559 per gallon
9) 19 gal. at $1.459 per gallon
10) 19 gal. at $1.689 per gallon

Gasoline from self-service pumps costs less per unit (gallon) than gas from full-service pumps. Customers save money by pumping their own gas. The difference between the posted prices may seem small, but the savings per tankful are considerable.

Saving money is one reason many people choose to use self-serve gas pumps.

EXAMPLE Donna needs to buy 8 gallons of gas. How much will she save by pumping her own? The price on the self-serve pump is 1.389 per gallon. The price on the full-service pump is 1.459 per gallon.

Step 1 Subtract. Find the difference in price per unit.

$ 1.459	Full-serve price
−1.389	Self-serve price
$ .070	Difference in prices

Step 2 To find the amount saved, multiply the the difference by the number of units purchased.

$.070	Difference in prices
× 8	Gallons purchased
$ .56	Savings

Exercise B Find the amount each customer saved by using the self-serve gasoline pump.

	Full-Serve	Self-Serve	Units	Savings
1)	$1.679	$1.599	20 gal.	____
2)	$1.899	$1.779	19 gal.	____
3)	$1.459	$1.429	10 gal.	____
4)	159.9¢	152.9¢	14 gal.	____
5)	135.9¢	129.9¢	15 gal.	____
6)	155.9¢	144.9¢	20 gal.	____
7)	$1.759	$1.689	14 gal.	____
8)	164.9¢	157.9¢	17 gal.	____
9)	$1.459	$1.399	17 gal.	____
10)	145.9¢	139.9¢	15 gal.	____

Lesson 14 Computing the Cost of Repairs

Parts and labor

Customer is charged for items to make a repair and the mechanic's time.

Rebuilt

Describing items that have been reconstructed or extensively repaired.

Cars need occasional repair. Regular tune-ups keep them running smoothly, but broken or worn parts must be replaced to prevent further damage. At an auto repair shop, you are charged for **parts and labor**. This terms means that you must pay the mechanic a certain amount per hour for any work done. It also means that you must pay for all the new or **rebuilt** items that the mechanic installs.

EXAMPLE A customer has her automatic transmission replaced for $500.00. The mechanic replaces 9 quarts of transmission fluid @ $3.50 per quart. It takes three hours of labor to complete the job. The cost for labor is $60.00 per hour. There is a 5% sales tax for all parts. No sales tax is charged on labor. What is the total cost?

Step 1 Find the total cost of the parts.

9 qt. × $3.50 = $31.50.

$ 31.50	Cost of fluid
+500.00	Transmission repair
$531.50	Total parts

Step 2 Compute the sales tax. Hint: Instead of computing 5% sales tax and adding it on, multiply by 105% and do it in one step. Round the answer to the next cent.

$531.50 × 105% (1.05)

$ 531.50	Total parts
× 1.05	Rate for parts plus tax
$558.075 ≈	$558.08 Parts plus tax

Step 3 Compute the labor.

$60.00 per hour for 3 hours

$60.00 × 3 = $180.00 Labor

Step 4 Add the parts plus tax and the labor together to find the total cost.

$ 558.08	Parts plus tax
+ 180.00	Labor
$ 738.08	Total cost

Consumer Humor

"Did you hear that James opened a new muffler shop?"

"Yes, I also heard that he is always exhausted!"

Exercise A Find the total cost of each repair job. Use $60 per hour as the labor rate. Include 5% tax on the parts.

1)	Parts:	Battery, $69.95	Labor: 0.3 hour
2)	Parts:	Muffler, $35.00 Tail pipe, $18.00 Clamps, $2.00	Labor: 1 hour
3)	Parts:	4 Shock Absorbers @ $17.94	Labor: 2 hours
4)	Parts:	Rebuilt alternator, $85.00 Fan belt, $10.00	Labor: $\frac{1}{2}$ hour
5)	Parts:	4 Radial tires 6R78x14 @ $65 per tire Federal excise tax @ $2.50 per tire Balanced and mounted @ $4.00 per tire	Labor: Included in price of tire
6)	Parts:	Filter, $7.50 6 cans oil @ $1.95 per can	Labor: 0.2 hours
7)	Parts:	Radiator, $150.00 2 gallons antifreeze @ $6.99	Labor: 1 hour
8)	Parts:	Disc brakes, $20.00 2 turn rotors @ $5.00 each	Labor: 2 hours
9)	Parts:	Power steering pump, $95.00 6 quarts fluid @ $1.75 per quart	Labor: 2 hours
10)	Parts:	2-Barrel carburetor, $75.00 6 plugs @ $1.45 each Points, $4.50	Labor: 3.2 hours

Chapter 5 Review

Solve these problems.

1) What is the total cost of a used car that sells for $6,399 if the dealer offers the buyer $299 on a trade-in car?

2) Compute the total amount paid for a used car with the following financing arrangements. The buyer agrees to pay $89 down plus $128.57 per month for 36 months.

3) What is the deferred cost of a car if the purchase price is $7,299, the down payment is $299, and the monthly payments are $165 per month for 48 months?

4) Stan Sampson has a good driver discount on his insurance policy. Compute his actual premium if he pays 86% of the $279 regular premium rate.

5) Write this odometer reading in words.

73804 | 5

6) The odometer in Ingrid's 3-year-old car reads 38465.2. What is her average yearly mileage?

7) At the beginning of a trip, the odometer reads 004157.8. At the end of the trip, the odometer reads 004360.7. Compute the distance traveled.

8) Find the gas mileage for a car that travels 473.3 miles on 13.6 gallons of gas.

9) If the EPA rating for a car is 22 mpg, then about how much fuel is needed for a 763 mile trip? Round your answer to the nearest gallon.

10) Brad is planning a 285-mile trip. His car's EPA rating is 18 mpg. How many gallons of gas will Brad need for his trip? Round your answer to the nearest gallon.

11) Calculate the average rate of speed on a 714-mile trip that takes 17 hours.

12) Find the number of hours it will take to drive 360 miles if a person averages 50 miles per hour.

13) How many hours will it take to travel 200 miles, if the driver averages 50 miles per hour?

14) Calculate the cost of 17 gallons of gasoline at a price of $1.599 cents per gallon. Round your answer to the nearest cent.

15) Calculate the cost of 7.3 hours of mechanical labor at a rate of $55 per hour.

Test Taking Tip

Sometimes it is easier to learn new vocabulary words if you make them a part of your speaking and writing in other discussions and subject areas.

Chapter 6

Working With Food

Today's consumer is becoming more aware of issues related to nutrition. The media provide much of the information about what types of foods are and are not healthy for you. The government requires food packagers to provide detailed information about the nutritional content of the foods they prepare. You may have noticed that food packaging includes labels that provide a wealth of information. These labels are designed to help you compare items and make informed decisions about the foods you purchase.

In Chapter 6, you will learn about some of the mathematics involved in selecting, preparing, and eating food.

Goals for Learning

- To calculate the number of calories consumed
- To use ratios and proportion to calculate fat calories and change recipe yields
- To read and interpret nutrition information found on food packages
- To find the number of calories your body uses when exercising
- To calculate the times food should begin cooking to be ready at a given time

Lesson 1 Counting Calories

Calorie

A measurement that indicates the energy value of foods.

Celsius

Temperature scale where 0° represents freezing and 100° represents boiling.

Many people are concerned about calories. A **calorie** is a measure of heat energy. It is the amount of energy needed to raise the temperature of one kilogram of water one degree **Celsius**. Calories measure food consumption because food contains energy for our bodies. The more energy that a food provides, the higher the number of calories that it contains.

EXAMPLE The following chart shows everything that Tamika eats in one day plus the calories in each food item.

Food for One Day		
Meal	**Serving**	**Calories**
Breakfast	Cereal, $\frac{2}{3}$ cup	100
	Skim milk, 4 oz.	50
	Strawberries, $\frac{1}{3}$ cup	15
Lunch	Yogurt, 8 oz.	250
	Chicken enchilada, 9.9 oz.	290
	Skim milk, 8 oz.	100
	Apple	80
Dinner	Broiled fish fillet, 3 oz.	120
	Broccoli, $\frac{1}{2}$ cup	25
	Refried beans, $\frac{1}{2}$ cup	110
	Rice, $\frac{1}{2}$ cup	120
	Tea	4
	Cherry pie, $\frac{1}{8}$ of a pie	220
Snacks	Popcorn, 3 cups	180
	Spring water, 1 quart	0
	Nectarine	65
	Bagel, 4 oz.	280

Exercise A Find the number of calories that Tamika consumes in each case.

1) For breakfast

2) For lunch

3) For dinner

4) For snacks

5) During the entire day

6) For breakfast, lunch, and dinner

7) Tamika is not overweight. Why do you think this is the case?

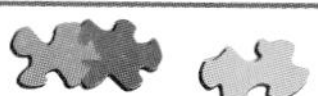

PROBLEM SOLVING

Exercise B Find the answers. Use the chart on page 126 to help you solve the first four problems.

1) If Tamika has another bowl of cereal with milk for breakfast, then how many more calories will she consume?

2) How many total calories are there in all of the fresh fruit Tamika eats?

3) How many calories are there in a whole cherry pie? (Hint: There are 220 calories in $\frac{1}{8}$ of a pie. There are eight $\frac{1}{8}$'s in a pie, so multiply 220 by 8 to find the total number of calories.)

4) How many calories are there in 1 cup of strawberries?

5) How many calories are contained in a gingerbread cake if $\frac{1}{9}$ of the cake contains 175 calories?

6) How many calories are contained in a whole piece of Matzo if $\frac{1}{2}$ piece contains 60 calories?

7) How many calories are contained in 6 glasses of lemon-lime drink if each glass contains 70 calories?

8) How many more calories are there in a piece of apple crumb pie (430 calories) than in a piece of pumpkin pie (180 calories)?

9) How many more calories are there in a serving of eggplant parmigiana (480 calories) than in a serving of angel hair pasta (240 calories)? Write what you notice about the result in a sentence.

10) One ounce of macadamia nuts has 200 calories. One ounce of almonds has 150 calories. What is the difference in calories? If you were choosing, which serving of nuts would you take? Write what you decide in a sentence.

Fruits and vegetables offer healthy choices for people watching their calorie intake.

Lesson 2 The Key to Ratio

Ratio
Number relationship between two or more things.

A **ratio** is a comparison of two quantities. Study the following examples.

EXAMPLES Suppose that there are 18 females and 14 males in your class.
The ratio of males to females is 14 to 18.
The ratio of females to males is 18 to 14.

A short way to write ratios is with fractions.

The ratio of males to females is $\frac{14}{18}$.

The ratio of females to males is $\frac{18}{14}$.

You can simplify a fraction by dividing both terms by their greatest common factor.

14 to 18 $\longrightarrow$ $\frac{14}{18} = \frac{14 \div 2}{18 \div 2} = \frac{7}{9}$

18 to 14 $\longrightarrow$ $\frac{18}{14} = \frac{18 \div 2}{14 \div 2} = \frac{9}{7}$

Exercise A Write each ratio as a fraction in simplest terms.

1) 2 to 4

2) 4 to 7

3) 6 to 8

4) 5 to 10

5) 8 to 36

6) a million to 1

7) two to three

8) 100 to 150

9) 160 calories to 2 cups

10) 34 miles to 2 gallons

11) 40 minutes to 50 miles

12) 120 miles to 3 hours

13) 145 calories to 15 ounces

14) eight to twelve

15) ten to fifteen

16) six to nine

The Key to Proportion

Proportion

An equal comparison.

Cross products

Multiplication of the denominator of one fraction with the numerator of another.

When two ratios are equal, we say that they form a **proportion**. One way to tell if two ratios are equal is to compare the **cross products**. This answer is obtained by multiplying the denominator of one fraction by the numerator of another.

EXAMPLES

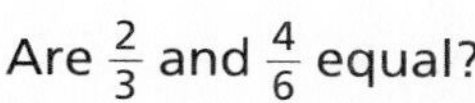

Are $\frac{2}{3}$ and $\frac{4}{6}$ equal?

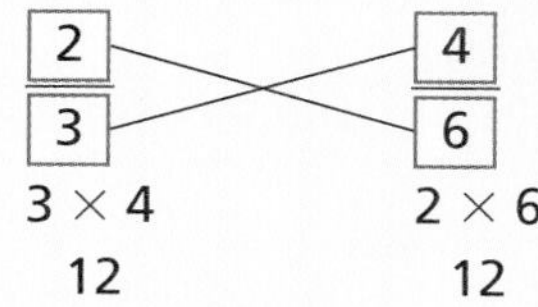

$3 \times 4 \quad 2 \times 6$

$12 \quad 12 \qquad \frac{2}{3} = \frac{4}{6}$

The cross products are both 12.
The cross products are equal, so the ratios form a proportion.

Do $\frac{7}{8}$ and $\frac{28}{32}$ form a proportion?

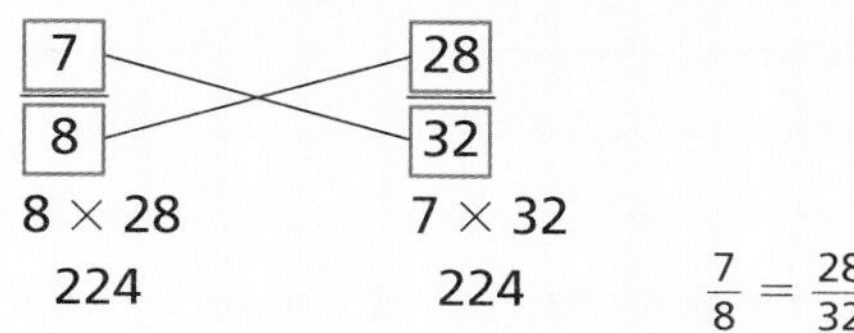

$8 \times 28 \quad 7 \times 32$

$224 \quad 224 \qquad \frac{7}{8} = \frac{28}{32}$

Both cross products are 224.
The cross products are equal, so the ratios form a proportion.

Exercise A Copy the following ratios. Check if the ratios are equal. Write an equal sign if the ratios form a proportion.

1) $\frac{3}{6} \quad \frac{5}{10}$

2) $\frac{1}{4} \quad \frac{2}{8}$

3) $\frac{5}{8} \quad \frac{3}{4}$

4) $\frac{2}{3} \quad \frac{9}{12}$

5) $\frac{10}{16} \quad \frac{5}{8}$

6) $\frac{7}{8} \quad \frac{15}{16}$

7) $\frac{1}{3} \quad \frac{5}{6}$

8) $\frac{4}{5} \quad \frac{20}{25}$

9) $\frac{10}{19} \quad \frac{30}{39}$

You may use cross products to find an unknown term in a proportion.

EXAMPLE

$\frac{2}{5} = \frac{\blacksquare}{15}$

Step 1 Find one cross product.

$\frac{2}{5} = \frac{\blacksquare}{15} \longrightarrow 2 \times 15 = 30$

Step 2 To find the missing term, divide the cross product by the other term.

$\frac{2}{5} = \frac{\blacksquare}{15}$

$5\overline{)30}$ = 6

6 Missing term
30 Cross product

Step 3 Write the complete proportion.

$\frac{2}{5} = \frac{6}{15}$

Step 4 Check by comparing cross products.

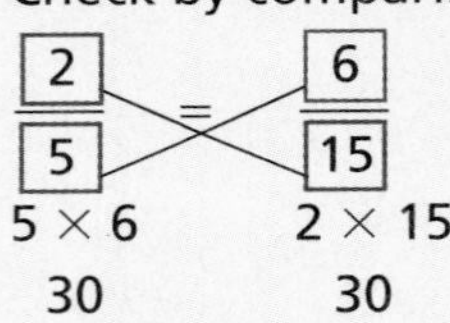

5×6 2×15

30   30

Exercise B Find the missing term in each proportion.

1) $\frac{1}{3} = \frac{\blacksquare}{12}$

2) $\frac{8}{150} = \frac{\blacksquare}{75}$

3) $\frac{2}{7} = \frac{24}{\blacksquare}$

4) $\frac{108}{18} = \frac{\blacksquare}{3}$

5) $\frac{5}{25} = \frac{25}{\blacksquare}$

6) $\frac{3}{4} = \frac{6}{\blacksquare}$

7) $\frac{5}{16} = \frac{25}{\blacksquare}$

8) $\frac{96}{180} = \frac{16}{\blacksquare}$

9) $\frac{2}{4} = \frac{4}{\blacksquare}$

10) $\frac{4}{\blacksquare} = \frac{16}{64}$

11) $\frac{\blacksquare}{12} = \frac{27}{36}$

12) $\frac{3}{\blacksquare} = \frac{9}{45}$

13) $\frac{72}{\blacksquare} = \frac{9}{7}$

14) $\frac{3}{9} = \frac{9}{\blacksquare}$

15) $\frac{1}{\blacksquare} = \frac{2}{4}$

Lesson 4 Finding Calories With Proportion

Read the calorie chart. When you drink a glass of punch, you do not always drink 12 ounces. You may want more than $\frac{1}{3}$ cup of cereal. How can you use the calorie chart to tell the number of calories in any amount of food? One way is to use proportions.

Calorie Chart

Food Item	Amount	Calories
Fruit punch	12 oz.	80
14″ pizza	$\frac{1}{8}$ pie	186
Bran cereal	$\frac{1}{3}$ cup	70
Chicken enchiladas	9 oz.	280
Zucchini	$\frac{2}{3}$ cup	12
Lentil and carrot soup	7.5 fl. oz.	70
Gefilte fish	1.7 oz.	60

EXAMPLES How many calories are in a 16 oz. bottle of fruit punch?

Step 1 Write a proportion.

$$\frac{12 \text{ ounces}}{80 \text{ calories}} = \frac{16 \text{ ounces}}{\blacksquare \text{ calories}}$$

Step 2 Find the cross product. $80 \times 16 = 1{,}280$

Step 3 Divide and round to the nearest whole number. $1{,}280 \div 12 = 106.7 \approx 107$ calories

At the Leaning Tower of Pizza Shop, pizzas are cut into six pieces instead of eight. How many calories are in one portion, or $\frac{1}{6}$ of a pizza?

Step 1 Write a proportion.

$$\frac{\frac{1}{8} \text{ pizza}}{186 \text{ calories}} = \frac{\frac{1}{6} \text{ pizza}}{\blacksquare \text{ calories}}$$

Step 2 Find the cross product. $186 \times \frac{1}{6} = 31$

Step 3 Divide. When dividing by a fraction, invert the divisor and multiply.

$31 \div \frac{1}{8} \longrightarrow 31 \times \frac{8}{1} = 248$ calories

Consumer Humor

Do you want your pizza cut into eight pieces today?

No, cut it into six pieces. I'm not sure I can eat eight.

Exercise A Calculate the number of calories in each portion by using a proportion. Round your answer to the nearest calorie. Follow the examples on page 131.

1) 8 oz. of fruit punch	12 oz. = 80 calories
2) 2 cups of bran cereal	$\frac{1}{3}$ cup = 70 calories
3) 16 oz. chicken enchiladas	9 oz. = 230 calories
4) 1 cup of zucchini	$\frac{2}{3}$ cup = 12 calories
5) 16 oz. lentil and carrot soup	7.5 fl. oz. = 70 calories
6) 4 oz. of gefilte fish	1.7 oz. = 60 calories
7) 4 oz. of beef Cantonese	9 oz. = 200 calories
8) 3 ounces of rice	7 oz. = 225 calories
9) One-sixth of a pie	one-seventh of a pie = 350 calories
10) One-fourth of a pizza	one-eighth of a pizza = 186 calories
11) 3.5 oz. of layer cake	2 oz. = 200 calories
12) 3 oz. of brownies	1 oz. = 95 calories

PROBLEM SOLVING

Exercise B Challenge yourself by solving these problems.

1) A can of chicken rice soup contains 2 servings. Each serving has 130 calories in it. How many calories are there in the whole can?

2) The chicken rice soup can holds 19 oz. How many calories are there in 16 oz.? (Hint: Use your answer to problem 1 for the total number of calories in the 19 oz. can.)

3) A can of water packed tuna contains 2.5 servings of 60 calories each. How many calories are in the whole can?

4) The tuna in the can weighs 6 ounces. How many calories are there in 3.5 ounces?

5) The product label on a certain can of spaghetti sauce says the can holds 6 servings of $\frac{1}{2}$ cup each. Each serving contains 60 calories. How many calories are in the whole can?

6) How many calories are in $1\frac{1}{2}$ cups of the spaghetti sauce?

7) How many calories are in 1 cup of the spaghetti sauce?

8) If you want to limit your spaghetti sauce calories to 100, then how much of this spaghetti sauce can you have?

Using Nutrition Information

Daily Value

Nutrient levels listed on a food label.

International Units (I.U.)

The amount of a nutrient or vitamin that produces an effect.

Nutrient

A substance that furnishes nourishment.

Recommended Dietary Allowance (RDA)

Nutrient levels required to maintain energy and growth.

Trace (T)

A very small amount.

The foods you eat affect your health and your body's functions. To help you make wise nutrition choices, food labels list **nutrient** amounts for one serving of a food product. If you have this nutrition information, you will know how much the food contributes to your daily needs to maintain energy and healthy growth.

The food label gives the percent of the **Daily Value** for each nutrient that one serving of the food provides. Percent Daily Values are based on a 2,000-calories-per-day diet. Your own daily values may be higher or lower depending on your calorie needs. You can use the Percent Daily Value information to estimate how much of a nutrient is in one serving.

Daily Values can also help you watch your intake of other food substances such as cholesterol, sodium, and dietary fiber. People with high blood pressure are often advised by their doctors to lower their sodium intake. Food labels tell how much sodium is in a food product so that you can track how much you consume. For example, the Daily Value for sodium is 2,400 mg. A food that has 1,150 mg of sodium per serving states on the label that it has 48% of the Daily Value.

Nutrition Facts

Serv. Size 1 cup (252g)
Servings about 2
Calories 260
Fat Cal. 100
* Percent Daily Values (DV) are based on a 2,000 calorie diet.

Amount/Serving	%DV*	Amount/Serving	%DV*
Total Fat 11g	**17%**	**Total Carb.** 31g	**10%**
Sat. Fat 5g	**25%**	Dietary Fiber 5g	**20%**
Cholest. 20mg	**7%**	Sugars 10g	
Sodium 1,150mg	**48%**	**Protein** 11g	

Vitamin A 10% • Vitamin C 2% • Calcium 4% • Iron 15%

The charts on page 134 show the **Recommended Dietary Allowances (RDA)** for certain nutrients and nutritional value of some beverages. You can use this information to help you decide how many calories and how much of each nutrient your body needs. Nutrient levels vary with a person's gender, age, and weight.

On the beverage chart, T means that only a **trace** amount of nutrient is present. I.U. or **International Units** is a standard measurement for some nutrients.

Recommended Dietary Allowances (RDA) of Chief Food Elements Source: Food and Nutrition Board, National Research Council											
	Age	Weight (lb.)	Calories	Protein (grams)	Calcium (mg.)	Iron (mg.)	Vit. A (I.U.)	Thia-min (mg.)	Ribo-flavin (mg.)	Niacin (mg.)	Vit. C (Ascorbic Acid) (mg.)
Male	11–14	99	2,500	45	1,200	12	5,000	1.3	1.5	17	50
	15–18	145	3,000	59	1,200	12	5,000	1.5	1.8	20	60
	19–24	160	2,900	58	1,200	10	5,000	1.5	1.7	19	60
	25–50	174	2,900	63	800	10	5,000	1.5	1.7	19	60
	51+	170	2,300	63	800	10	5,000	1.2	1.4	15	60
Female	11–14	101	2,200	46	1,200	15	4,000	1.1	1.3	15	50
	15–18	120	2,200	44	1,200	15	4,000	1.1	1.3	15	60
	19–24	128	2,200	46	1,200	15	4,000	1.1	1.3	15	60
	25–50	138	2,200	50	800	15	4,000	1.1	1.3	15	60
	51+	143	1,900	50	800	10	4,000	1.0	1.2	13	60

The U.S. Department of Agriculture lists these nutrients in beverages:

Nutritional Value of Beverages										
Beverage	Volume (fluid oz.)	Calories	Protein (grams)	Calcium (mg.)	Iron (mg.)	Vit. A (I.U.)	Thiamin (mg.) (mg.)	Ribo-flavin (mg.)	Niacin (mg.)	Vit. C (Ascorbic Acid) (mg.)
Whole milk	8	157	8	290.4	T	240	T	.41	T	T
Skim milk	8	100	9.7	351.8	T	400	.1	.5	T	T
Apple juice	8	117	.2	T	.9	T	T	T	T	T
Cranberry juice	8	144	T	T	T	T	T	T	T	89.7
Grapefruit juice	8	94	1.3	T	T	T	.1	T	T	72.1
Grape juice	8	154	1.4	T	.6	T	T	.1	T	T
Orange juice	8	112	1.7	T	T	T	.22	T	1.0	124
Prune Juice	8	182	1.6	T	3	T	T	.2	2.0	10.5
Club soda	12	0	0	0	0	0	0	0	0	0
Cola	12	152	0	0	0	0	0	0	0	0
Diet cola	12	4	.4	0	0	0	0	0	0	0
Orange soda	12	179	0	0	0	0	0	0	0	0
Ginger ale	12	124	0	0	.7	0	0	0	0	0
Root beer	12	154	0	0	0	0	0	0	0	0
T = Trace I.U. = International Units										

PROBLEM SOLVING

Exercise A Write the answers. Use information from the charts on page 134 to help you.

1) Which beverage is highest in Vitamin A?

2) Which beverage is highest in Vitamin C (ascorbic acid)?

3) Which two beverages have the lowest number of calories?

4) Which beverage is highest in calcium?

5) Which juice is highest in thiamin?

6) List the juices and milk in order of their protein content. Begin with the highest.

7) List the beverages in order of their iron content. Begin with the highest.

8) List the beverages in order of their riboflavin content. Begin with the lowest.

9) Which three beverages supply more than the Recommended Dietary Allowance (RDA)of Vitamin C?

10) Compared with the RDA for protein, are juices high or low in protein? Are juices a good source for protein?

11) What do you think is meant by this statement: "Soft drinks contain empty calories"?

One serving of food may provide part of the Recommended Dietary Allowance for a certain nutrient. You can find out what percent of the RDA for nutrient is supplied in one serving by using a ratio.

EXAMPLE What percent of the RDA of iron for an 18-year-old female is provided by 8 ounces of grape juice? Follow these steps.

Step 1 Write the ratio.

$$\frac{\text{iron in grape juice}}{\text{RDA of iron}} = \frac{.6 \text{ mg}}{15 \text{ mg}}$$

Step 2 Change the fraction to a percent by dividing.

$$\frac{.6}{15} = 15\overline{).60}\text{ (quotient } .04\text{)} = 4\%$$

Eight ounces of grape juice provides an 18-year-old female with 4% of the RDA for iron.

Exercise B Find the percent of the RDA of the nutrient that is supplied by 8 ounces of each beverage. Use the charts on page 134 to help you.

1) Calcium in skim milk for a 16 year old

2) Vitamin C in orange juice for a 50-year-old male

3) Iron in apple juice for a 25-year-old female

4) Thiamin in orange juice for a 15-year-old male

5) Niacin in prune juice for a 14-year-old female

6) Riboflavin in whole milk for a 37-year-old male

7) Protein in grapefruit juice for a 22-year-old female

Calculator Practice Use this method to calculate the percent of the RDA of a nutrient found in a certain food.

Step 1 Key in the amount in the food.

Step 2 Press ÷ .

Step 3 Key in the RDA for that nutrient.

Step 4 Press × .

Step 5 Key in 100.

Step 6 Press = .

Step 7 Round to the nearest whole number and affix the percent sign.

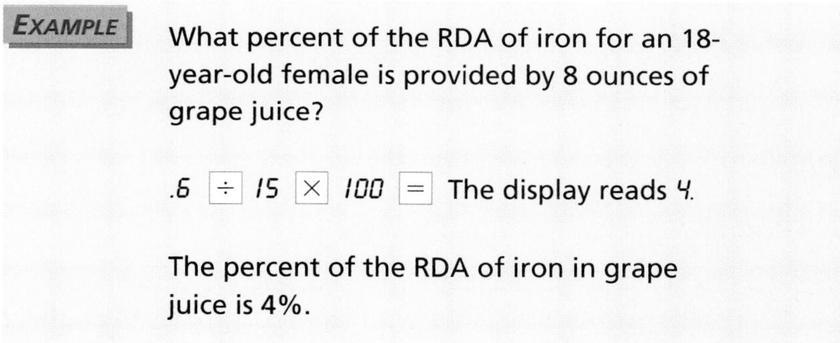

EXAMPLE

What percent of the RDA of iron for an 18-year-old female is provided by 8 ounces of grape juice?

.6 ÷ 15 × 100 = The display reads 4.

The percent of the RDA of iron in grape juice is 4%.

Check your work for Exercise B by using this method.

Lesson 6 Fat Grams and Calories

You should eat more of foods shown at the bottom of the food pyramid than those shown at the top.

Consumers are becoming health conscious. They are concerned about the amount of fat in their diet. The U.S. Department of Agriculture and the U.S. Department of Health and Human Services have designed a Guide to Daily Food Choices called the Food Guide Pyramid. Many foods naturally contain fats. While some fat is necessary, added fat should be used sparingly in your diet. A guide is to limit your fat intake to less than 30% of calories.

EXAMPLE Suppose you eat 2,300 calories a day. How many calories of fat is your limit? Calculate 30% of 2,300 calories. Write 30% as a decimal.

30% = .30 = .3

$$\begin{array}{r} 2{,}300 \\ \times \quad .3 \\ \hline 690.0 \end{array}$$

You should eat less than 690 calories of fat in a day.

Exercise A Calculate the number of fat calories allowed for each of the groups in the following chart.

Recommended Dietary Allowances (RDA) of Chief Food Elements Source: Food and Nutrition Board, National Research Council				
	Age	Weight (lb.)	Calories	Calories From Fat
Male	11–14	99	2,500	______
	15–18	145	3,000	______
	19–22	160	2,900	______
	23–50	174	2,900	______
	51+	170	2,300	______
Female	11–14	101	2,200	______
	15–18	120	2,200	______
	19–22	128	2,200	______
	23–50	138	2,200	______
	51+	143	1,900	______

Nutritional labels on prepared foods indicate fat content in grams. Each gram (g) of fat is 9 calories. You will need to make a calculation to determine the number of calories from fat in a food product.

EXAMPLE In one brand of soup, there are 5 g of fat per serving. Each serving provides 180 calories. What percent of these calories are from fat?

Step 1 Find the number of calories from fat.
$5 \text{ g} \times 9 \text{ calories/g} = 45$ calories from fat

Step 2 Find the ratio of fat calories to the soup calories.

$$45 \text{ to } 180 \rightarrow \frac{45}{180} \rightarrow \frac{45 \div 9}{180 \div 9} \rightarrow \frac{5}{20} \rightarrow \frac{5 \div 5}{20 \div 5} \rightarrow \frac{1}{4}$$

Step 3 Write the fraction as a percent.

$$4\overline{)1.00} = 0.25 = 25\%$$

The fat calories are 25% of the calories in the soup. This is less than the 30% guideline.

Exercise B Decide which of the following foods have less than 30% of their calories from fat.

	Food	Serving Size	Total calories per serving	Grams of fat per serving
1)	Hoagie sesame roll	1 roll	260	4 g
2)	Chunk white tuna in water	3 oz.	90	1 g
3)	Chunk white tuna in oil	3 oz.	240	18 g
4)	Applesauce	4 oz. can	90	0 g
5)	Skim milk	8 fl. oz.	100	<1 g
6)	Refried beans	$\frac{1}{2}$ cup	110	1 g
7)	Rigatoni (uncooked)	1 oz.	110	<1 g
8)	Oat and honey granola bar	.8 oz. bar	110	5 g
9)	Fresh romaine lettuce	$\frac{2}{3}$ cup	6	0 g
10)	Chicken con queso burritos	5.2 oz.	280	8 g
11)	Tortilla chips	1 oz.	140	6 g
12)	Chicken, white meat with skin	3 oz.	190	9 g
13)	Chicken, white meat no skin	3 oz.	145	4 g

Lesson 7 Using Calories

Calories are necessary for carrying on basic processes such as heartbeat, breathing, and digestion. The average person uses 1,400 to 1,650 calories each day just to live. Other activities may require between 700 and 1,400 more calories.

This graph shows how many calories are burned per hour by different activities. The amount shown may vary from person to person, depending on age, weight, and gender.

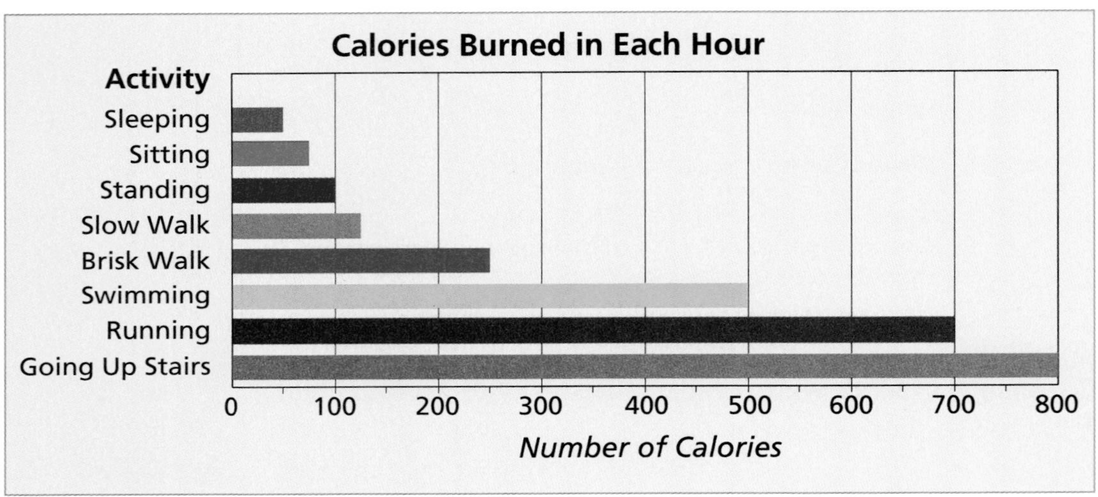

PROBLEM SOLVING

Exercise A Use the graph to answer these questions.

1) How many calories are used in an hour-long brisk walk?

2) How many calories are burned by swimming for 2 hours?

3) How many calories are burned in 8 hours of sleep?

4) How many more calories are used in one hour by a person who stands than by a person who sits?

5) In two hours, how many more calories are burned while running than while swimming?

You may use proportions to find out how many calories are burned during a different length of time than one hour.

EXAMPLE

Ms. Ling runs for 45 minutes. How many calories does she use? Use information from the graph on page 140.

Step 1 Write a proportion.
The ratio will be minutes to calories.

$$\frac{\text{minutes}}{\text{calories}} \rightarrow \frac{\overset{\textit{Graph}}{\text{1 hour}}}{\text{700 calories}} = \frac{\overset{\textit{Ms. Ling}}{\text{45 minutes}}}{\blacksquare\ \text{calories}}$$

Step 2 Change the time to minutes. $\frac{60}{700} = \frac{45}{\blacksquare}$

Step 3 Find the cross product. $700 \times 45 = 31{,}500$

Step 4 Divide by 60 (minutes in one hour)

$$60 \overline{)31{,}500} = 525 \text{ calories}$$

Ms. Ling uses 525 calories.

Exercise B Calculate the number of calories used in each activity. Use the graph on page 140. Round your answer to the nearest calorie.

	Activity	Time Spent
1)	Walking slowly	20 minutes
2)	Sleeping	$1\frac{1}{2}$ hours
3)	Running	1 hour, 25 minutes
4)	Walking up stairs	15 minutes
5)	Sitting in class	45 minutes
6)	Swimming	9 hours, 15 minutes
7)	Standing	2 hours, 15 minutes
8)	Walking briskly	55 minutes
9)	Sleeping	4 hours, 35 minutes
10)	Sitting in front of TV	3 hours, 40 minutes

Lesson 8 Losing Pounds

Each extra pound in a person's body contains about 3,500 calories. One way to lose a pound is to exercise enough to burn 3,500 calories.

EXAMPLE How long does Sabrina have to run to burn up one extra pound? Use the information from the graph to help you.

Divide 3,500 by the number of calories burned while running one hour.

$$\begin{array}{r} 5 \text{ hours} \\ 700\overline{)3{,}500} \\ -3{,}500 \\ \hline 0 \end{array}$$

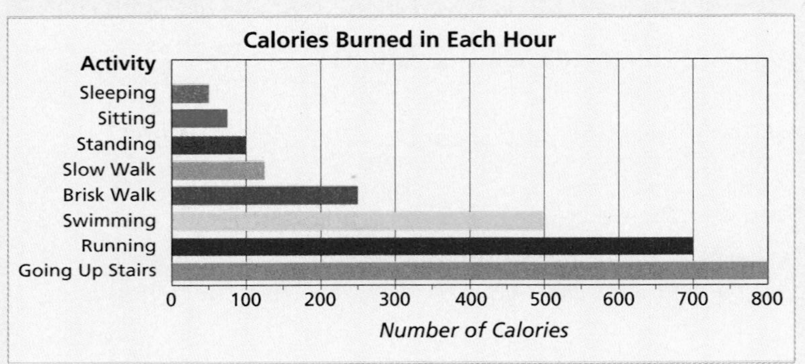

Of course, these exercises should not be overdone. They should be spread over a number of days. Stamina and conditioning are also important factors in exercise and maintaining a healthy body. Check with your doctor before beginning any exercise program.

Exercise A Find the length of time each exercise must be carried out to lose weight. Use the graph to help you.

	Exercise	Pounds to Lose
1)	Walking briskly	1
2)	Standing	1
3)	Swimming	2
4)	Walking up steps	1
5)	Walking slowly	2
6)	Running	2
7)	Swimming	1
8)	Walking briskly	2

Another way for a person to lose a pound is to consume 3,500 calories less than the body uses. A person's body will burn a pound of body fat for the energy he or she needs.

EXAMPLE Mike wants to lose 2 pounds in 21 days. How many fewer calories should he consume each day?

Step 1 Multiply 3,500 times the number of pounds to be lost.
$3{,}500 \times 2 = 7{,}000$ total number of calories

Step 2 Divide the total number of calories by the number of days.

$$21\,\overline{)\,7{,}000}\;=\;333$$

333 calories per day
21) 7,000 total number of calories

Mike must consume 333 fewer calories per day for 21 days to lose 2 pounds.

Exercise B Compute how many fewer calories per day should be consumed to lose the following amounts of weight. Remember to change all time periods to days.

1) 1 pound in 7 days

2) 4 pounds in 10 days

3) 2 pounds in 1 week

4) 10 pounds in 3 months

5) 3 pounds in 2 weeks

6) 4 pounds in 3 weeks

7) 5 pounds in 8 weeks

8) 12 pounds in 6 months

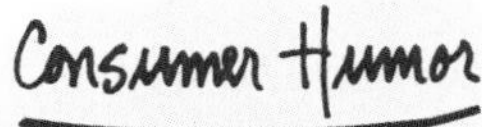

Did you see the height and weight chart in today's newspaper?

Yes! According to that chart, I'm not overweight, I'm just too short!

Lesson 9 Changing Recipe Yields

Yield

The number of servings provided by a given recipe.

Recipes are designed to provide a given number of servings. For example, this recipe for Chicken Casserole has a **yield** of 6 servings. You may need to make a larger or smaller casserole.

Chicken Casserole

6 chicken breasts, cooked and sliced
2 packages frozen broccoli, cooked
$10\frac{1}{2}$ oz. condensed cream of chicken soup
$\frac{1}{2}$ cup non-fat yogurt
1 Tbsp. lemon juice
$\frac{1}{2}$ cup skim milk
2 tsp. tarragon leaves

Spread broccoli in a glass baking dish. Arrange chicken over broccoli. Mix soup, yogurt, milk and lemon juice. Pour over chicken. Sprinkle tarragon leaves over top. Microwave 20 minutes on low. Yield: 6 servings

Remember Use these steps to multiply fractions.

1. Multiply the numerator times the numerator.
2. Multiply the denominator times the denominator.
3. Simplify your answer if possible.

EXAMPLES

Numerator → Denominator → $\frac{2}{5} \times \frac{3}{7} = \frac{6}{35}$

Numerator → Denominator → $\frac{2}{10} \times \frac{4}{8} = \frac{8}{80} = \frac{1}{10}$

To serve fewer than six people, you will need to decrease the quantity for each ingredient.

EXAMPLE Compute the quantity of each ingredient in Chicken Casserole needed to serve 3 people.

Step 1 Find the ratio of desired portions (3) to recipe portions (6).

$\frac{\text{desired}}{\text{recipe}} = \frac{3}{6} = \frac{1}{2}$

Step 2 Multiply every quantity by the ratio $\frac{1}{2}$.

Recipe for 6 Servings	**Recipe for 3 Servings**
6 chicken breasts	$\frac{6}{1} \times \frac{1}{2} =$ 3 chicken breasts
2 pkgs. broccoli	$\frac{2}{1} \times \frac{1}{2} =$ 1 pkg. broccoli
$10\frac{1}{2}$ oz. soup	$10\frac{1}{2} \times \frac{1}{2} =$
(Write mixed numbers as fractions, $10\frac{1}{2} = \frac{21}{2}$)	$\frac{21}{2} \times \frac{1}{2} = \frac{21}{4}$ or $5\frac{1}{4}$ oz. soup
$\frac{1}{2}$ cup non-fat yogurt	$\frac{1}{2} \times \frac{1}{2} = \frac{1}{4}$ cup non-fat yogurt
$\frac{1}{2}$ cup skim milk	$\frac{1}{2} \times \frac{1}{2} = \frac{1}{4}$ cup skim milk
1 Tbsp. lemon juice	$1 \times \frac{1}{2} = \frac{1}{2}$ Tbsp. lemon juice
2 tsp. tarragon leaves	$\frac{2}{1} \times \frac{1}{2} =$ 1 tsp. tarragon leaves

Exercise A Find the amounts of ingredients needed to make Chicken Casserole for each of these numbers of servings.

1) 2

2) 4

3) 5

If you plan to prepare more servings than the original recipe will yield, you will need to increase the quantity for each of the ingredients.

EXAMPLE Find how much of each ingredient in Chicken Casserole is needed to serve 8 people.

Step 1 Write the ratio: $\frac{\text{desired}}{\text{recipe}} = \frac{8}{6} = \frac{4}{3}$

Step 2 Multiply each amount by $\frac{4}{3}$.

Recipe for 6 Servings

6 chicken breasts

2 pkgs. broccoli

$10\frac{1}{2}$ oz. soup

$\frac{1}{2}$ cup non-fat yogurt

$\frac{1}{2}$ cup skim milk

1 Tbsp. lemon juice

2 tsp. tarragon leaves

Recipe for 8 Servings

$\frac{6}{1} \times \frac{4}{3} = \frac{24}{3} = 8$ chicken breasts

$\frac{2}{1} \times \frac{4}{3} = \frac{8}{3} = 2\frac{2}{3}$ pkgs. broccoli

$\frac{21}{2} \times \frac{4}{3} = \frac{84}{6} = 14$ oz. soup

$\frac{1}{2} \times \frac{4}{3} = \frac{4}{6} = \frac{2}{3}$ cup non-fat yogurt

$\frac{1}{2} \times \frac{4}{3} = \frac{4}{6} = \frac{2}{3}$ cup skim milk

$1 \times \frac{4}{3} = \frac{4}{3} = 1\frac{1}{3}$ Tbsp. lemon juice

$\frac{2}{1} \times \frac{4}{3} = \frac{16}{3} = 2\frac{2}{3}$ tsp. tarragon leaves

Exercise B Find the amounts of ingredients needed to make Chicken Casserole for each of these number of servings.

	No. of Servings	Chicken Breasts	Broccoli (pkg.)	Soup (oz.)	Non-fat Yogurt (cup)	Skim Milk (cup)	Lemon Juice (Tbsp.)	Tarragon Leaves (tsp.)
1)	12	____	____	____	____	____	____	____
2)	18	____	____	____	____	____	____	____
3)	15	____	____	____	____	____	____	____
4)	36	____	____	____	____	____	____	____
5)	21	____	____	____	____	____	____	____
6)	9	____	____	____	____	____	____	____
7)	24	____	____	____	____	____	____	____
8)	30	____	____	____	____	____	____	____

Lesson 10 Timing Food Preparation

Some recipes require preparation time for mixing ingredients or chopping vegetables in addition to the cooking time.

One of the most challenging parts of making a meal is scheduling the preparation so that all the food is ready at the same time.

EXAMPLE Amy and Paul are planning to serve the following items at 7:30 P.M. When must each item begin cooking to be ready at 7:30?

Item	**Cooking Time**
Roast lamb (7 lbs.)	30 min./lb. + 15 min. standing time
Brown rice	40 minutes
Broccoli	12 minutes

Roast Lamb: Multiply the weight times the cooking time per pound. Add the standing time.

$7 \times 30 = 210$ min. $\quad 210 + 15 = 225$ minutes

Change to hours and minutes by dividing by 60.

$$\begin{array}{r} 3 \text{ Hours} \\ 60\overline{)225} \\ -180 \\ \hline 45 \text{ Minutes} \end{array}$$

Total time: 3 hours, 45 minutes.

Subtract 3 hours, 45 minutes from 7:30.

$$\begin{array}{r} 7 \text{ hrs. } 30 \text{ min.} \\ -\ 3 \text{ hrs. } 45 \text{ min.} \\ \hline \end{array} \quad = \quad \begin{array}{r} 6 \text{ hrs. } 90 \text{ min.} \\ -\ 3 \text{ hrs. } 45 \text{ min.} \\ \hline 3 \text{ hrs. } 45 \text{ min.} \end{array}$$

The lamb should go in the oven at 3:45 P.M.

Brown Rice: Subtract 40 minutes from 7:30.

$$\begin{array}{r} 7 \text{ hrs. } 30 \text{ min.} \\ -\ 40 \text{ min.} \\ \hline \end{array} \quad = \quad \begin{array}{r} 6 \text{ hrs. } 90 \text{ min.} \\ -\ 40 \text{ min.} \\ \hline 6 \text{ hrs. } 50 \text{ min.} \end{array}$$

The rice should begin cooking at 6:50 P.M.

Broccoli: Subtract 12 minutes from 7:30.

$$\begin{array}{r} 7 \text{ hrs. } 30 \text{ min.} \\ -\ 12 \text{ min.} \\ \hline 7 \text{ hrs. } 18 \text{ min.} \end{array}$$

The broccoli should begin cooking at 7:18 P.M.

Exercise A Calculate the times these foods should begin cooking to be ready at the given time.

1) Dinner at 8:00 P.M.

Roast beef (6 lbs.)	35 min./lb. + 20 min. standing time
Mixed vegetables	18 minutes
Boiled potatoes	40 minutes
Rolls	17 minutes

2) Dinner at 7:00 P.M.

Baked chicken (5 lbs.)	25 minutes per pound
Noodles Romanoff	55 minutes
Acorn squash	$1\frac{1}{2}$ hours
Biscuits	15 minutes

3) Dinner at 4:30 P.M.

Roast turkey (20 lbs.)	20 min./lb. + 25 min. standing time
Sauerkraut casserole	1 hour, 20 minutes
Baked potatoes	$1\frac{1}{2}$ hours
Lima beans	15 minutes

Exercise B Calculate the times you should begin to prepare these foods to be ready at the given time.

1) Dinner at 6:30 P.M.

Herbed chicken à la Française	Prepare 20 minutes, bake 30 minutes, add topping, bake 15 minutes
Vegetable stir fry	10 minutes
Lime mousse	Mixing time 25 minutes, chill 4 hours

2) Dinner at 5:15 P.M.

Vegetable cheese soufflé	Prepare 35 minutes, bake 55 minutes
Tabouleh–seafood salad	Prepare 10 minutes, chill 2 hours
Broiled orange boats	Mix 20 minutes, broil 6 minutes

Chapter 6 Review

Look at the Calorie Chart. Find the number of calories consumed in each meal described below:

1) Breakfast: yogurt, corn muffin, iced tea with sugar.

2) Snack: granola bar, carrot, lemonade

3) Dinner: spaghetti with meat sauce, spinach salad, two slices wheat bread, peach, spring water

Calorie Chart Source: McCall's Cook Book and Package Labels	
Food	**Calories per Serving**
Carrot	20
Corn muffin	130
Granola bar	120
Lemonade	105
Peach	45
Spinach salad	140
Spring water	0
Spaghetti with meat sauce	400
Iced tea with sugar	50
Wheat bread, one slice	55
Yogurt	250

Solve these problems.

4) Use cross products to check if these ratios are equal.

$\frac{5}{6}$ $\frac{30}{360}$

5) Find the missing term in this proportion.

$\frac{30}{360} = \frac{■}{12}$

6) There are 350 calories in $1\frac{1}{2}$ cups of spaghetti. How many calories are in two cups?

7) There are 1.5 mg of iron in 8 ounces of apple juice. How many ounces would contain 100% of the RDA for iron if 18 mg are recommended?

8) There are 6 grams fat per serving in granola. Each serving provides 180 calories. What percent of these calories are from fat? (Remember, there are 9 calories of fat in each gram.)

9) Look at the two nutrition labels from different cereals. Which has more calories per serving? Which has fewer calories from fat?

10) Which cereal would you choose? Explain your answer.

11) Running consumes 700 calories per hour. How many calories are used in 40 minutes of running?

12) How many fewer calories per day must be consumed in order to lose 6 pounds in 5 weeks? (Remember, each pound is about 3,500 calories.)

13) A salad recipe that serves 10 people requires $1\frac{1}{2}$ cups of celery. How much celery is needed for 5 servings?

14) A recipe that serves six calls for 4 ounces of tomato sauce. Compute the amount of tomato sauce necessary to serve eight people. Round your answer to the nearest ounce.

15) A roast requires 3 hours and 40 minutes to prepare. When must it be put into the oven in order to be ready to be served at 6:30 P.M.?

Toasted Oats

Nutrition Facts
Serving Size: 1 box (21 g; 3/4 oz.)
Servings Per Container: 1

Amount Per Serving	Cereal
Calories	80
Calories from Fat	10
	% Daily Value**
Total Fat 1g*	**2%**
Saturated Fat 0g	**0%**
Cholesterol 0mg	**0%**
Sodium 10mg	**0%**
Potassium 80mg	**2%**
Total Carbohydrate 16g	**5%**
Dietary Fiber 1g	**4%**
Sugars 1g	
Protein 2g	
Vitamin A	0%
Vitamin C	0%
Calcium	10%
Iron	2%

Bran with Raisins

Nutrition Facts
Serving Size: 1 box (35 g; 1 1/4 oz.)
Servings Per Container: 1

Amount Per Serving	Cereal
Calories	110
Calories from Fat	5
	% Daily Value**
Total Fat 0.5g*	**1%**
Saturated Fat 0g	**0%**
Cholesterol 0mg	**0%**
Sodium 10mg	**0%**
Potassium 210mg	**6%**
Total Carbohydrate 27g	**9%**
Dietary Fiber 5g	**20%**
Sugars 7g	
Protein 3g	
Vitamin A	0%
Vitamin C	0%
Calcium	0%
Iron	6%

Test Taking Tip

Studying together in small groups and asking questions of one another is one way to review material for tests.

13

Chapter 7 Improving Your Home

When people mention home improvements, we usually think about things like painting, wallpapering, a new roof, or a new addition. But home improvements also include making changes outside the home. Some people spend a great deal of time and money working in their yards and gardens. A well-kept yard can make a home a more attractive and inviting place.

In Chapter 7, you will explore the calculations and expenses related to home improvements. These include items that are purchased for the home, as well as changes made to the structure of the home and its surroundings.

Goals for Learning

- To compute payments for purchases of items, including comparing and computing regular price, discount rate, and sale price
- To use elapsed time to determine date of payment
- To estimate the quantity of materials and the costs associated with painting a room, papering a wall, covering a floor, building an addition, and insulating an attic
- To calculate the amount and cost of grass seed or fertilizer required for a lawn
- To find the length of fencing required to enclose a yard

Lesson 1 Buying Furniture and Appliances

Furniture stores will offer you many different styles and fabrics when you choose a new sofa.

Furniture and appliances are expensive. Smart shoppers may find the items that they want on sale.

EXAMPLE Rosa Arroyo purchases a couch at a "40% off" sale. If the sale price is $539.99, what was the original cost?

Rule To find the original cost, subtract the discount rate from 100%. Then divide the sale price by this difference.

Step 1 Subtract the discount from 100%.

$$\begin{array}{rl} 100\% & \\ -\ 40\% & \text{Percent discount} \\ \hline 60\% & \text{Percent paid} \end{array}$$

The sale price is 60% of the original cost.

Step 2 Round the sale price to the nearest dollar to make the calculation easier.

$539.99 ≈ $540.00 Rounded sale price

Step 3 To find the original cost, divide the rounded sale price by the percent paid.

60% = .60

$$\begin{array}{rl} \$900. & \text{Original cost} \\ .60.\overline{)\,\$540.00.} & \text{Rounded sale price} \end{array}$$

The original cost is $900. Note that this original price may have actually been listed as $899.99.

Exercise A Find the original cost of each item. Round your answer to the nearest dollar.

Item	Discount	Sale Price
1) full-size mattress set	50%	$299.99
2) twin-size mattress set	50%	$199.99
3) 4-piece living room set	35%	$584.99
4) rocking chair	26%	$140.60
5) coffee table	25%	$97.50
6) window air conditioner	50%	$144.99
7) recliner	27%	$510.99
8) stereo	28%	$215.98
9) dining room set	20%	$559.99
10) refrigerator	12%	$571.97
11) ceiling fan	16%	$92.40
12) VCR	16%	$209.99
13) queen-size bed	5%	$688.75
14) microwave oven	20%	$199.99
15) electric range	10%	$359.95
16) television	32%	$183.60
17) bunk beds	50%	$174.98
18) hide-a-bed	40%	$419.99
19) washing machine	13%	$304.50
20) clothes dryer	23%	$230.99

You can compute the sale discount when you know the sale price and the regular price of the item.

EXAMPLE Frank Lee buys a lamp for $49.99. The regular price is $79.99. What discount does he receive?

Step 1 Round the prices to the nearest dollar.

$\$49.99 \approx \$50$
$\$79.99 \approx \$80$

Step 2 Subtract the sale price from the regular price to find the amount saved.

$ 80	Regular price
− 50	Sale price
$ 30	Amount saved

Step 3 Write the ratio. $\frac{\text{amount saved}}{\text{regular price}}$

Simplify this ratio.

$\frac{\$30}{\$80} = \frac{3}{8}$

Step 4 Write the ratio as a percent.

$8\overline{)3.000}$ = .375

$.375 \approx .38 = 38\%$

Consumer Humor

What a sale! I bought a dresser, a refrigerator, and a TV! I saved over $300!

Now the bills are coming due. I don't know if I can afford to save that much money.

Exercise B Find the discount in each case.

	Item	Regular Price	Sale Price
1)	bookcase	$169.95	$149.50
2)	desk	$149.98	$124.98
3)	4-piece bedroom suite	$1,258.99	$994.60
4)	sectional sofa	$599.98	$449.99
5)	gas range	$249.95	$201.95
6)	outdoor grill	$149.99	$119.97
7)	king-size bed	$950.99	$799.95
8)	pine finish rocker	$129.99	$59.95
9)	5-piece dinette set	$499.95	$439.95
10)	refrigerator	$599.98	$499.98
11)	kitchen table and chairs	$415.99	$389.99
12)	window fan	$329.99	$249.99
13)	chandelier	$224.99	$129.99
14)	color television	$429.95	$359.95
15)	dishwasher	$369.98	$279.95
16)	freezer	$549.98	$349.95
17)	microwave oven	$149.95	$119.95
18)	TV/VCR combination	$299.99	$259.99
19)	washing machine	$269.95	$209.95
20)	clothes dryer	$188.98	$159.99

Lesson 2 90-Day Purchase Plan

Ninety Days Same As Cash

A plan in which a purchase is paid in 90 days with no interest.

Some businesses offer their customers a **Ninety Days Same As Cash** plan with the purchase of large or expensive items. Rather than pay interest on a charge account, some customers choose this plan because they have 90 days to pay with no interest. The term means that within 90 days after the date of purchase, the purchase price must be paid in full. No interest is charged for the use of this plan.

EXAMPLE Mr. Angello purchases a living room suite on January 14 and uses the "Ninety Days Same As Cash" plan. By what date must he pay the total purchase price?

Step 1	Find the number of days left in January. January has 31 days.	31	Days in January
		− 14	Date of purchase
		17	Days left in January
Step 2	Subtract the days left in January from 90, the total number of days in the purchase plan.	90	Days in plan
		− 17	Days left in January
		73	
Step 3	Subtract the days in February from 73. There are usually 28 days in February.	73	Days left in plan
		− 28	Days in February
		45	
Step 4	Subtract the days in March from 45. March has 31 days.	45	Days left in plan
		− 31	Days in March
		14	Days left in plan

There are 14 days left after March. The next month is April. April 14 is the final payment date.

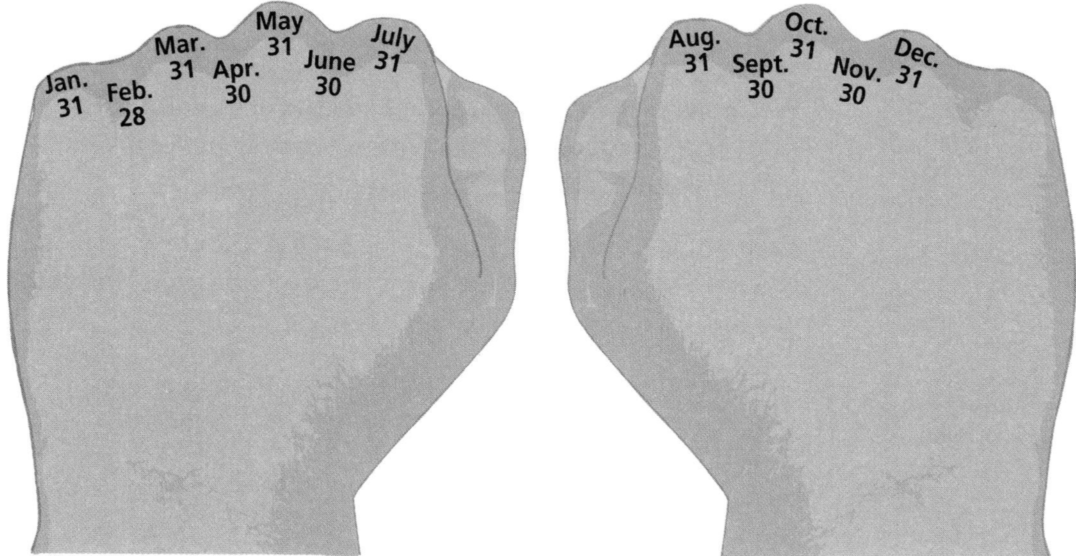

Use a Knuckle Calendar to help you remember how many days are in each month. Make a fist with your left hand. Name the months as you touch each knuckle and valley in succession. When you reach July at your last knuckle, make a fist with your right hand, and name August through December.

All the months named on the knuckles have 31 days. All the rest have 30 days, except February, which has 28 (29 days in a leap year).

Exercise A Find the payment date for each of these "Ninety Days Same As Cash" plans. The purchase dates are listed below. Any leap years are indicated.

1) January 20
2) March 10
3) December 30
4) June 22
5) May 10
6) June 28
7) September 7
8) August 22
9) July 16
10) February 2 (Leap year)
11) November 10
12) July 30
13) June 6
14) December 24
(Next year is a leap year)
15) July 10
16) February 6
17) December 7
18) July 4
19) February 22
20) May 5

Lesson 3 The Key to Perimeter and Area

Perimeter
The whole outer boundary of a figure or region.

Area
The amount of surface within a boundary.

Perimeter is the distance around a figure or region. Notice the word "rim" in pe*rim*eter. Remember that perimeter is the measure of the *rim* of a figure.

Area is the number of squares of a given size that cover a surface. It is the surface included inside a perimeter. Notice that the last three letters in squ*are* are in *are*a.

Certain figures have formulas to use for finding perimeter and area. Study the following examples for a rectangle and a square. Note that some symbols are used in this chapter: 5″ means 5 inches; 5′ means 5 feet.

Rectangle

w = width
l = length

Rule To find the perimeter of a rectangle, add the length and width, then multiply by 2.

Perimeter
$P = 2(l + w)$

Rule To find the area of a rectangle, multiply the length by the width.

Area $A = l \times w$

EXAMPLE What is the perimeter of this rectangle?
What is the area of this rectangle?

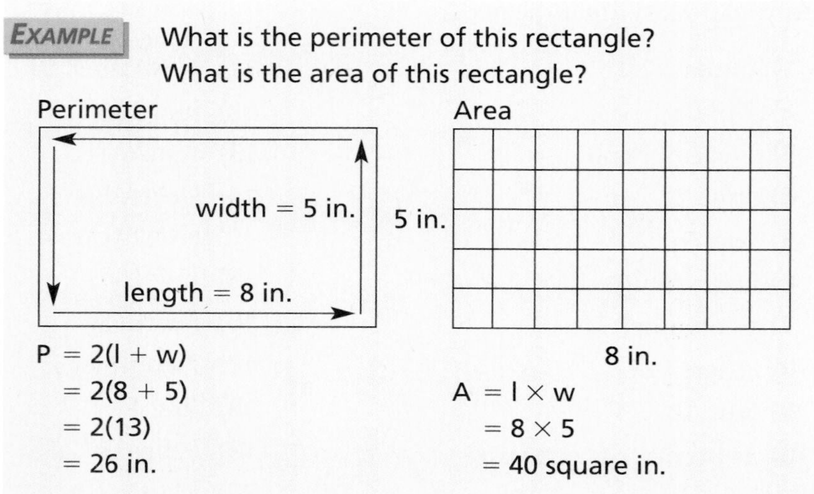

$P = 2(l + w)$
$= 2(8 + 5)$
$= 2(13)$
$= 26$ in.

$A = l \times w$
$= 8 \times 5$
$= 40$ square in.

Square

s = side

Rule To find the perimeter of a square, multiply the length of one side by 4.

Perimeter
P = 4 × s or P = 4s

Rule To find the area of a square, multiply the length of one side by itself, or **square** it. Another way to express this is s^2, which is read as side squared.

Area A = s × s or A = s^2

Square
The product of a number multiplied by itself.

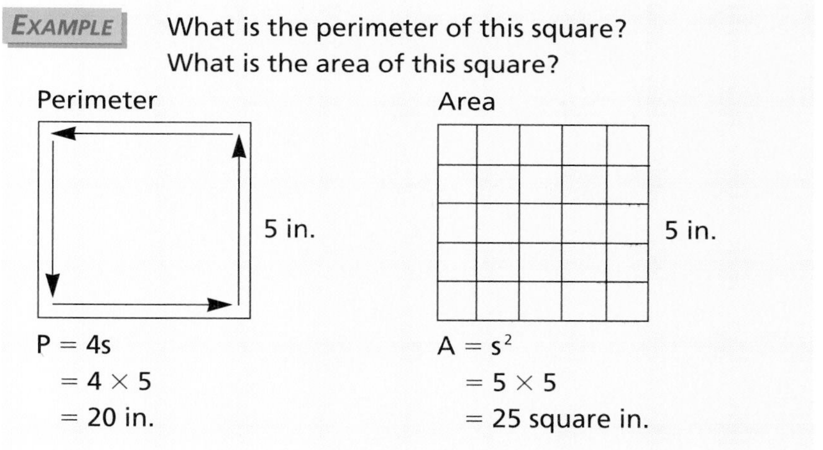

EXAMPLE What is the perimeter of this square?
What is the area of this square?

Perimeter

P = 4s
= 4 × 5
= 20 in.

Area

A = s^2
= 5 × 5
= 25 square in.

Exercise A Find the perimeter and area of each of these figures. Label each answer with the correct units.

Rectangles		Perimeter	Area
1) l = 4 in.	w = 6 in.	________	________
2) l = 1″	w = 5″	________	________
3) l = 7 ft.	w = 2 ft.	________	________
4) l = 25 in.	w = 14 in.	________	________
5) l = 38′	w = 39′	________	________

Squares	Perimeter	Area
6) s = 3″	________	________
7) s = 5 in.	________	________
8) s = 10 in.	________	________
9) s = 7″	________	________
10) s = 32 ft.	________	________

Irregular Shapes You can find the area of some irregular shapes by dividing them into rectangles or squares.

What is the area of this irregular shape?

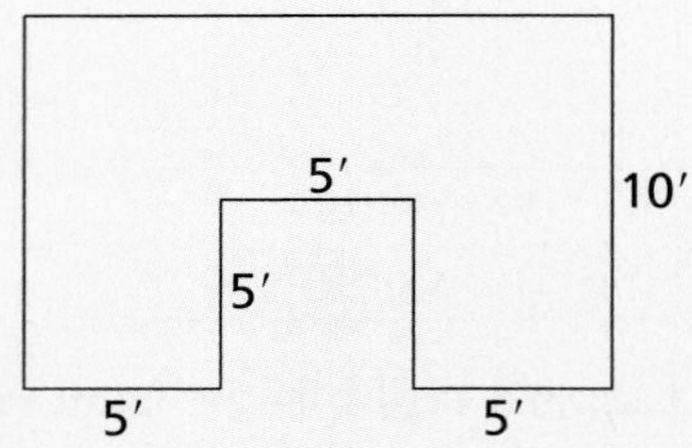

Step 1 Divide the irregular shape into rectangles or squares.

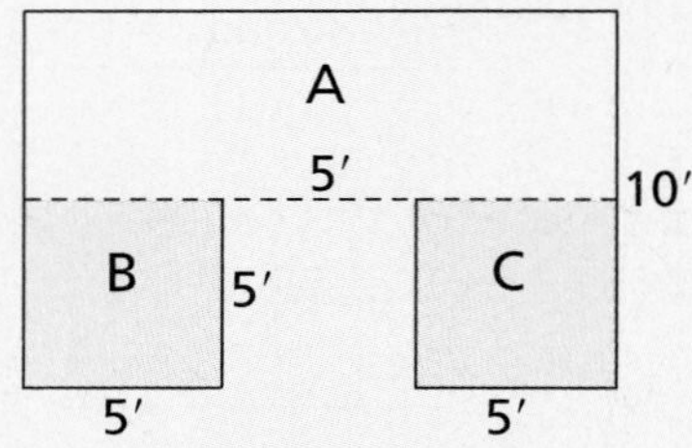

Step 2 Find any missing dimensions.

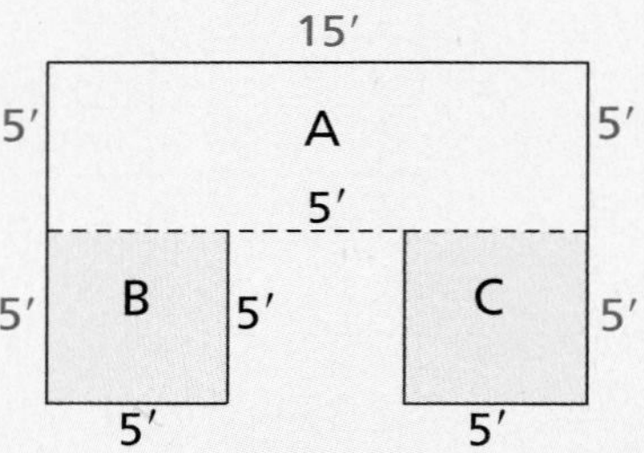

Step 3 Calculate the areas of the rectangles or squares.

Rectangle A:	$5' \times 15'$	=	75 sq. ft.
Square B:	$5' \times 5'$	=	25 sq. ft.
Square C:	$5' \times 5'$	=	25 sq. ft.

Step 4 Add these areas to find the total area of the irregular shape.

75 sq. ft.	Rectangle A
25 sq. ft.	Square B
+ 25 sq. ft.	Square C
125 sq. ft.	Total area

The area of this irregular shape is 125 square feet.

Exercise B Find the area of each of irregular shape.

1)

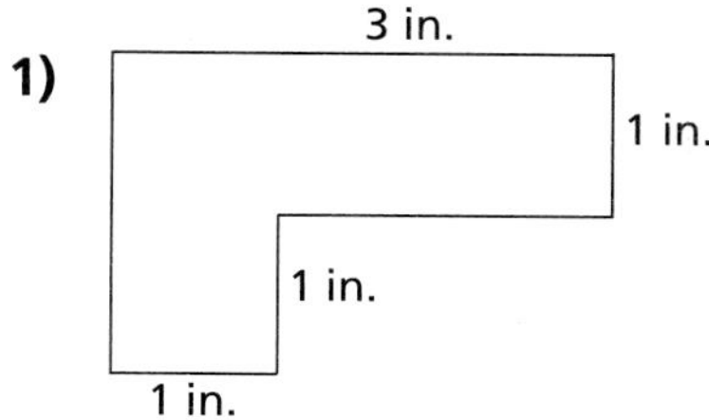

2)

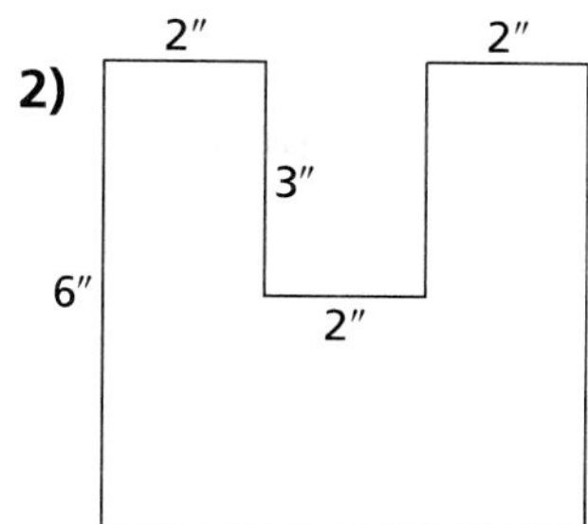

3)

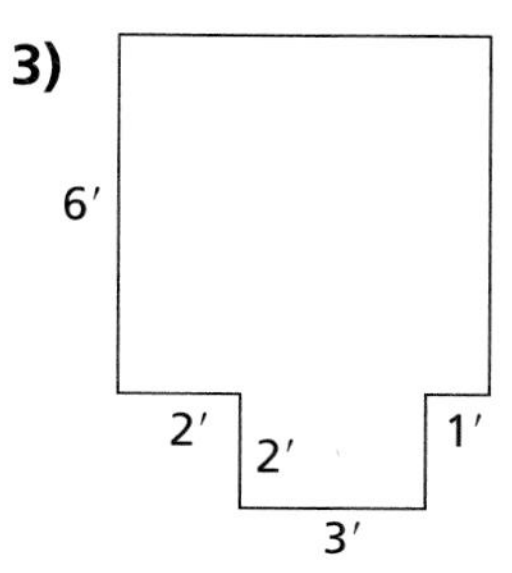

4)

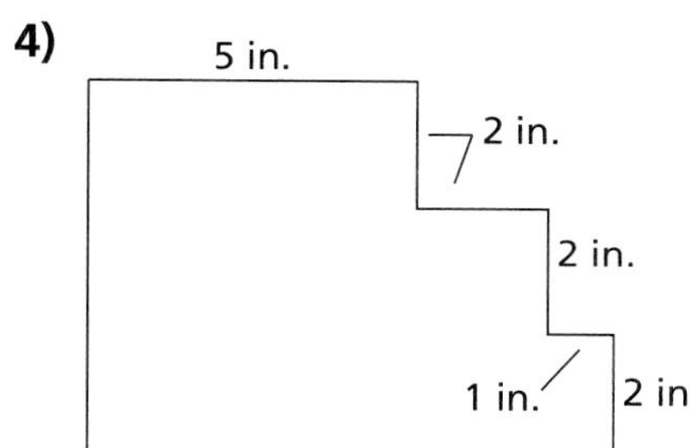

5)

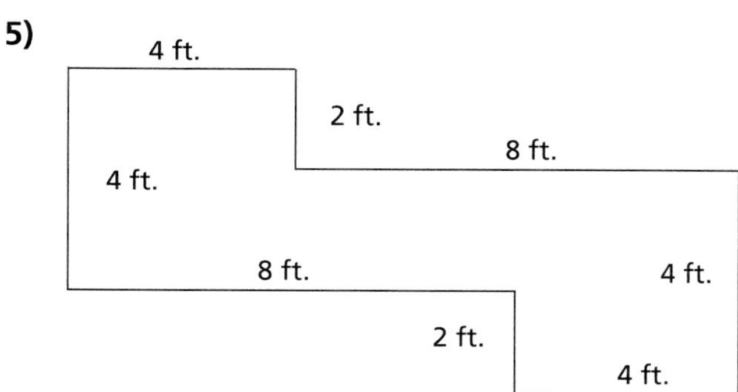

6)

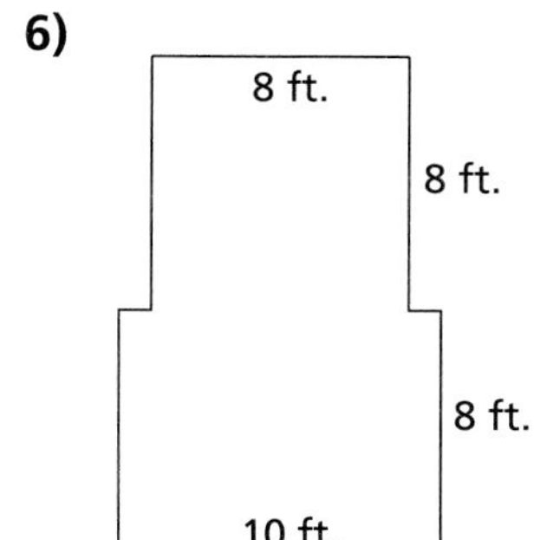

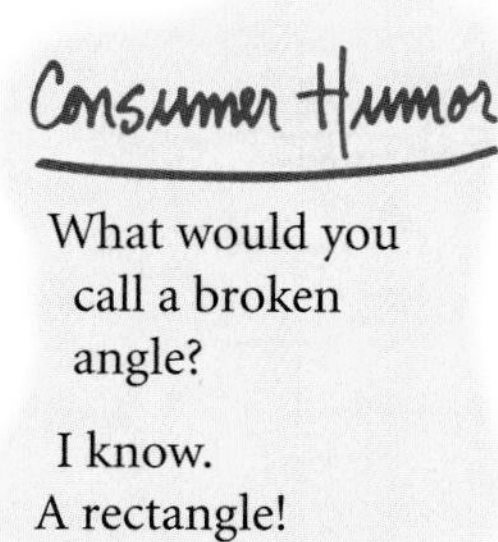

What would you call a broken angle?

I know. A rectangle!

Lesson 4 Painting a Room

How much paint to buy? That's the question! If you buy too much, you waste money. If you buy too little, you have to return to the store for more. Mathematics will help you to buy the correct amount.

> *Coverage*
>
> *The area of wall that a can of paint is supposed to cover.*

Each can of paint is marked with the area of wall that it is supposed to cover. This **coverage** is listed in square feet per quart or per gallon. Painters need to know the total area to be painted. Remember: There are four quarts in one gallon.

EXAMPLE Sarah wants to paint her living room. The paint she selects will cover 100 square feet per quart or 400 square feet per gallon. How many gallons should she buy?

Step 1 Measure the living room. Round to the nearest foot.

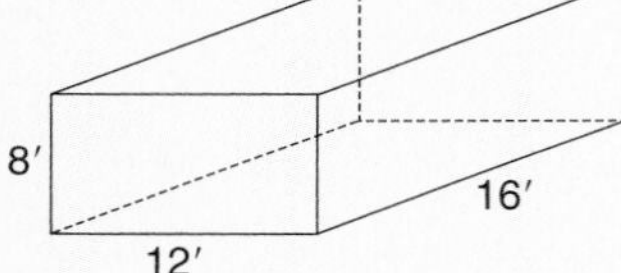

Step 2 Calculate the total area of the walls.

8′ × 12′	=	96 sq. ft.
8′ × 12′	=	96 sq. ft.
8′ × 16′	=	128 sq. ft.
8′ × 16′	=	128 sq. ft.
Total area	=	448 sq. ft.

Step 3 Divide the total area by the coverage per gallon.

1	Gallon
400) 448	Total area in square feet
− 400	
48	Remaining square feet

Step 4 Because each quart covers 100 square feet, one quart should be purchased for the extra 48 square feet remaining. Sarah should buy one gallon and one quart.

PROBLEM SOLVING

Exercise A Find these answers.

1) Suppose that Sarah wants to paint the ceiling of the living room in the example on page 164. How much paint does she need?

2) José wants to paint three rooms the same color. The total area to be painted is 1,375 square feet. How many gallons of paint will he need if each gallon covers 500 square feet?

Michelle wants to paint her basement walls with waterproof paint. Each gallon covers 75 square feet. The dimensions of this basement are 20′ by 30′. The walls are 7′ high.

3) Draw a diagram of the basement.

4) Find the area of each wall.

5) Find the total area to be painted.

6) Find the number of gallons needed.

To prepare a wall for painting, you may need to repair holes in the wall with spackle or drywall mud.

Exercise B Find the amount of paint needed to paint the walls of each of these rooms.

	Length	Width	Height	Coverage	Amount Needed
1)	8′	10′	8′	100 sq. ft./quart	______
2)	11′	20′	8′	125 sq. ft./quart	______
3)	15′	7′	7′	75 sq. ft./quart	______
4)	25′	17′	8′	100 sq. ft./quart	______
5)	18′	19′	10′	110 sq. ft./quart	______

Calculator Practice

Sometimes it is useful to press the [=] key before a problem is finished to get an *intermediate*, or part of the way, result. This is the same as putting parentheses around the intermediate calculation. Here we will press the equal key to find the perimeter of the room.

Use this method to calculate the amount of paint needed to cover a room.

Step 1 Key in the length of the room.
Step 2 Press [+].
Step 3 Key in the width of the room.
Step 4 Press [=].
Step 5 Press [×].
Step 6 Key in 2.
Step 7 Press [=]. This is the perimeter.
Step 8 Now, press [×].
Step 9 Key in the height of the room.
Step 10 Press [÷].
Step 11 Key in the coverage for each can of paint.
Step 12 Press [=].
Step 13 Round up to the *next* can of paint.

EXAMPLE How much paint should you buy to paint a room 12′ by 14′ by 8′ high? One gallon covers 450 square feet.

12 [+] 14 [=] [×] 2 [=] [×] 8 [÷] 450 [=]

The display reads 0.9244444
You should purchase 1 gallon of paint.

Use a calculator to check your answers in Exercise B.

Lesson 5 Buying Paint

Paint is sold by the quart and by the gallon. Sometimes you need to purchase paint in both of these sizes to get the best value for your money.

Paint is sold in different sizes. You may find a bargain by comparing prices.

Read the following example on pages 167 through 169. Follow the steps to find out how to buy paint.

EXAMPLE Michael is at the hardware store and must decide whether to buy paint in 9 individual quart cans or to buy it in both gallon and quart cans. Here are the facts:

4 quarts = 1 gallon
1 quart costs $3.99
1 gallon costs $11.99
What should Michael do?

EXAMPLE *(continued)*

Step 1 Find the cost of 4 quarts.

$ 3.99	Cost of 1 quart
× 4	Number of quarts
$15.96	Cost of 4 quarts

Step 2 Find the difference in price between 1 gallon and 4 quarts.

$15.96	Cost of 4 quarts
−11.99	Cost of 1 gallon
$ 3.97	Difference

One gallon of paint is less expensive than 4 quarts. The amount you save, $3.97, is just about the price of 1 quart of paint. When you buy the gallon, you get nearly 1 quart free.

Step 3 Find out how many gallons to buy. Divide the total number of quarts needed by 4. This answer will tell Michael the number of gallons and quarts he needs.

$$\begin{array}{r l} 2 & \text{Gallons} \\ 4\overline{)9} & \\ -\ 8 & \\ \hline 1 & \text{Quart} \end{array}$$

Two gallons and 1 quart are equal to 9 quarts.

EXAMPLE *(continued)*

Step 4 Find the cost.

$11.99	Cost per gallon
× 2	
$23.98	Cost of 2 gallons

$ 3.99	Cost per quart
× 1	
$ 3.99	Cost of 1 quart

$23.98	Cost of 2 gallons
+ 3.99	Cost of 1 quart
$27.97	Total cost

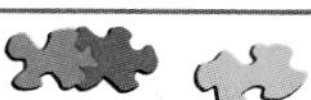

PROBLEM SOLVING

Exercise A Copy and complete this chart. The first line describes the completed example problem on pages 167–169. Its answers are provided for you.

Remember: 1 gallon costs $11.99 and 1 quart costs $3.99.

	Quarts Required	Amount to Buy		Cost		
		Gallons	Quarts	Gallons	Quarts	Total
1)	9	2	1	$23.98	$3.99	$27.97
2)	10	____	____	____	____	____
3)	6	____	____	____	____	____
4)	7	____	____	____	____	____
5)	13	____	____	____	____	____
6)	46	____	____	____	____	____

Lesson 6 Buying Wallpaper

Wall area

The surface of a wall that is to be covered.

Wallpaper is measured in two sizes: single roll and double roll. Each single roll of wallpaper covers 72 square feet. Some patterns are sold only by the double roll. Before you purchase wallpaper, you need to calculate the **wall area** to be covered.

EXAMPLE Paul uses an easy way to estimate the wall area to be papered.

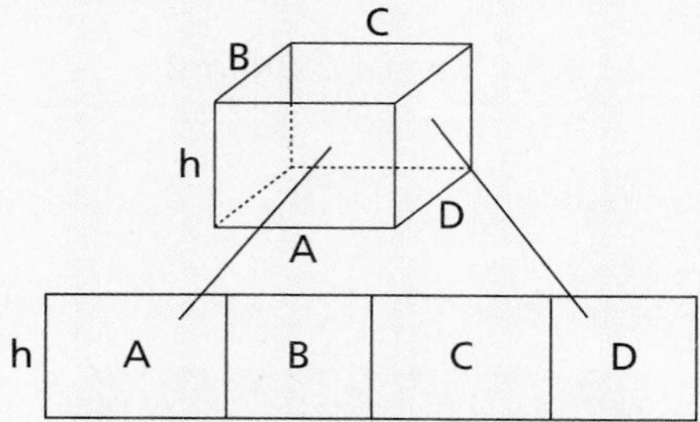

Visualize the walls moved into a straight line to form a large rectangle. The length of this rectangle is the perimeter of the original floor. The width of this rectangle is the height of the original room. The total wall area of the room equals the perimeter of the floor times the height of the room.

Rule Wall area = perimeter of floor × height of room

EXAMPLE Ann plans to paper her bedroom, which measures 10′ by 12′ by 8′. How much wallpaper should she buy?

Step 1 Find the perimeter of a floor 10′ × 12′.

$$P = 2(10' + 12')$$
$$= 2(22')$$
$$= 44'$$

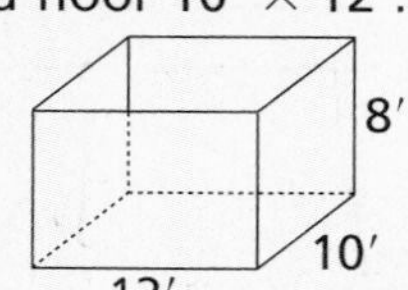

EXAMPLE *(continued)*

Step 2 Find the area of the 4 walls.
Multiply the perimeter by the height.

$$\begin{array}{rl} 44' & \text{Perimeter} \\ \times\ 8' & \text{Height} \\ \hline 352 \text{ sq. ft.} & \text{Area of 4 walls} \end{array}$$

Step 3 Divide the area by 72 square feet to find the number of single rolls needed. Because of the remainder, Ann needs to buy 5 single rolls.

$$\begin{array}{rl} 4 & \text{Single rolls of wallpaper} \\ 72\overline{)352} & \text{Area of room} \\ -288 & \\ \hline 64 & \text{Square feet remaining} \end{array}$$

Step 4 Divide the number of single rolls by 2 to find the number of double rolls. Because of the remainder, Ann needs to buy 3 double rolls.

$$\begin{array}{rl} 2 & \text{Double rolls} \\ 2\overline{)5} & \\ -4 & \\ \hline 1 & \text{Roll remaining} \end{array}$$

Exercise A Calculate the number of double rolls of wallpaper needed to paper each of these rooms. The third measurement for each room is the height.

1) $7' \times 10' \times 8'$

2) $11' \times 12' \times 8'$

3) $15' \times 12' \times 10'$

4) $9' \times 10' \times 8'$

5) $9.5' \times 10.5' \times 8'$

6) $8' \times 11' \times 8'$

7) $16' \times 14' \times 8'$

8) $9' \times 11' \times 8'$

9) $13' \times 21' \times 8'$

10) $25' \times 17' \times 8'$

Lesson 7 Covering the Floor

Whenever a person decides to buy floor covering, the area of the floor needs to be determined before the purchase is made.

EXAMPLE Soo Lee decides to buy square tiles to cover her kitchen floor. Each square measures 12″ by 12″ and costs $1.39. How much will it cost to cover her 10′ × 7′ floor?

Step 1 Find the area that each tile covers.
12 inches = 1 foot
1′ × 1′ = 1 square foot

1 square foot
12″
12″

Step 2 Find the number of square feet of floor that needs to be covered.

Area = l × w
= 10′ × 7′
= 70 square feet

10′
7′

Since each tile covers 1 square foot, Soo Lee needs 70 tiles.

Step 3 Multiply the number of tiles by the cost per tile.

$ 1.39	Cost per tile
× 70	Number of tiles
$97.30	Total cost

Exercise A Find the cost of covering these floors with 12″ by 12″ tiles.

	Cost per Tile	Floor Dimensions		Cost per Tile	Floor Dimensions
1)	$.89	10′ × 7′	**6)**	$.99	10′ × 16′
2)	$1.29	8′ × 11′	**7)**	$2.79	13′ × 17′
3)	$2.59	10′ × 15′	**8)**	$4.39	18′ × 17′
4)	$1.89	11′ × 16′	**9)**	$3.59	9′ × 17′
5)	$1.79	12′ × 18′	**10)**	$1.59	19′ × 16′

The dimensions of a floor rarely measure a whole number of feet. To simplify calculations and to be sure you get enough covering, round to the next foot.

EXAMPLE Help Zenta compute the cost of covering the floor of his dining room. The floor measures 15 feet 6 inches by 12 feet 7 inches. Each tile covers 1 square foot. A box of 45 tiles costs $29.25.

Step 1 Round the dimensions to the next foot.

$15'\,6'' \longrightarrow 16'$

$12'\,7'' \longrightarrow 13'$

Step 2 Find the area of the floor.

$$\begin{aligned} \text{Area} &= \text{l} \times \text{w} \\ &= 16' \times 13' \\ &= 208 \text{ square feet} \end{aligned}$$

Since each tile covers 1 square foot, Zenta needs 208 tiles.

Step 3 Find the number of boxes needed. Divide the number of tiles by 45, the number of tiles in one box. Round your answer up to the next whole number.

$$45 \overline{)208.0} = 4.6 \longrightarrow 5 \text{ boxes}$$

208.0 Number of tiles

Step 4 Find the cost. Multiply the cost per box by the number of boxes.

$ 29.25	Cost per box
× 5	Number of boxes
$146.25	Total cost

Zenta needs 5 boxes of tiles to cover the floor of his dining room. The cost of putting floor tiles in his dining room will be $146.25.

Exercise B Follow the example on page 173 to find the cost of covering the floor of each room. Each tile measures 12″ by 12″. Round floor dimensions to the next foot. Round the number of boxes of floor tiles to the next whole number.

	Cost per Box (45 tiles)	Floor Dimensions
1)	\$39.95	10′5″ × 9′8″
2)	\$14.99	15′6″ × 17′10″
3)	\$26.59	25′3″ × 15′8″
4)	\$35.55	11′2″ × 7′9″
5)	\$16.39	12′3″ × 8′3″
6)	\$20.99	14′6″ × 15′2″
7)	\$16.17	10′11″ × 7′9″
8)	\$15.99	12′4″ × 16′7″
9)	\$17.99	13′10″ × 14′6″
10)	\$26.85	26′10″ × 17′5″

Keeping straight lines and even spaces between tiles will make your finished floor look like a professional did the work.

Lesson 8 Computing Length of Molding

Molding

A decorative strip at the edge of walls or around windows.

Molding is a decorative strip used to finish a room. After the floor is covered, molding is usually installed at the base of the walls. You can determine the length of molding you need by finding the perimeter of the room.

EXAMPLE Soo Lee wants to finish her kitchen by installing molding around the room. How much quarter-round molding should she buy for the 10′ by 7′ room?

Find the perimeter of the room.

$$\begin{aligned} P &= 2(l + w) \\ &= 2(10' + 7') \\ &= 2(17') \\ &= 34' \end{aligned}$$

Soo Lee needs 34 feet of molding.

Exercise A Find the amount of molding needed for each of the floors described.

1) $10' \times 7'$

2) $8' \times 11'$

3) $10' \times 15'$

4) $11' \times 16'$

5) $12' \times 18'$

6) $10' \times 16'$

7) $13' \times 17'$

8) $18' \times 17'$

9) $9' \times 17'$

10) $19' \times 16'$

EXAMPLE Maurice wishes to finish his dining room with quarter-round molding. The room is 15′6″ by 12′7″. How much molding should he buy? Follow these steps to calculate the perimeter of the room.

Step 1 Write the formula to find the perimeter of the room.

$$\begin{aligned} P &= 2(l + w) \\ &= 2(15'6'' + 12'7'') \end{aligned}$$

Step 2 Add the feet and inches.

a) Add feet together.
b) Add inches together.
c) If total inches are 12 or more, then rename to feet and inches.

15 feet	6 inches
+ 12 feet	7 inches
27 feet	13 inches (13 inches = 1 foot, 1 inch)

or 28 feet 1 inch or 28 feet + 1 inch

Step 3 Multiply the feet and inches by the whole number.
a) Multiply the feet by the whole number.
b) Multiply the inches by the whole number.
c) Rename the inches to feet if necessary.

$$\begin{aligned} P &= 2(28 \text{ feet} + 1 \text{ inch}) \text{ or } 2(28' + 1'') \\ &= (2 \times 28') + (2 \times 1'') \\ &= 56' + 2'' \\ &= 56'2'' \end{aligned}$$

Maurice needs 56 feet and 2 inches of molding.

Exercise B Find the length of molding needed for each of the floors described.

1) $10'5'' \times 9'8''$

2) $15'6'' \times 17'10''$

3) $25'3'' \times 15'8''$

4) $11'2'' \times 7'9''$

5) $12'3'' \times 8'3''$

6) $14'6'' \times 15'2''$

7) $10'11'' \times 7'9''$

8) $12'4'' \times 16'7''$

9) $13'10'' \times 14'6''$

10) $26'10'' \times 17'5''$

Lesson 9 Wall-to-Wall Carpeting

Wall-to-wall carpeting is sold by the square yard. You can estimate the amount needed.

EXAMPLE Ernesto wants wall-to-wall carpeting in his room, which measures 8′ by 11′. Carpeting is on sale for $10.99 per sq. yd. Estimate the cost. Round answers where possible.

Step 1 Find the area of the floor in square feet.

A = l × w
= 11′ × 8′
= 88 square feet

Step 2 Find the area in square yards. One square yard = 9 square feet. Divide by 9 to find the number of square yards. Round 9 sq. yd. and 7 sq. ft. to 10 sq. yd.

$$\begin{array}{r} 9 \text{ sq. yd.} \approx 10 \text{ sq. yd.} \\ 9\overline{)88} \\ -\ 81 \\ \hline 7 \text{ sq. ft.} \end{array}$$

1′	1′	1′	
1	2	3	1′
4	5	6	1′
7	8	9	1′

1 sq. yd.

Step 3 Round the cost per square yard to the next whole number. Multiply the number of square yards by the cost per square yard.

$10.99 ≈ $11.00
10 × $11.00 = $110.00
Ernesto's estimated cost is $110.00.

Exercise A Estimate the cost of carpeting for each room.

	Room	Cost per Sq. Yd.		Room	Cost per Sq. Yd.
1)	8′ × 10′	$12.99	**6)**	12′ × 15′	$7.99
2)	25′ × 18′	$10.95	**7)**	10′ × 17′	$8.90
3)	14′ × 16′	$9.98	**8)**	9′6″ × 11′	$7.99
4)	10′3″ × 15′8″	$10.99	**9)**	13′5″ × 16′9″	$12.99
5)	15′8″ × 17′9″	$14.99	**10)**	12′6″ × 13′10″	$15.99

Lesson 10 Additions to Existing Homes

Contractors

People who agree to perform work.

Materials

Supplies needed for making or doing something.

Some homeowners want to add a room to their existing house. **Contractors** who erect buildings or additions estimate a job based on its area and on the cost of the **materials** required.

EXAMPLE Brad and Penny plan to build a family room. The new 10′ by 15′ room will cost an average of \$50 per square foot. The fireplace will cost \$2,500 more. What will be the total cost?

Step 1 Find the area of the addition.

$$A = l \times w$$
$$= 10' \times 15'$$
$$= 150 \text{ square feet}$$

Step 2 Multiply the area by the cost per square foot.

150	Square feet
× 50	Cost per square foot
\$7,500	Cost of addition

Step 3 Add the cost of any extras to find the total cost.

\$ 7,500	Cost of addition
+ 2,500	Cost of fireplace
\$10,000	Total cost of addition

A homeowner may decide to add a room to an existing home rather than to buy a larger home.

Exercise A Compute the total cost of each addition.

	Addition	Dimensions	Cost per Sq. Ft.	Cost of Extras
1)	Family room	$18' \times 10'$	$45.00	$2,400
2)	Sun porch	$14' \times 25'$	$20.00	$650
3)	Master bedroom	$20' \times 30'$	$40.00	$3,200
4)	Bathroom	$7' \times 10'$	$50.50	$756
5)	Garage	$20' \times 30'$	$20.50	$309
6)	Breakfast nook	$8' \times 8'$	$20.75	$497
7)	Sun deck	$25' \times 30'$	$10.85	None
8)	Bedroom and bath	$12' \times 13'$	$40.50	$1,379
9)	Bedroom	$10' \times 12'$	$30.57	$1,847
10)	Den and TV room	$16' \times 25'$	$37.50	$1,575

Insulation

Insulation
Material that prevents electricity, heat, or sound from entering or leaving an area.

Insulation is a term describing materials used to prevent transfer of electricity, heat, or sound. Installing insulation in an attic will cut heating and cooling bills. Consumers compare prices to decide which insulation is least expensive.

Exercise A Find the cost per square foot of insulation described in each of the following ads. Round answers to the nearest cent.

1) Brand A

2) Brand B

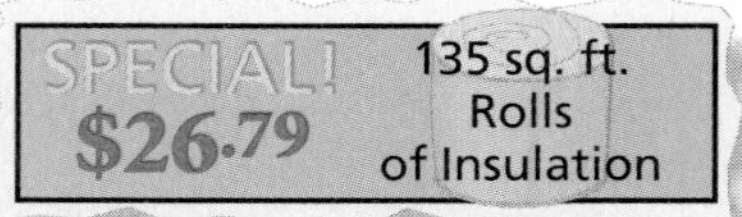

3) Brand C

4) Brand D

EXAMPLE Jennifer plans to put Brand A insulation in her attic. How much will it cost? The dimensions are as shown.

Step 1 Divide the irregular figure into rectangles.

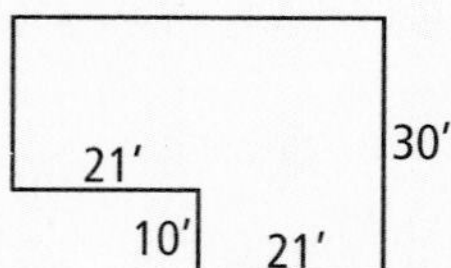

Step 2 Find the missing dimensions.

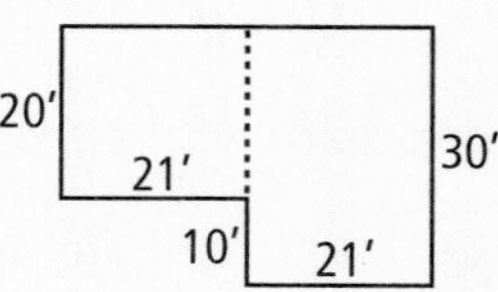

Step 3 Find the areas.

Area A = l × w
= 21′ × 20′
= 420 square feet

Area B = l × w
= 30′ × 21′
= 630 square feet

EXAMPLE *(continued)*

Step 4 Add these areas to find the total area.

$$\begin{array}{rl} 420 & \text{sq. ft.} \\ +\ 630 & \text{sq. ft.} \\ \hline 1{,}050 & \text{sq. ft.} \end{array}$$

Step 5 Divide the total area by the number of square feet per roll of insulation.

$$88\,\overline{)\,1{,}050} = 11.9 \longrightarrow 12 \text{ rolls}$$

Round up for any remainder.

Step 6 Multiply the cost per roll times the number of rolls of insulation needed.

$$\begin{array}{rl} \$\ 17.49 & \text{Cost per roll} \\ \times\quad 12 & \text{Number of rolls} \\ \hline \$209.88 & \text{Total cost to insulate attic} \end{array}$$

Exercise B Find the cost of insulating each of these attics.

1) Brand A

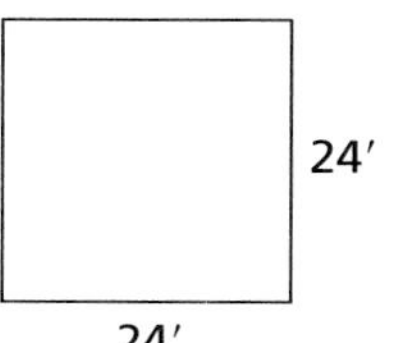

2) Brand C

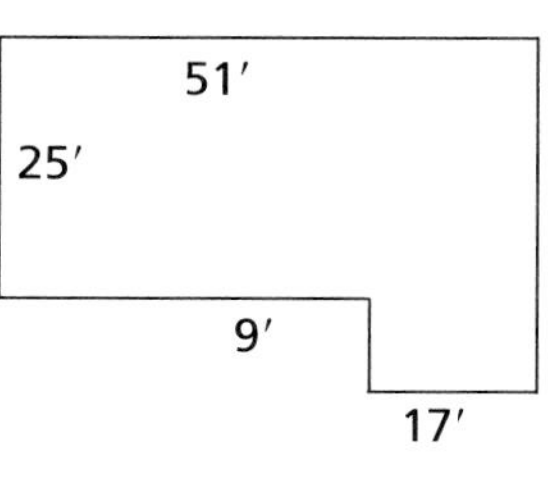

3) Brand A

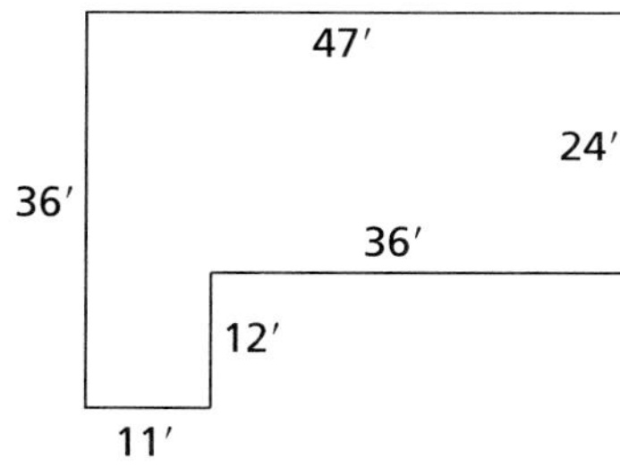

4) Brand B

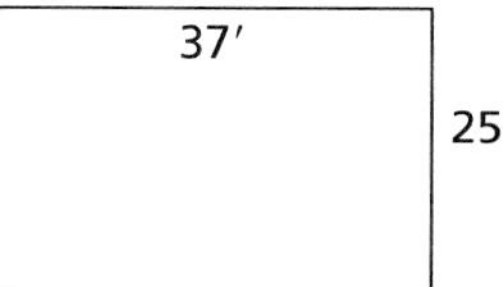

5) Brand D

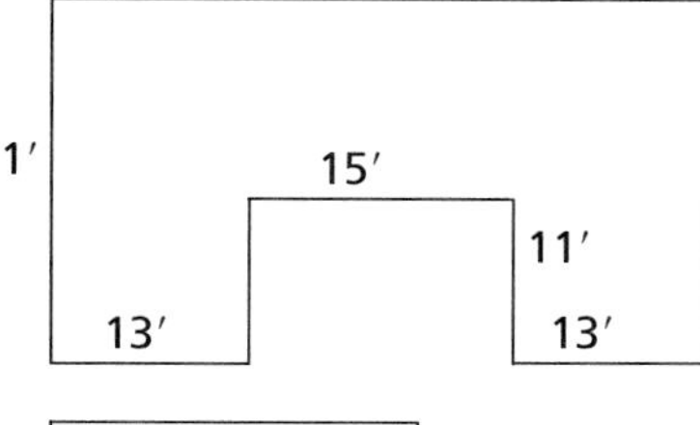

6) Brand C

23′ 17′ 17′ 17′

Lesson 12 Seeding and Feeding Lawns

Fertilizer

Natural or chemical mixture applied to soil to help grass grow.

Square meters (m^2)

A metric unit used for measuring area.

Grass seed and **fertilizer** are sold in quantities to cover a certain size area. Before you buy grass seed or fertilizer, you need to know how much ground is to be covered.

The table below shows the coverage rates and prices for sample grass seeds and fertilizer. The coverage figures are for established lawns that have thin grass and are in need of more seed and fertilizer. The coverage rates are listed in **square meters** (m^2).

Coverage Rates		
Variety	**Coverage per Box**	**Cost per Box**
A. Shady Seed	275 m^2	$11.79
B. Show Seed	200 m^2	$7.59
C. Hardy Seed	450 m^2	$9.99
D. Kentucky Bluegrass Seed	400 m^2	$10.49
E. Generic Seed	400 m^2	$5.69
F. Fertilizer	100 m^2	$9.49

Exercise A Find the cost per square meter of each of the five grass seeds. Round your answer to the nearest cent.

1) Shady seed ($11.79 ÷ 275)

2) Show seed

3) Hardy seed

4) Kentucky Bluegrass seed

5) Generic seed

EXAMPLE Mo wants to reseed his lawn. He selects variety A, Shady Seed. The total area of his property is 600 m². His house and driveway cover 150 m². What does the seed cost?

Lawn
House
Driveway

Step 1 Find the area to be seeded. Subtract the area of the house and driveway from the total area.

$$\begin{array}{rl} 600 & m^2 \\ -\ 150 & m^2 \\ \hline 450 & m^2 \end{array} \quad \text{Area to be seeded}$$

Step 2 Find the number of boxes of seed needed. Divide the area to be seeded by the coverage per box. Round your answer to the next box.

$$275\,\overline{)\,450.0} = 1.6 \longrightarrow 2 \text{ boxes}$$

Step 3 Multiply the cost per box times the number of boxes needed.

$11.79	Cost per box
× 2	Number of boxes
$23.58	Total cost

The cost of seed for Mo's lawn is $23.58.

Exercise B Find the cost of seed for each of these lots.

	Area of Lot	Area of House and Driveway	Variety of Seed
1)	1,000 m^2	100 m^2	A
2)	975 m^2	75 m^2	B
3)	827 m^2	129 m^2	C
4)	2,010 m^2	68 m^2	D
5)	1,575 m^2	103 m^2	E

Exercise C Find the annual cost of fertilizing each lawn above twice a year. Use Fertilizer F from the chart on page 182.

Lesson 13 Fencing a Yard

People sometimes fence their property for privacy or for protection. The amount of fencing you need is determined by the *perimeter* of the property that you are enclosing.

EXAMPLE Denise and Richard decide to fence their property. They live on a rectangular lot 90 feet long and 60 feet wide.

$$
\begin{aligned}
P &= 2(l + w) \\
&= 2(90 \text{ ft.} + 60 \text{ ft.}) \\
&= 2(150 \text{ ft.}) \\
&= 300 \text{ ft.}
\end{aligned}
$$

60 ft.

90 ft.

They need 300 feet of fencing to surround their lot.

You can use many different materials such as wood, metal, and stone to fence a yard.

Exercise A Find the length of fencing needed for each of these lots.

1) 51 ft. × 57 ft.

2) 45 ft. × 75 ft.

3) 81 ft. × 117 ft.

4) $31\frac{1}{2}$ ft. × 54 ft.

5) 66 ft. × $67\frac{1}{2}$ ft.

6) 129 ft. × 258 ft.

7) 69 ft. × 135 ft.

8) 66 ft. × 129 ft.

9) 69 ft. × 96 ft.

10) 123 ft. × $97\frac{1}{2}$ ft.

11) 72 ft. × 125 ft.

12) 47 ft. × $91\frac{1}{2}$ ft.

13) 70 ft. × 143 ft.

14) 63 ft. × 75 ft.

15) 92 ft. × 147 ft.

Consumer Humor

Why does a competitor take lumber to the Olympic Games?

He wants to participate in the fencing event.

Chapter 7 Review

Solve these problems.

1) Find the original cost of a rocker selling for $159.95 at 20% off.

2) Find the discount if a $69.99 item is on sale for $39.99.

3) Find the due date on a "Ninety Days Same As Cash" agreement. The purchase date is October 10.

4) Calculate the number of cans of paint needed to cover the walls of a room 11′ × 12′ × 8′. Each can covers 300 square feet.

5) Paint sells for $4.99 a quart and $15.99 a gallon. How many gallons and quarts should be purchased if 9 quarts are needed? What will this paint cost?

6) A special variety of wallpaper covers only 60 square feet per roll. How many single rolls are needed to paper a room measuring 19′ by 12′ by 8′6″?

7) Estimate the number of square yards of carpeting needed to cover a floor 10′3″ by 15′9″?

Find the total cost of each of these additions.

	Addition	Dimensions	Cost per Sq. Ft.	Cost of Extras
8)	Bathroom	7′ × 10′	$60.25	$932.00
9)	Sun Deck	8′ × 12′	$14.00	$732.00
10)	Garage	20′ × 24′	$21.00	$170.00

11) Compute the cost of insulation for this attic. The insulation comes in 49 sq. ft. rolls, which cost $15.97 each.

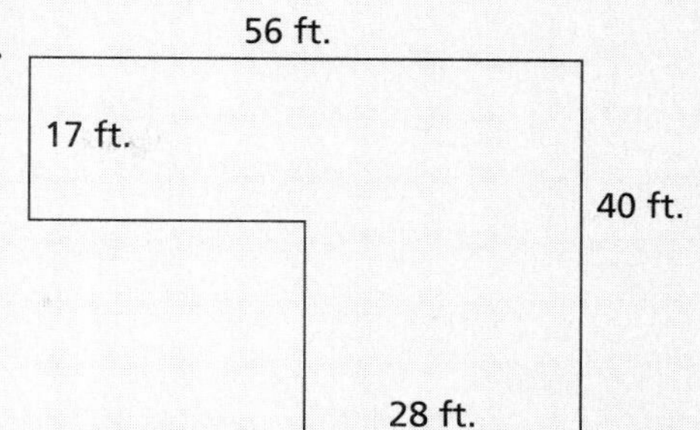

Find the total cost of grass seed for each of these lawns. Use the table to help you.

	Area of Lot	Area of House and Driveway	Variety of Seed
12)	1,325 m^2	120 m^2	B
13)	2,010 m^2	70 m^2	D

Coverage Rates		
Variety	**Coverage per Box**	**Cost per Box**
A. Shady Seed	275 m^2	$11.79
B. Show Seed	200 m^2	$7.59
C. Hardy Seed	450 m^2	$9.99
D. Generic Seed	400 m^2	$5.69

14) Compute the length of fencing needed to enclose this yard.

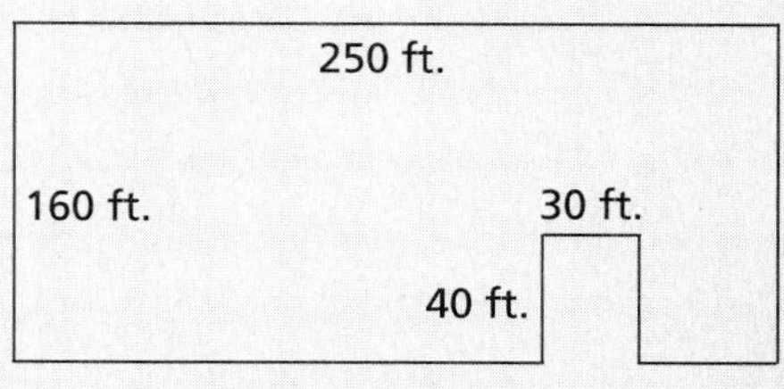

15) Calculate the length of fencing needed to enclose this yard.

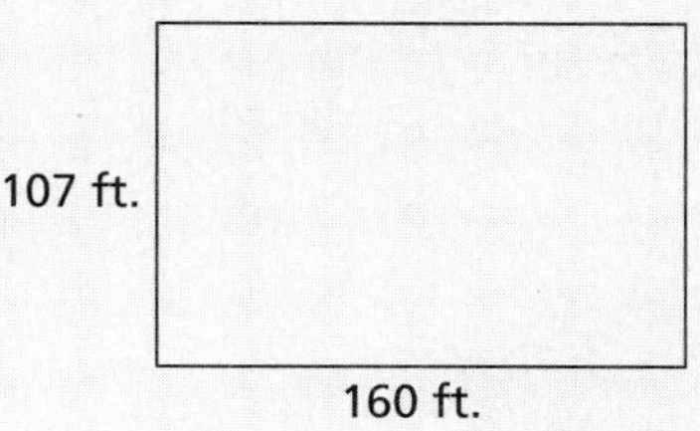

Test Taking Tip

Read test questions carefully to identify those questions that require more than one answer.

Chapter 8

Traveling

Many people enjoy traveling both within the United States and abroad. You can use mathematics to answer many questions about your travel plans.

"How far is it to a given destination?"

"How much will the ticket cost?"

"How much time will be spent traveling?"

"What will be the arrival time?"

"Is a rental car needed?"

"How much is a U.S. dollar worth in another country?"

In Chapter 8, you will learn about several tools used by travelers. You will also learn how to compute travel expenses here and in foreign locations.

Goals for Learning

- To read maps and compute distance
- To compute travel fares and hotel expenses
- To find the exchange value of U.S. dollars and foreign currency
- To compute the cost of car rentals and parking charges
- To compare time in different time zones
- To calculate flight times between different time zones

Lesson 1 Reading a Map

> ***Legend***
> *A chart that explains the symbols used on a map.*

Using a map can simplify travel by car. The distances between towns and road junctions are shown by small numbers. A road map usually has a **legend** on it to explain the symbols used on that particular map. The legend may show highway markers, different kinds of roads, sizes of towns and cities, mileages, and points of interest. A sample legend is shown below.

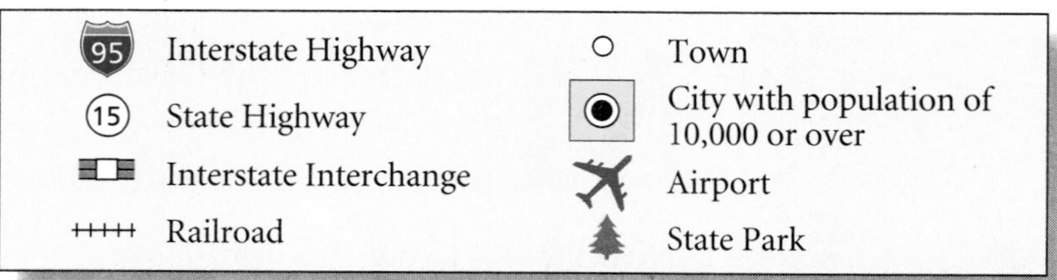

Study the following road map. Notice the names of the towns, the highways, and the symbols used on this map.

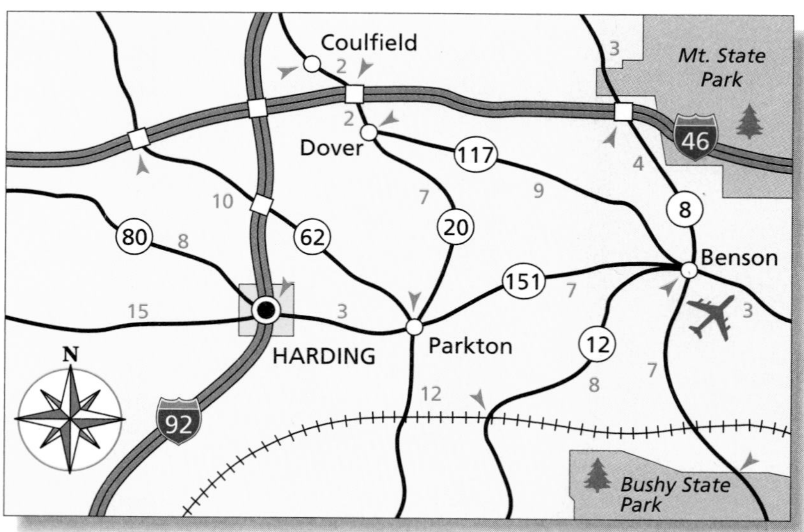

PROBLEM SOLVING

Exercise A Answer these questions. Use the road map on page 190.

1) How many interstate highways are shown on this map?

2) What is the route number of the interstate highway that heads north and south?

3) What is the route number of the interstate highway that heads east and west?

4) What is the route number of the state highway that goes from Benson toward Mt. State Park?

5) Where is an airport located?

6) How many state parks are located near Benson?

7) What route would you take to travel from Benson to Harding?

8) How many miles is it from Benson to Harding?

9) How many miles is it from Interstate 46 to Bushy State Park?

10) Does the train stop in Benson?

11) What city has a population over 10,000?

12) What cities have populations under 10,000?

13) In what direction do you travel to go from Parkton to Dover?

14) Is Dover closer to Parkton or Benson?

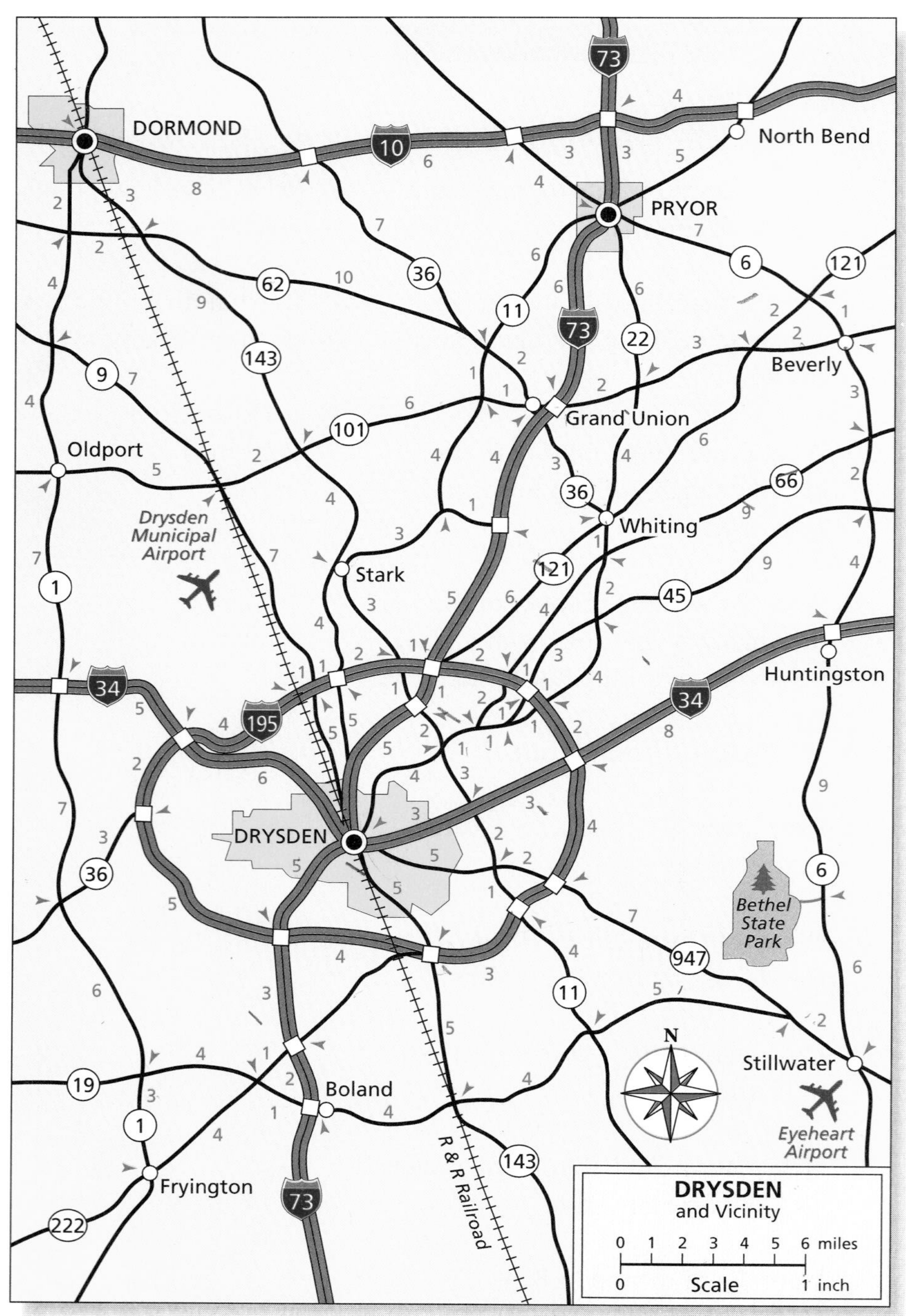
DORMOND
PRYOR
North Bend
Beverly
Grand Union
Oldport
Drysden Municipal Airport
Whiting
Stark
Huntingston
DRYSDEN
Bethel State Park
Boland
Stillwater
Eyeheart Airport
Fryington
R & R Railroad
N
DRYSDEN
and Vicinity
0 1 2 3 4 5 6 miles
0 Scale 1 inch

EXAMPLE Rhoda drives from Fryington to Huntingston. How many miles does she travel?

Step 1 Read the map and choose a route. Locate Fryington. Use Route 222 to Route 73 to Route 34 to Huntingston.

Step 2 Read each mileage number along the route.

Step 3 Find the total. It is 27 miles from Fryington to Huntingston.

Route 222	4
	1
Route 73	3
	5
Route 34	3
	3
	+8
Total	27

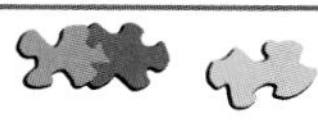

PROBLEM SOLVING

Exercise B Read the map to help you find the distance in miles in each case.

1) Between Grand Union and Beverly

2) Between Dormond and Stark

3) Between Dormond and Fryington

4) From Grand Union to Dormond on Routes 36 and 10

5) From Grand Union to Dormond on Routes 36, 62, and 143

6) From Pryor to North Bend on Routes 73 and 10

7) From Pryor to North Bend on Route 11

8) From Oldport to Drysden on Routes 1 and 34

9) From Oldport to Drysden on Routes 101 and 9

10) What is the road distance between the airports?

11) How far is it from Pryor to the state park on Route 6?

12) What is the shortest route from Boland to Oldport?

13) What is the shortest road distance from Stillwater to Fryington?

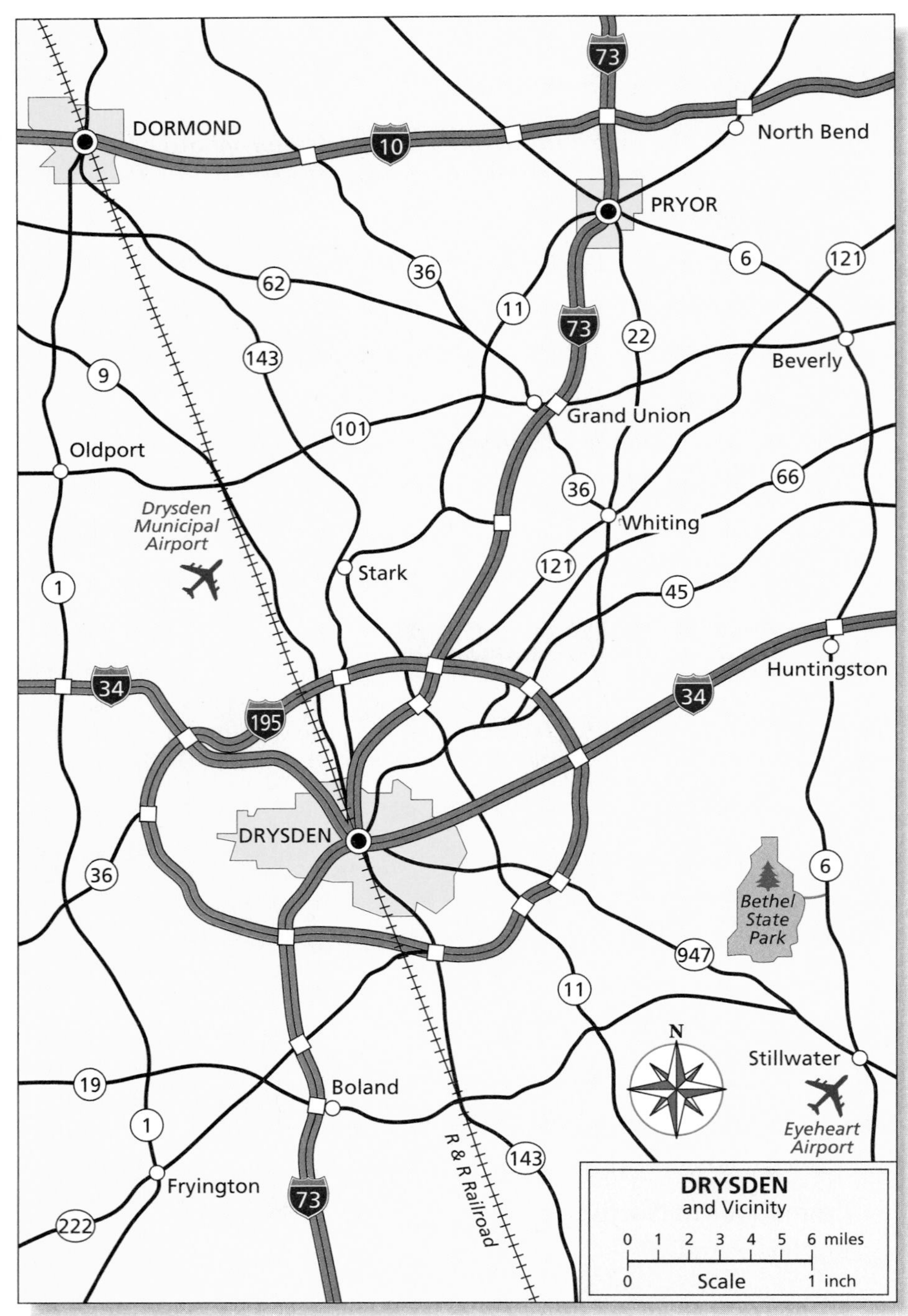

DORMOND
North Bend
PRYOR
Beverly
Grand Union
Oldport
Drysden Municipal Airport
Whiting
Stark
Huntingston
DRYSDEN
Bethel State Park
Stillwater
Boland
Eyeheart Airport
Fryington
R & R Railroad
N
DRYSDEN
and Vicinity
0 1 2 3 4 5 6 miles
0 Scale 1 inch

Lesson 2 Estimating Distances

Straightline distance

The shortest distance between two points on a map.

Scale

A ratio of the distance on a map to actual distance.

You can estimate the shortest or **straightline distance** between towns by using the **scale**. It indicates the relationship between the distances on a map and the corresponding actual distances. Look at the map and the scale on page 194.

EXAMPLE Charise wants to know about how far it is between Boland and Pryor.

Step 1 With a ruler, measure the distance between Boland and Pryor. It is about $5\frac{1}{4}''$.

Step 2 Read the scale at the bottom of the map. It indicates that 1 inch = 6 miles.

Step 3 Multiply the measured distance in inches by the number of miles to the inch.

$$\begin{array}{r} 5.25 \\ \times \quad 6 \\ \hline 31.50 \text{ miles} \end{array}$$

It is about $31\frac{1}{2}$ miles between Boland and Pryor.

According to the road map, the driving distance between Boland and Pryor is 45 miles. Compare the estimate above with that driving distance. Which is larger? Why do you think this is so?

Exercise A Use the scale on the map to estimate the distance between these towns. Copy the following chart and complete it.

	Towns	Distance in Inches	Distance in Miles
1)	Whiting to Stark	____	____
2)	Stillwater to Dormond	____	____
3)	Oldport to Stillwater	____	____
4)	Beverly to Boland	____	____
5)	Grand Union to Fryington	____	____
6)	Drysden to Fryington	____	____
7)	Huntingston to North Bend	____	____

Mileage Map

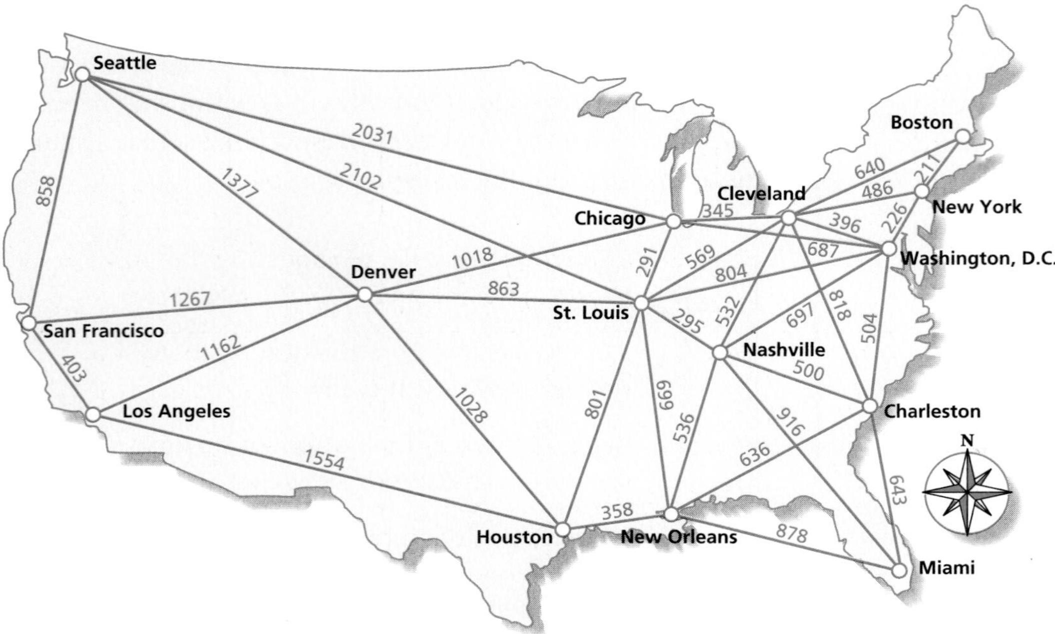

Mileage map
A map that gives distances between cities.

EXAMPLE The **mileage map** shown above gives the driving distance in miles between major cities. Dianna wants to know the shortest route between Nashville and Chicago.

Step 1 Find a likely route and add the distances.

Nashville to St. Louis	295 miles
St. Louis to Chicago	+291 miles
	586 miles

Step 2 Find another likely route and add the distances.

Nashville to Cleveland	532 miles
Cleveland to Chicago	+345 miles
	877 miles

Step 3 Choose the route with the shorter distance: 586 miles.

Exercise B Copy this chart on grid paper and complete it with the shortest distance between each pair of cities. Use the mileage map to help you. Leave plenty of room for the numbers.

		Boston	Charleston	Chicago	Cleveland	Denver	Houston	Los Angeles	Miami	Nashville	New Orleans	New York	San Francisco	Seattle	St. Louis
1)	Charleston														
2)	Chicago														
3)	Cleveland														
4)	Denver														
5)	Houston														
6)	Los Angeles														
7)	Miami														
8)	Nashville			586											
9)	New Orleans														
10)	New York														
11)	San Francisco														
12)	Seattle														
13)	St. Louis														
14)	Washington, D.C.														

Calculator Practice

When planning a trip, it is good to know about how long the trip will take. Use your calculator to help you estimate.

Step 1 Key in the estimated distance.

Step 2 Press ÷.

Step 3 Key in the estimated average rate of speed.

Step 4 Press =.

Step 5 Round to the nearest hour.

EXAMPLE Estimate the time for a trip of 350 miles, if you average 45 miles per hour.

350 ÷ 45 =

The display reads 7.777777778

The trip will take about 8 hours.

Using the calculator might make you think that the times are exact. But, remember that we started with numbers that were estimates and the best we can do with those numbers is to find another estimate.

If you wish to estimate the minutes, subtract the whole number of hours and multiply the remainder by 60. This is true because the remainder is a fraction of an hour and there are 60 minutes in each hour.

7.777777778 − 7 = × 60 =

The display reads 46.66666667.
The trip will take an estimated 7 hours and 47 minutes. That is about $7\frac{3}{4}$ hours.

Exercise C Estimate the amount of time each of the following trips will take. Round to a reasonable unit of time. Sometimes, it will be to the nearest quarter hour, sometimes to the nearest day. You decide.

	Estimated Distance	Estimated Average Speed
1)	100 miles	40 mph
2)	115 miles	35 mph
3)	15 miles	50 mph
4)	327 miles	47 mph
5)	762 miles	55 mph
6)	1,000 miles	40 mph
7)	1,356 miles	55 mph
8)	2,500 miles	45 mph
9)	2,456 miles	55 mph
10)	2,680 miles	40 mph

Lesson 3 Reading a Bus Schedule

Bus schedule

A chart or table that shows the times a bus stops on a route.

Bus schedules are charts or tables that indicate arrival and departure times at all the stops on a given route. To find the time to travel any given distance, subtract the departure time from the arrival time.

THE NUMBER LINE

READ UP ↑	STOPS	READ DOWN ↓
3:52 p	Appleton	5:44 p
3:45 p	Bell	5:49 p
3:15 p	Davis	6:01 p
2:43 p	Evanston	6:39 p
1:43 p	Fordham	7:47 p
12:50 p	DP Hopedale AR	8:58 p
12:40 p	AR Hopedale DP	9:08 p
11:48 a	Largo	10:00 p
11:10 a	DP Taft AR	10:40 p
10:55 a	AR Taft DP	11:00 p
10:40 a	Opala	11:15 p
9:52 a	Pikerton	12:08 a
9:15 a	Union	12:50 a

DP = Departure Time a = a.m.
AR = Arrival Time p = a.m.

EXAMPLE Find the time for the trip from Opala to Fordham.

Step 1 To get from Opala to Fordham on the schedule, you read up. Therefore, use the times given in the first column, "READ UP."

1:43 p	Fordham
10:40 a	Opala

Step 2 Subtract 10:40 (the departure time) from 1:43 (the arrival time). Rename 1:43. Add the 12 morning hours to 1:43 so that it becomes 13:43.

Arrival time at Fordham	1:43	+ 12 hours ⟶	13:43
Departure time at Opala	−10:40		−10:40
			3:03

The trip from Opala to Fordham takes 3 hours and 3 minutes.

EXAMPLE Find the time for the trip from Bell to Evanston.

Step 1 Read down to get from Bell to Evanston.

Bell	5:49 p
Evanston	6:39 p

Step 2 Subtract the departure time from the arrival time. Rename 1 hour to 60 minutes so that 6:39 becomes 5:99.

Arrives at Evanston	6:39	Rename →	5:99
Departs Bell	−5:49	(1 hour = 60 minutes)	−5:49
			50

The trip from Bell to Evanston takes 50 minutes.

Exercise A Find the time for each trip. Use the bus schedule on page 200.

	Point of Departure	Destination
1)	Appleton	Union
2)	Taft	Pikerton
3)	Pikerton	Hopedale
4)	Davis	Opala
5)	Pikerton	Bell
6)	Union	Appleton
7)	Largo	Evanston
8)	Fordham	Hopedale
9)	Bell	Fordham
10)	Evanston	Davis

PROBLEM SOLVING

Exercise B Use the bus schedule to help you answer the following questions.

1) How long does the bus stay in the station at Hopedale on the trip from Union to Appleton?

2) How long does the bus stay in the station at Hopedale on the trip from Appleton to Union?

3) How long does the bus stay in the station at Taft on the trip from Union to Appleton?

4) How long does the bus stay in the station at Taft on the trip from Appleton to Union?

Lesson 4 Computing Bus Fares

Off-peak hours

A time period in which a minimum number of people travel.

Peak hours

A time period in which the maximum number of people travel.

Knowing the special rates for bus fares can help travelers to save money. A sample rate chart is shown below. Fares during **off-peak hours** are lower. Extra fares are charged for **peak hours**.

Bus Fares Rate Chart

Service Between Appleton and:	Off-Peak Hours	Peak Hours
Bell	$1.50	$3.00
Davis	$2.00	$4.25
Evanston	$3.75	$8.00
Fordham	$8.50	$13.25
Hopedale	$12.00	$17.75
Largo	$15.50	$21.75
Taft	$16.50	$23.75
Opala	$17.75	$26.50
Pikerton	$20.90	$33.50
Union	$24.25	$37.25

Here are money-saving plans that apply to this rate chart:

1. Children under 12 may ride at half fare when accompanied by one or more adults. Otherwise, full fare is charged.
2. One infant under 2, not occupying a separate seat and accompanied by a person aged 12 or older, may ride free. Otherwise, half fare is charged.
3. A round-trip fare is double the one-way fare.

EXAMPLE Annette, her husband, and their three children (ages 6, 8, and 10) will ride the bus from Appleton to Largo. If they choose the off-peak fare, what will their fares be?

Step 1	Read the rate table for adult off-peak fare between Appleton and Largo.	\$15.50	Off-peak for adult
Step 2	Multiply the off-peak fare by 2. (2 adults)	\$15.50 × 2 \$31.00	Off-peak fare Fare for parents
Step 3	Find the child's fare by dividing by 2.	\$ 7.75 2)\$15.50	Fare for child under 12
Step 4	Multiply child's rate by the number of children. (3)	\$ 7.75 × 3 \$23.25	Fare for child under 12 Fare for children
Step 5	Add the adult fares and children's fares to find total fares.	\$31.00 +23.25 \$54.25	Fare for parents Fare for children Fare for family

The family will pay \$54.25 for their bus fares.

Exercise A Find the fares from Appleton for each of these groups. Use the rate chart on page 202.

	Adults	Children	Infants	Destination	Trip	Service
1)	1	0	0	Opala	One way	Peak
2)	2	0	0	Hopedale	One way	Peak
3)	2	3	0	Fordham	Round	Off-peak
4)	1	2	1	Taft	Round	Peak
5)	2	3	0	Bell	One way	Off-peak
6)	3	0	1	Union	Round	Off-peak
7)	4	5	1	Largo	One way	Off-peak
8)	2	0	2	Evanston	One way	Peak
9)	3	1	0	Pikerton	Round	Peak
10)	4	2	0	Davis	Round	Off-peak

Lesson 5 Staying in Hotels

Double occupancy
A hotel room for two people.

Peak season
The time of year when business is greatest.

Single occupancy
A hotel room for one person.

Suite
A group of connected hotel rooms.

Tourist season
A period of the year when many people visit a given area.

Most hotel rooms are designed for **single** or **double occupancy**. These terms mean rooms for one or two persons. **Suites**, or sets of rooms, are usually designed for groups of more than two persons. Rates, or prices, for the rooms may change depending on the **tourist season**. The highest prices are in effect during the peak season when many people visit a given area. The term **peak season** is used to describe the time of year when business is at its best; for instance, at the beach in summer or in the mountains during ski season. Below is a list of the rates available at the High Gate Inn in Sunnyvale, Florida.

High Gate Inn — Daily Rates — High Gate Inn

April 20 - Sept. 8		Sept. 9 - Dec. 19	
Single	$47.50	Single	$39.50
Double	$59.50	Double	$49.50
Suite	$135.50	Suite	$115.50
Dec. 20 - Jan. 31		**Feb. 1 - April 19**	
Single	$59.50	Single	$79.50
Double	$67.50	Double	$87.50
Suite	$170.50	Suite	$190.50

Daily rates apply to persons who arrive after 1 P.M. on the first day and leave by checkout time (11 A.M.) on the last day. Anyone who arrives too early or leaves too late must pay for an extra day.

EXAMPLE Virginia and Georgia plan to stay at the High Gate Inn from March 24 to March 31. They plan to arrive on March 24 and leave by checkout time on March 31. They will not be charged for March 31. What will be the cost per person?

Use a four-step method to solve this problem.

Step 1 Calculate the number of days. Subtract the earlier date from the later date.

$$\begin{array}{r} \text{March } 31 \\ -\text{March } 24 \\ \hline 7 \text{ Days} \end{array}$$

EXAMPLE *(continued)*

Step 2 Find the daily rate in the schedule. A double room from February 1 to April 19 is $87.50 daily.

Step 3 Multiply the daily rate times the number of days to find the total cost.

$ 87.50	Daily rate
× 7	Days
$612.50	Total cost

Step 4 To find the cost per person, divide the total cost by the number of people.

$$\begin{array}{r l} \$306.25 & \text{Cost per person} \\ 2\,\overline{)\,\$612.50} & \text{Total cost} \end{array}$$

The cost per person will be $306.25.

Exercise A Copy and complete the information for this table. Use the rate chart on page 204 to help you.

	Dates		Number of Days	Number of Persons	Daily Rate	Total Cost	Cost per Person
	Arrive	Depart					
1)	Jan. 4	Jan. 11	___	1	___	___	___
2)	Oct. 10	Oct. 11	___	2	___	___	___
3)	Apr. 11	Apr. 19	___	2	___	___	___
4)	May 10	May 20	___	5	___	___	___
5)	Dec. 5	Dec. 14	___	4	___	___	___
6)	Feb. 14	Feb. 20	___	2	___	___	___
7)	May 5	May 9	___	1	___	___	___
8)	Aug. 10	Aug. 21	___	2	___	___	___
9)	June 7	June 21	___	3	___	___	___
10)	Dec. 25	Dec. 31	___	3	___	___	___

Exercise B Hotel guests are often charged a special tax. Find a 15% tax for each cost per person in Exercise A. To find a 15% tax, multiply .15 times the cost per person. What would the tax be in each case?

Often a person's stay in a hotel happens to include days in two different months.

EXAMPLE DeAndra is staying at the High Gate Inn from July 29 to August 15. What is the cost? Use the rate chart on page 204.

Step 1 Calculate the number of days she stays in July. Subtract the arrival date from the number of days in the month. Add one day. (Why?)

31	Days in July
−29	Arrival day
2	
+1	Add a day
3	Days stayed

Step 2 Find the number of days in August that DeAndra stays. She leaves on the 15th, so she will not be charged for that day. Subtract 1 from the date she leaves. (Why?)

15	Departure
−1	
14	Days stayed

Step 3 Add the days stayed in each month.

3	July
+14	August
17	Total days

Step 4 Find the total cost. Multiply the daily rate by the number of days. DeAndra's total cost is $807.50.

$ 47.50	Daily rate
× 17	Days
$807.50	Total cost

Exercise C Copy and complete the information for this table. Use the rate chart on page 204 to help you.

	Dates		Number of Days	Number of Persons	Daily Rate	Total Cost	Cost per Person
	Arrive	Depart					
1)	Apr. 25	May 5	____	2	____	____	____
2)	Dec. 28	Jan. 3	____	5	____	____	____
3)	Oct. 25	Nov. 4	____	2	____	____	____
4)	Nov. 20	Dec. 10	____	1	____	____	____
5)	Mar. 29	Apr. 10	____	7	____	____	____

Sometimes a guest's stay spans two rental seasons.
Study this example.

EXAMPLE Mark and his cousin visit the High Gate Inn from September 5 to 15. What is their cost per person? Use the rate chart on page 204.

		Season 1		Season 2
Step 1	Find the number of days stayed.	Sept. 5–8 8 − 5 = 3	3 + 1 Add a day = 4 Days	Sept. 9–15 15 − 9 = 6 Days
Step 2	Find the daily rate.	\$ 59.50		\$ 49.50
Step 3	Multiply the rate by the number of days.	\$ 59.50 × 4 = \$238.00		\$ 49.50 × 6 = \$297.00

Step 4 Find the total cost. Add.

\$238.00 Cost for Sept. 5–8
+297.00 Cost for Sept. 9–15
\$535.00 Total cost

Step 5 Find the cost per person. Divide the total cost by the number of persons. The cost per person is \$267.50.

2) \$535.00 Total cost = \$267.50 Cost per person

Exercise D Copy and complete the information for this chart. Use the rate chart on page 204 to help you.

	Dates: Arrive	Dates: Depart	Season	Number of Days	Number of Persons	Daily Rate	Total Cost	Cost per Person
1)	Apr. 15	Apr. 25	1	____	3	____	____	____
			2	____		____		
2)	Sept. 1	Sept. 14	1	____	2	____	____	____
			2	____		____		
3)	Jan. 27	Feb. 4	1	____	1	____	____	____
			2	____		____		
4)	Aug. 28	Sept. 12	1	____	2	____	____	____
			2	____		____		
5)	Dec. 15	Jan. 15	1	____	5	____	____	____
			2	____		____		

Lesson 6 Package Travel Plans

Package plans
Low-priced trips planned for groups of people.

Travel agencies and travel groups will plan a trip for a large number of people. Because of the large volume of such sales, discounts are given. These low-priced trips are called **package plans.** They often provide for hotel rooms, transportation, some meals, tours or side trips, and other special services.

EXAMPLE Mary and her friend each purchase a $939 package plan to travel to London for seven days. What is their daily cost?

Divide the number of days into the total cost.

$$7\overline{)\$939.00} = \$134.14$$

$134.14 — Cost per day
$939.00 — Total cost

Exercise A Find the cost per day for each of these package plan tours.

	Trip	Cost	Number of Days	Cost per Day
1)	Cruise to Nassau	$795	7 days	_______
2)	Health Spa and Inn	$297	3 days	_______
3)	Brazil	$1,699	7 days	_______
4)	Hawaii	$1,134	8 days	_______
5)	Bermuda	$1,044	7 days	_______
6)	Italy	$1,420	10 days	_______
7)	Spain	$1,499	8 days	_______
8)	China	$4,037	12 days	_______
9)	Peru	$1,519	7 days	_______
10)	Ireland	$1,255	8 days	_______

Lesson 7 Exchanging Currency

Sometimes Americans who travel must exchange their dollars for another nation's money, or currency. Some countries use the word *dollar* to describe their currency, but its value and appearance are different from a United States (U.S.) dollar.

> ***Exchange rate***
>
> *The ratio at which the principal unit of money of two countries may be exchanged.*

The value of the U.S. dollar compared to other countries' currencies can change daily. Travelers must find out the current **exchange rate** at the time of their trip.

Exchange rates can change daily for some currencies. When you travel, check the rates frequently so that you get the most for your dollars.

The following table shows various countries' currencies and their values compared to the U.S. dollar.

	Comparison of Currencies to U.S. Dollar				
	Country	**Currency Name**	**Currency Symbol**	**Number of Units That Equal One U.S. Dollar**	**Value of Unit in U.S. Dollars**
1)	Australia	dollar	A$	.92 dollars	$1.09
2)	Belgium	franc	BF	40 francs	$0.025
3)	Brazil	cruzado	Cz	79 cruzados	$0.013
4)	Britain	pound	£	.60 pounds	$1.67
5)	Canada	dollar	C$	1.22 dollars	$0.82
6)	China	yuan	RMB¥	6.81 yuan	$0.15
7)	Denmark	krone	Dkr	5.18 krones	$0.19
8)	Finland	markka	Fmk	4.49 markkas	$0.22
9)	France	franc	F	5.02 francs	$0.199
10)	Germany	mark	DM	1.50 marks	$0.67
11)	Greece	drachma	Dr	218 drachmas	$0.0045
12)	India	rupee	Re	31.66 rupees	$0.0315
13)	Israel	shekel	IS	1.98 shekels	$0.50
14)	Italy	lira	Lit	1481 lire	$0.0006
15)	Japan	yen	¥	94.50 yen	$0.01
16)	Mexico	peso	Mex $	6.34 pesos	$0.16
17)	South Africa	rand	R	3.35 rands	$0.30
18)	Sweden	krona	Skr	5.73 krona	$0.17
19)	Switzerland	franc	SwF	2.21 francs	$0.45

EXAMPLE Mrs. Osaka wants to exchange 25 United States dollars for Japanese yen. How many yen will she receive?

Rule To convert United States dollars to foreign currency, multiply the currency rate from the fourth column of the chart by the number of U.S. dollars.

94.50	Currency rate of yen per dollar
× 25	U.S. dollars
2,362.50	Yen

Mrs. Osaka will receive 2,362.50 yen for $25.

Exercise A For each of the countries listed on page 210, find out how much currency you will receive for 70 United States dollars. Use the currency rate listed in the fourth column of the chart. Round each answer to the nearest whole number.

Exercise B Convert the United States currency below to currency of other countries.

U.S. Dollars	Country	Number of Units
1) $100	Britain	__________
2) $50	Canada	__________
3) $25	Mexico	__________
4) $40	Germany	__________
5) $85	Italy	__________
6) $37	France	__________
7) $423	China	__________
8) $10,500	Israel	__________
9) $798	Japan	__________
10) $25,000	Greece	__________

EXAMPLE William sees a chess set for sale in Switzerland for 65 francs. How much would it cost in United States dollars?

Rule To convert foreign currency to United States dollars, multiply the currency rate in the fifth column of the chart on page 210 by the amount of foreign money.

65	Swiss Francs
× .45	Currency rate (value in U.S. dollars)
$29.25	U.S. Dollars

The chess set costs $29.25 in U.S. dollars.

Exercise C Convert the currency below to United States dollars. Use the chart on page 210. Round each answer to the nearest cent.

	Country	Amount
1)	Australia	26 dollars
2)	Belgium	6,754 francs
3)	Brazil	30,985 cruzados
4)	South Africa	75 rands
5)	Canada	50 dollars
6)	China	403 yuan
7)	Denmark	987 krones
8)	Finland	100 markkas
9)	Greece	309 drachmas
10)	India	1,300 rupees
11)	Israel	967 shekels
12)	Italy	135,879 lire
13)	Mexico	685 pesos
14)	France	50 francs
15)	Germany	300 marks
16)	Sweden	6,790 krona

Lesson 8 Renting a Car

A traveler may find it necessary or convenient to rent a car while away from home. Two sample rate charts are shown below. As you can see on the chart, rates are usually higher for larger cars than they are for smaller cars.

Ace Rental	
Daily Rates	
Subcompact	$43
Compact	$50
Midsize	$54
Full Size	$57
Weekly Rates	
Subcompact	$159
Compact	$189
Midsize	$209
Full Size	$229

Bekins Rent-A-Car	
Daily Rates	
Compact	$18.98 + 20¢ / mile
Midsize	$22.95 + 20¢ / mile
Full Size	$24.95 + 20¢ / mile
Monthly Rates (No charge for first 3,000 miles)	
Compact	$420 + 20¢ / mile > 3,000
Midsize	$525 + 20¢ / mile > 3,000
Full Size	$545 + 20¢ / mile > 3,000

EXAMPLE Carlotta rents a midsized car from Bekins Rent-A-Car for three days. She drives 657 miles. What is the rental fee?

Step 1	Find the daily rate.	$22.95	
Step 2	Multiply the daily rate by the number of days.	$22.95	Daily rate
		× 3	Number of days
		$68.85	Daily cost
Step 3	Find the mileage cost. Multiply the mileage by $.20.	657	Mileage
		× $.20	Rate per mile
		$131.40	Mileage cost
Step 4	Add the daily cost and the mileage cost to find the total rental fee.	$ 68.85	Daily cost
		+131.40	Mileage cost
		$200.25	Total rental fee

Here is another sample rate chart for car rentals.

Carl's Easy Rentals	
Daily Rate	$19.95 + 10¢/mile + $3.50 insurance For all models
Weekly Plan 1	Daily rate (plus $3.50 insurance fee) x 7 with unlimited mileage.
Weekly Plan 2	$125/week + $3/day insurance +18¢/mile over 1,000 miles/week.

EXAMPLE Katherine rents a small automobile from Carl's Easy Rentals. She selects Weekly Plan 2 and travels 1,156 miles in seven days. What is her rental fee?

Step 1 Find the weekly rate.

$125

Step 2 Find the insurance cost for one week. Multiply the insurance rate by 7.

$ 3	Cost of insurance per day
× 7	Number of days
$21	Insurance per week

Step 3 Find the number of miles over 1,000 that Katherine drives.

1,156	Miles traveled
−1,000	Miles allowed free
156	Excess miles

Step 4 Find the mileage cost. Multiply the excess miles by the rate per mile.

1 56	Excess miles
× .18	Mileage rate
1,2 48	
1 5 6	
$28.08	Mileage cost

Step 5 Find the total cost by adding the separate costs.

$125.00	Weekly rate
21.00	Insurance per week
+ 28.08	Mileage cost
$174.08	Total rental fee

Katherine's rental fee is $174.08.

Ace Rental		Bekins Rent-A-Car	
Daily Rates		**Daily Rates**	
Subcompact	$43		
Compact	$50	Compact	$18.98 + 20¢ / mile
Midsize	$54	Midsize	$22.95 + 20¢ / mile
Full Size	$57	Full Size	$24.95 + 20¢ / mile
Weekly Rates		**Monthly Rates** (No charge for first 3,000 miles)	
Subcompact	$159		
Compact	$189	Compact	$420 + 20¢ / mile > 3,000
Midsize	$209	Midsize	$525 + 20¢ / mile > 3,000
Full Size	$229	Full Size	$545 + 20¢ / mile > 3,000

Exercise A Find the cost of renting each of these cars. Use the rate charts on page 214 and above to help you.

	Rental Agency	Size of Car	Time Rented	Miles Traveled
1)	Bekins	Midsize	5 days	329
2)	Ace	Full Size	2 weeks	897
3)	Carl's	Midsize	3 weeks, Plan 1	2,567
4)	Ace	Subcompact	3 days	158
5)	Carl's	Compact	6 weeks, Plan 2	2,514
6)	Bekins	Full Size	3 months	9,254
7)	Ace	Subcompact	8 days	1,400
8)	Bekins	Compact	4 months	14,259
9)	Carl's	Midsize	4 weeks, Plan 1	5,000
10)	Carl's	Midsize	4 weeks, Plan 2	5,000

Exercise B Find the cost of renting each of these cars from Ace Rental and Bekins Rent-A-Car. Then choose one plan from Carl's Easy Rentals and find its cost for each car.

	Size of Car	Time Rented	Miles Traveled
1)	Compact	1 week	1,500
2)	Midsize	6 days	759
3)	Full Size	2 weeks	1,100
4)	Compact	3 days	548
5)	Full Size	8 weeks	6,623

Lesson 9 Parking Expenses

One of the expenses of driving a car in a city is parking.

Manny's Garage
PARKING
$1.00 For first hour
75¢ Each extra hour
$7.00 Maximum

EXAMPLE Miguel Sanchez leaves his car at Manny's Garage. Miguel returns 2 hours and 15 minutes later. What is his parking fee?

Add.		
	$1.00	First hour
	.75	Second hour
	+ .75	15 minutes (Note that any
	$2.50	portion of an hour counts as a whole hour.)

Miguel's parking fee is $2.50.

Exercise A Find the total parking fee at Manny's for each of these times.

1) 2 hours

2) 3 hours

3) 4 hours

4) 5 hours

5) 6 hours

6) 10 hours

7) 5 hours, 30 minutes

8) 3 hours, 20 minutes

9) 4 hours, 5 minutes

10) 2 hours, 54 minutes

Consumer Humor

I'm sorry to hear about your accident. How did it happen?

Everything was fine until I passed the sign for the town of Merging Traffic.

Some parking lots use an electronic ticket dispenser. It prints the date and time of your car's arrival at the parking lot. When you leave, an attendant uses another electronic device that prints the leaving time and date. The attendant subtracts the times and computes your parking fee.

Notice the use of the 24-hour clock. Any number below 12:00 stands for morning hours. Numbers greater than 12:00 stand for afternoon and evening times.

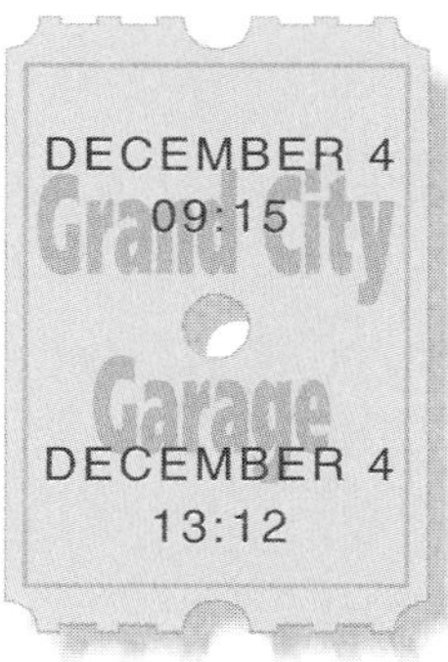

12-Hour Clock	24-Hour Clock
1:00 A.M.	01:00
2:00 A.M.	02:00
3:00 A.M.	03:00
:	:
:	:
10:00 A.M.	10:00
11:00 A.M.	11:00
12:00 noon	12:00
1:00 P.M.	13:00
2:00 P.M.	14:00
:	:
:	:
11:00 P.M.	23:00
12:00 P.M.	24:00

EXAMPLE Michael uses an electronic ticket machine at his parking lot. His rates are posted on a sign. A sample ticket from Michael's lot is shown at the right. The numbers 5/12 stand for the date, May 12. The other numbers stand for the times. What is the cost for parking for a car with this ticket?

$1.25 First hour
$1.00 Each additional hour
$9.00 Maximum per day

5/12 — 08:45
5/12 — 12:20
Michael's

Step 1 Find the parking time. Subtract earlier time from the later time. Round answers to the next full hour.

~~12:20~~ (11:80)	Rename 12:20 to 11:80
−8:45	Remember, 60 minutes is one hour.
3:35 →	4 hours

Step 2 Find the total cost. Add the hourly rates.

$1.25	First hour
+3.00	3 additional hours
$4.25	Total cost

The parking fee for this ticket is $4.25.

Exercise B Find the cost to park at Michael's lot for each of these tickets.

1) 11/10 — 12:15
11/10 — 15:20

2) 5/10 — 07:00
5/10 — 09:15

3)
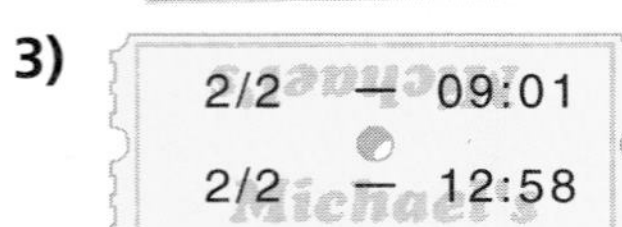

4) 6/28 — 11:28
6/28 — 15:12

5) 9/7 — 06:30
9/7 — 15:29

6) 10/20 — 20:30
10/20 — 23:30

7) 7/10 — 10:12
7/10 — 12:15

8) 6/6 — 14:15
6/6 — 16:02

9) 7/30 — 09:10
7/30 — 17:02

10) 12/24 — 04:25
12/24 — 19:20

Lesson 10 Time Zones

Time zone

A geographical region in which the same standard time is used.

The world is divided into 24 different **time zones**. The same standard time is used within each zone. The United States falls into seven different time zones of the world. Beginning at the Atlantic Ocean and moving west, one crosses these four time zones: Eastern, Central, Mountain, and Pacific. The state of Alaska is so large that it falls into the next three time zones: Yukon, Alaska-Hawaii, and Bering. Hawaii is also located in the Alaska-Hawaii time zone.

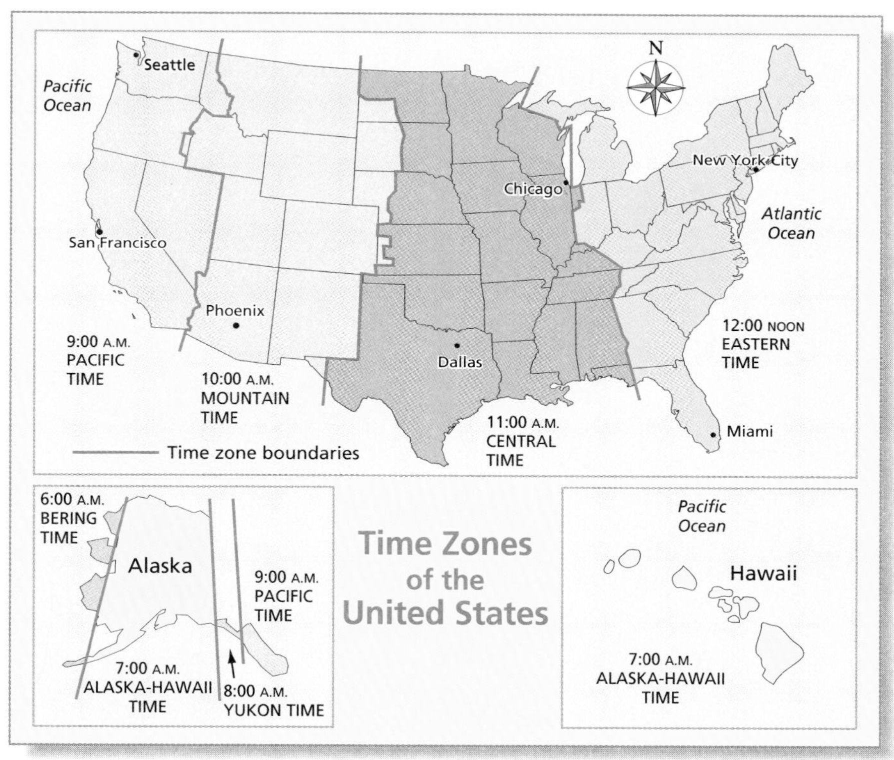

When every zone is using standard time, each zone's time is one hour later than the next zone to the west. For example, when it is 12:00 noon in the Eastern Time Zone, it is 11:00 A.M. in the Central Time Zone. Likewise, each zone is one hour earlier than the next zone to the east.

EXAMPLE What is the time in San Francisco when it is 7 P.M. in Miami?

Step 1 Look at the map on page 219. Start at Miami in the Eastern Time Zone. Count the number of time zones one passes through to reach San Francisco.

Central	—	1 hour
Mountain	—	2 hours
Pacific	—	3 hours

The difference in time is three hours.

Step 2 You are moving west. So you will subtract 3 hours.

7:00	P.M.
−3:00	Hours
4:00	P.M.

When it is 7 P.M. in Miami, it is 4 P.M. in San Francisco.

EXAMPLE What is the time in Dallas when it is 11 A.M. in Seattle?

Step 1 Dallas is two time zones away from Seattle. The difference in time is two hours.

Step 2 You are moving east. So you will add 2 hours.

11:00	A.M.
+2:00	Hours
13:00	

13:00 is the same as 1:00 P.M. When it is 11 A.M. in Seattle, it is 1 P.M. in Dallas.

EXAMPLE When it is 1:43 P.M. in Phoenix, what time is it in Hawaii?

Step 1 The time zones are Pacific, Yukon, and Alaska-Hawaii. Three time zones mean a difference of three hours.

Step 2 You are moving west, so you will subtract the 3 hours.

1:43 P.M. + 12 Hours	→	13:43	Rename 1:43 as 13:43
−3:00 Hours		−3:00	
		10:43	

When it is 1:43 P.M. in Phoenix, it is 10:43 A.M. in Hawaii.

Exercise A Find the missing time for each of the zones indicated. Use the time zone map on page 219.

1) 2:00 P.M. Central
_______ Eastern

2) 3:04 P.M. Eastern
_______ Pacific

3) 9:37 P.M. Alaska-Hawaii
_______ Mountain

4) 10:15 A.M. Bering
_______ Mountain

5) 1:36 A.M. Mountain
_______ Pacific

6) 4:01 P.M. Eastern
_______ Yukon

7) 11:52 P.M. Eastern
_______ Alaska-Hawaii

8) 6:25 A.M. Mountain
_______ Eastern

9) 8:59 A.M. Central
_______ Bering

10) 2:48 A.M. Central
_______ Yukon

Consumer Humor

One time I stayed up all night, wondering where the sun went. Finally, it dawned on me.

Lesson 11 Traveling by Air

For each airline flight, a schedule is available that states the time of departure and the time of arrival at its destination.

Most airports have large displays where you can find the arrival and departure times for your flight.

Notice the following example.

Flight	Departure from Baltimore	Arrival in New York City	
1	7:00 a	8:00 a	Kennedy
2	10:10 a	11:15 a	Kennedy
3	11:45 a	1:05 p	Kennedy
4	5:24 p	7:09 p	La Guardia

EXAMPLES

Rule To find the length of flying time for a trip, subtract the departure time from the arrival time.

How long does Flight 2 take?

11:15	Arrival
−10:10	Departure
1:05	

Flight 2 takes 1 hour and 5 minutes.

How long does Flight 3 take?

					12:65
Arrival	1:05	→	13:05	→	~~13:05~~
Departure	−11:45		−11:45		−11:45
					1:20

Flight 3 takes 1 hour and 20 minutes.

Exercise A Calculate the length of time for each flight.

	Departure	Arrival
1)	3:35 p	6:46 p
2)	5:05 p	7:10 p
3)	3:45 p	8:00 p
4)	9:50 a	2:20 p
5)	7:50 a	5:00 p
6)	10:35 p	1:20 a
7)	7:44 p	11:15 p
8)	9:35 p	2:12 a
9)	12:30 a	8:15 a
10)	11:40 a	4:13 p

Time Differences Between Some Cities and Four U.S. Time Zones									
City	**PST**	**MST**	**CST**	**EST**	**City**	**PST**	**MST**	**CST**	**EST**
Baltimore	3	2	1	—	Nome	3	4	5	6
Bermuda	4	3	2	1	Ottawa	3	2	1	—
Chicago	2	1	—	1	Paris	9	8	7	6
Detroit	3	2	1	—	Phoenix	1	—	1	2
Dallas	2	1	—	1	St. Louis	2	1	—	1
Honolulu	2	3	4	5	San Diego	—	1	2	3
Juneau	—	1	2	3	San Francisco	—	1	2	3
Los Angeles	—	1	2	3	San Juan	4	3	2	1
Miami	3	2	1	—	Seattle	—	1	2	3
Minneapolis	2	1	—	1	Vancouver	—	1	2	3
New York City	3	2	1	—	Washington, D.C.	3	2	1	—

PST = Pacific Standard Time
MST = Mountain Standard Time
CST = Central Standard Time
EST = Eastern Standard Time

When calculating travel time, you need to consider the time differences between zones. Use the chart shown above.

EXAMPLE What is the time of a flight that leaves Baltimore at 8 A.M. (EST) and arrives in Honolulu at 3:15 P.M. Alaska-Hawaii Standard Time (A-HST)?

Step 1 Express both times in terms of the same time zone. Find the equivalent time in EST for 3:15 P.M. Honolulu time. Use the table to find the differences in time zones.

Step 2 According to the table, there is a 5-hour difference in time between Honolulu and EST. Since you are converting to Eastern time, add hours.

$$\begin{array}{rl} 3{:}15 & \text{P.M.} \\ +5{:}00 & \text{Hours} \\ \hline 8{:}15 & \text{P.M.} \end{array}$$

Step 3 Subtract the departure time from the converted arrival time.

$$\begin{array}{r} 8{:}15 \text{ P.M.} \\ -8{:}00 \text{ A.M.} \\ \hline \end{array} \quad +12 \text{ hours} \quad \begin{array}{r} 20{:}15 \\ -\ 8{:}00 \\ \hline 12{:}15 \end{array}$$

The trip takes 12 hours and 15 minutes.

Exercise B Calculate the travel time for each flight. Use the chart on page 224 to help you.

	Departure		Arrival	
1)	Baltimore	11:10 a	San Francisco	6:05 p
2)	St. Louis	2:15 p	Washington, D.C.	5:07 p
3)	Chicago	4:05 p	Seattle	6:58 p
4)	Los Angeles	7:20 a	New York City	4:47 p
5)	Detroit	10:35 a	Bermuda	2:19 p
6)	Vancouver	7:45 a	Baltimore	5:00 p
7)	Miami	4:40 p	Ottawa	9:03 p
8)	Nome	2:05 a	New York City	10:15 p
9)	Honolulu	7:15 p	San Francisco	1:05 a
10)	Baltimore	6:20 p	Los Angeles	9:00 p
11)	Los Angeles	9:30 a	Baltimore	5:15 p
12)	Washington, D.C.	10:50 a	Minneapolis	1:35 p
13)	Minneapolis	5:05 p	Washington, D.C.	9:30 p
14)	Phoenix	3:25 p	Dallas	6:13 p
15)	Dallas	8:45 p	Phoenix	9:50 p
16)	San Diego	3:15 p	Juneau	7:10 p
17)	Juneau	11:10 a	San Diego	3:15 p
18)	Washington, D.C.	11:10 a	Chicago	12:06 p
19)	Chicago	11:35 a	Washington, D.C.	2:10 p
20)	Chicago	5:10 p	San Juan	2:10 a
21)	San Juan	5:40 p	Chicago	11:35 p
22)	New York City	5:10 p	Paris	8:30 a
23)	Paris	12:45 p	New York City	4:30 p
24)	Washington, D.C.	11:45 a	Paris	7:50 p
25)	Paris	4:35 p	Washington, D.C.	3:05 p

Chapter 8 Review

Solve these problems.

1) Three towns are on a route. What is the distance between Town A and Town C?

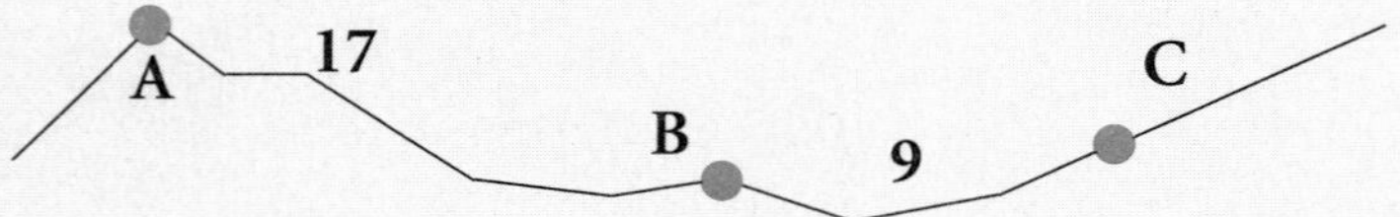

2) A map has a scale of 1 in. = 5 mi. What distance is represented by a line 6 in. long? What distance is represented by a line 2.5 in. long?

3) A passenger on a bus pays the fare for herself and three children. The peak fare for an adult is $45.00 and peak fare for each child is $22.50. How much is the total peak fare? The off-peak fares are $5.00 less per ticket. How much is the total off-peak fare?

4) How many nights are spent in a hotel by a guest who arrives on May 28 and leaves early on June 11? If the daily rate is $79.95, then what is the total amount of money the guest pays?

5) What is the cost per day of a 7-day trip that has a total cost of $756.00?

6) If the conversion rate for Swiss francs is 2.21 francs = 1 U.S. dollar, then how many Swiss francs can be exchanged for $79.00 in U.S. currency?

7) What is the cost of renting a car for 4 days at $17.59 per day and driving 237 miles at 19¢ per mile?

8) Use the chart for parking rates shown below. What is the cost of parking 3 hours and 15 minutes?

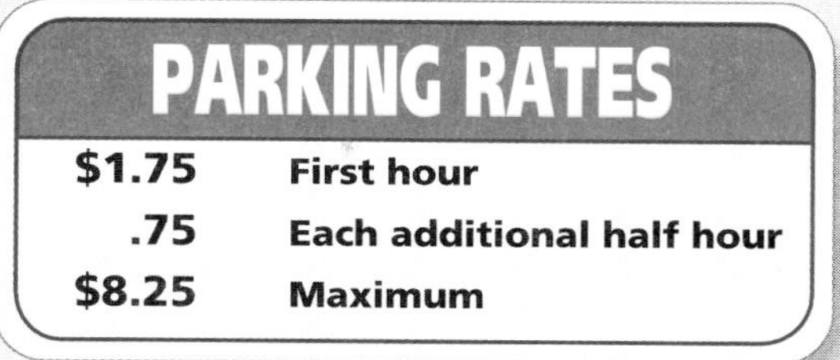

PARKING RATES	
$1.75	First hour
.75	Each additional half hour
$8.25	Maximum

9) When it is 3:45 P.M. in Phoenix, what time is it in New York City? Use the time zone map to help you.

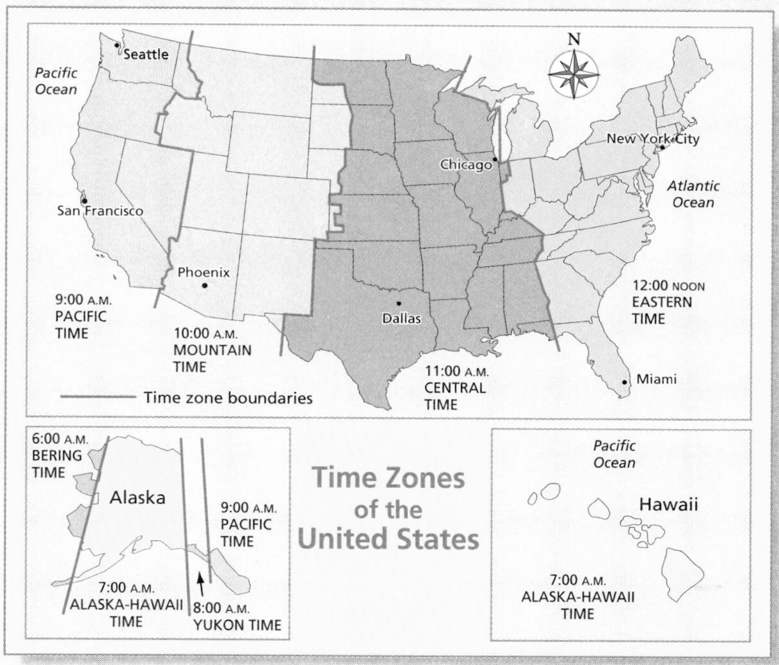

10) If a flight departs at 3:05 P.M. EST and arrives at 6:35 P.M. MST, then how long is the flight? Use the time zone map above.

Test Taking Tip

When you review your notes to prepare for an exam, use a marker to highlight key words and example problems.

Chapter 9 Budgeting Your Money

A budget is a plan for managing income and expenses. The plan is usually related to a set period of time, such as monthly or yearly. People make budgets to plan their spending so that they can afford necessary expenses. Budgets contribute to financial stability. Government agencies, large companies, and small businesses also create budgets. This allows them to adjust spending from year to year.

In Chapter 9, you will learn the steps necessary for preparing, adjusting, and balancing a budget. You will also develop the mathematical skills needed to plan for financial stability.

Goals for Learning

- To compute average income
- To compute the percent of income to be spent on each budget item
- To read and create circle graphs as summaries of budget spending
- To complete records to determine if a budget is balanced

Lesson 1 Finding Average Income

Budget

A plan to manage income and expenses.

When you compute the average monthly income available for a **budget**, use only the net or take-home pay. This is the money you have left after taxes and other deductions. Net pay is the actual amount of money available for budgeting.

EXAMPLE Buddy is paid $516.56 biweekly. This term means that he is paid every other week. What is his average monthly net income?

Step 1 Find his yearly income. Multiply his biweekly income by the number of pay periods per year.

26	Pay periods
$2\overline{)52}$	Weeks in a year

$ 516.56	Biweekly income
× 26	No. of pay periods
$13,430.56	Yearly income

Step 2 Find monthly income. Divide yearly income by 12 months.

$1,119.21	Monthly income
12) $13,430.56	Yearly income

Buddy's average monthly net income is $1,119.21.

Rule To find average monthly income, multiply the regular take-home pay by the number of pay periods per year. Then divide this yearly income by 12 months.

Exercise A Find the average monthly income for each pay. Semimonthly means twice a month.

	Pay Period	Net Pay
1)	Biweekly	$1,425.00
2)	Biweekly	$135.96
3)	Weekly	$570.21
4)	Weekly	$128.75
5)	Semimonthly	$376.89
6)	Semimonthly	$1,300.47
7)	Weekly	$159.32
8)	Biweekly	$287.16
9)	Biweekly	$312.10
10)	Weekly	$196.88

EXAMPLE Vera works different hours each week and wants to estimate her average monthly income. These figures show her net pay for the last seven weeks.

$156.19	$154.57	$167.98	$148.76
$137.82	$172.08	$187.19	

Step 1 Find the average weekly income. Add the seven net pays. The sum of the net pay is $1,124.59.

Step 2 Divide this sum by the number of pays. The average weekly income is $160.66.

$$\begin{array}{r} \$160.66 \\ 7\,\overline{)\,\$1{,}124.59} \end{array}$$

Average weekly income
Total of net pays

Step 3 Compute the estimated yearly income. Multiply the weekly income by 52.

$$\begin{array}{r} \$\ \ 160.66 \\ \times \qquad 52 \\ \hline \$8{,}354.32 \end{array}$$

Average weekly income
Yearly income

Step 4 Divide the yearly income by 12 to find the average monthly income.

$$\begin{array}{r} \$696.19 \\ 12\,\overline{)\,\$8{,}354.32} \end{array}$$

Average monthly income
Yearly income

Vera's average monthly income is $696.19.

Exercise B Find the average monthly income for each set of weekly net pays.

1)	$356.10	$159.25	$267.84	$192.90	$212.88		
2)	$105.16	$174.87	$97.59	$110.03	$126.48	$95.70	
3)	$88.88	$102.15	$90.76	$101.18	$129.87	$135.18	$116.05
4)	$256.00	$243.50	$252.05	$261.18	$225.93	$250.47	
5)	$131.07	$139.10	$133.48	$128.79	$127.56		
6)	$175.89	$177.50	$172.10	$175.89	$182.46	$180.14	
7)	$101.01	$175.64	$152.17	$136.49	$143.00		
8)	$84.16	$102.36	$95.75	$97.19			
9)	$302.01	$335.75	$317.75	$328.99	$297.48		
10)	$162.10	$175.18	$167.90	$172.44	$177.67	$168.46	$164.33

Lesson 2 Preparing a Budget

Expenses
Money spent to pay for specific costs.

The first step in preparing a budget is to determine how much income is available. The second step is to decide what kinds of **expenses** or costs you will have. It is helpful to list expenses in large categories.

Exercise A List two kinds of expenses that can be included in each category.

1) Housing
2) Clothing
3) Insurance
4) Entertainment
5) Health
6) Food
7) Transportation
8) Gifts
9) Savings
10) Miscellaneous

Budget guidelines
An outline of budget policies.

Circle graph
Circular chart divided into sections to show relative sizes.

Some consumer groups publish **budget guidelines**, or plans. One such plan is shown by the **circle graph**, or pie chart, below. The family's income is divided into portions so that a certain amount of the money can be used for each expense. Dividing the circle into sections shows the relative size of each category.

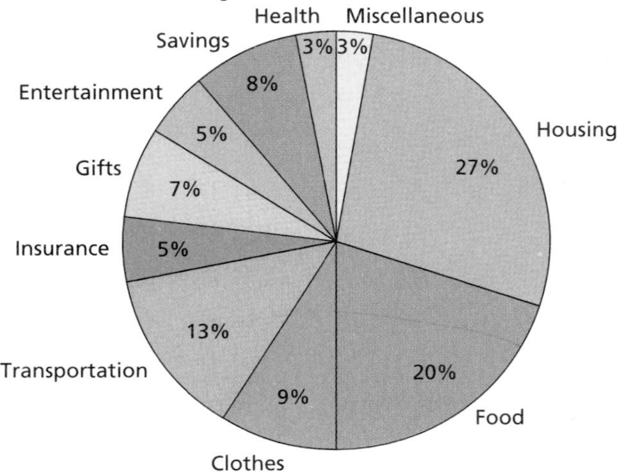

EXAMPLE Manuel has an average monthly income of $945.10. He uses the budget plan shown in the circle graph. How much money does he budget for each expense?

Step 1 Multiply each percent by the amount available.

a) Housing	27% × $945.10 =	$255.18
b) Food	20% × $945.10 =	$189.02
c) Clothes	9% × $945.10 =	$85.06
d) Transportation	13% × $945.10 =	$122.86
e) Insurance	5% × $945.10 =	$47.26
f) Gifts	7% × $945.10 =	$66.16
g) Entertainment	5% × $945.10 =	$47.26
h) Savings	8% × $945.10 =	$75.61
i) Health	3% × $945.10 =	$28.35
j) Miscellaneous	3% × $945.10 =	+ $28.35
		$945.11

Step 2 Add the individual amounts to check for errors. The difference of 1¢ is due to rounding.

Exercise B Follow the example and use the budget plan shown in the circle graph for each of these monthly incomes. Find the amount of money that is to be budgeted for each category. Check your work by adding. The total may vary slightly from original figures due to rounding.

1) $810.15
2) $696.45
3) $992.80
4) $713.28
5) $1,128.03
6) $1,037.69
7) $755.07
8) $876.19
9) $857.13
10) $937.21
11) $505.08
12) $622.49

Lesson 3 Adjusting a Budget

Some people examine their spending patterns before they plan their budgets. They calculate the yearly totals and then compute the percent spent in each category. Study the following example.

Part of Anaka's Yearly Expenditures,

Month	Food	Housing	Clothes	Car
January	$140.00	$251.50	—	$152.77
February	$152.10	$251.50	—	$150.12
March	$97.38	$251.50	$25.90	$158
April	$102.76	$302.67	$146.56	
May	$95.59	$251.50	$10.50	
June	$111.21	$251.50	—	
July	$93.85	$287.10	—	
August	$108.72	$251.50		
September	$134.67	$251.50		
October	$166.44	$251.50		
November	$99.93	$251.50		
December	$110.84	$251.50		
Totals	$1,413.49	$3,104.77		

EXAMPLE Anaka spends $1,413.49 on food. Approximately what percent of her $15,804.19 net income is this?

Step 1 Write the ratio. $\frac{\text{expenses}}{\text{income}}$ $\frac{1{,}413.49}{15{,}804.19}$

If you have a calculator, then perform the division.
$1{,}413.49 \div 15{,}804.19 = .0894377 \approx .09$ or 9%

Step 2 If not, then round the numbers and estimate the answer.

$$\frac{1{,}400}{16{,}000}$$

Step 3 Simplify the ratio.

$$\frac{1{,}400}{16{,}000} = \frac{14}{160} = \frac{7}{80}$$

Step 4 Divide to find the decimal.

$$80\,\overline{)\,7.000} = .087 \approx .09$$

Step 5 Write answer as a percent. $.09 = 9\%$

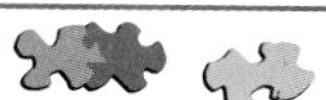

PROBLEM SOLVING

Exercise A Solve the following problems.

1) What percent of the net income of $17,307.20 is spent on each category?

a) Housing	$5,538.30
b) Food	$4,153.73
c) Clothes	$1,730.72
d) Transportation	$2,596.08
e) Insurance	$865.36
f) Gifts	$692.29
g) Entertainment	$519.22
h) Savings	$173.07
i) Health	$1,038.43

2) What percent of the net income of $23,695.06 is spent on each category?

a) Housing	$6,160.72
b) Food	$4,975.96
c) Clothes	$2,132.56
d) Transportation	$3,317.31
e) Insurance	$1,421.70
f) Gifts	$1,895.61
g) Entertainment	$1,184.75
h) Savings	$1,658.65
i) Health	$947.80

3) Katrina has a part-time job and earns a net income of $162.33 per month. This is how she spends her money each month.

CDs and Tapes $13.00
Savings $100.00
Entertainment $29.25
Miscellaneous $20.08

What percent of her income is spent in each category?

4) A small business has an average monthly gross income of $39,000.
   a) What percent is spent in each of these categories?

Rent	$4,265
Operations	$1,325
Materials	$5,756
Payroll	$20,950
Advertising	$1,450

   b) What percent remains as profit?

Lesson 4 Using Circle Graphs

Sector
A wedge-shaped section of a circle graph.

You can make a circle graph to show the relative sizes of budget categories.

Every circle contains 360°. To find out how large to make a **sector,** or section of the circle, multiply 360° by the percent of income. The result will tell you the number of degrees to include in that sector.

EXAMPLE Sally's family spends 23% of their income for food.

360° × .23 = ■ degrees of the circle

$$\begin{array}{rl} 360 & \text{Number of degrees in a circle} \\ \times\ .23 & \text{Percent of income} \\ \hline 1{,}080 & \\ +720 & \\ \hline 82.80 \approx 83^\circ & \end{array}$$

The food sector represents 83°.

We hope to buy a new home some day.

Why wait? Is your income too low?

No, our income is fine. It's our outgo that is too high.

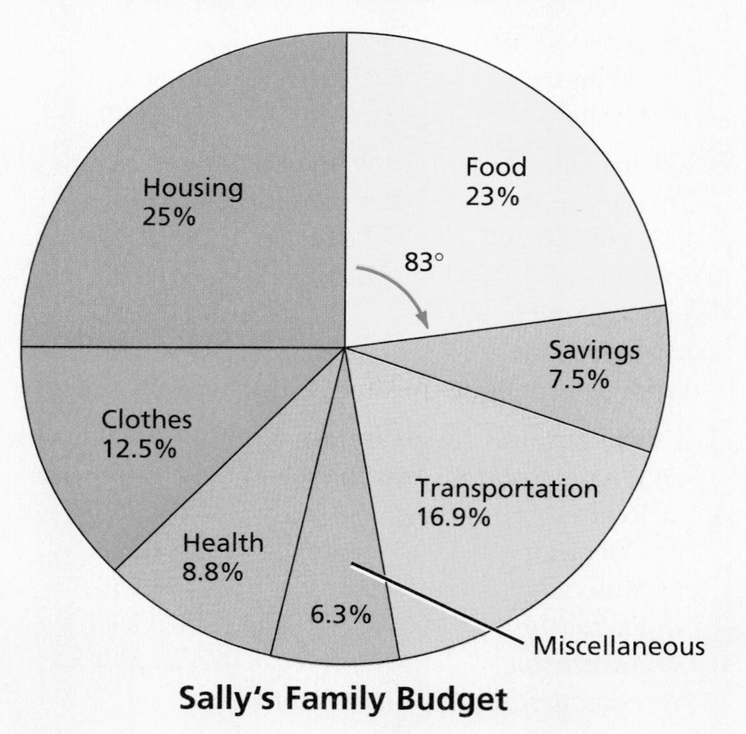

Sally's Family Budget

PROBLEM SOLVING

Exercise A Solve these problems. Use the example on page 236 to help you.

1) Find the number of degrees for each of the sectors of Sally's family budget circle graph. Note that the total number of degrees may not be 360, due to rounding.

   a) Housing
   b) Clothes
   c) Savings
   d) Health
   e) Transportation
   f) Miscellaneous

2) List some possible reasons why food and transportation are such large expenditures for this family.

3) Use a protractor to help you draw a circle graph to display the following budget.

Food	24%
Housing	15%
Clothing	20%
Cars	10%
Health	10%
Miscellaneous	21%

4) A family has a monthly net income of $2,895.00. The average monthly expenses are listed below. Draw a circle graph to show the percent of income that is spent in each category.

Housing	$723
Food	$579
Clothes	$435
Transportation	$375
Health	$348
Investments	$144
Miscellaneous	$291

Calculator Practice

Sometimes it is convenient to use a calculator's memory to do steps we repeat in doing a problem. This is true for Exercise A, problem 4 on page 237.

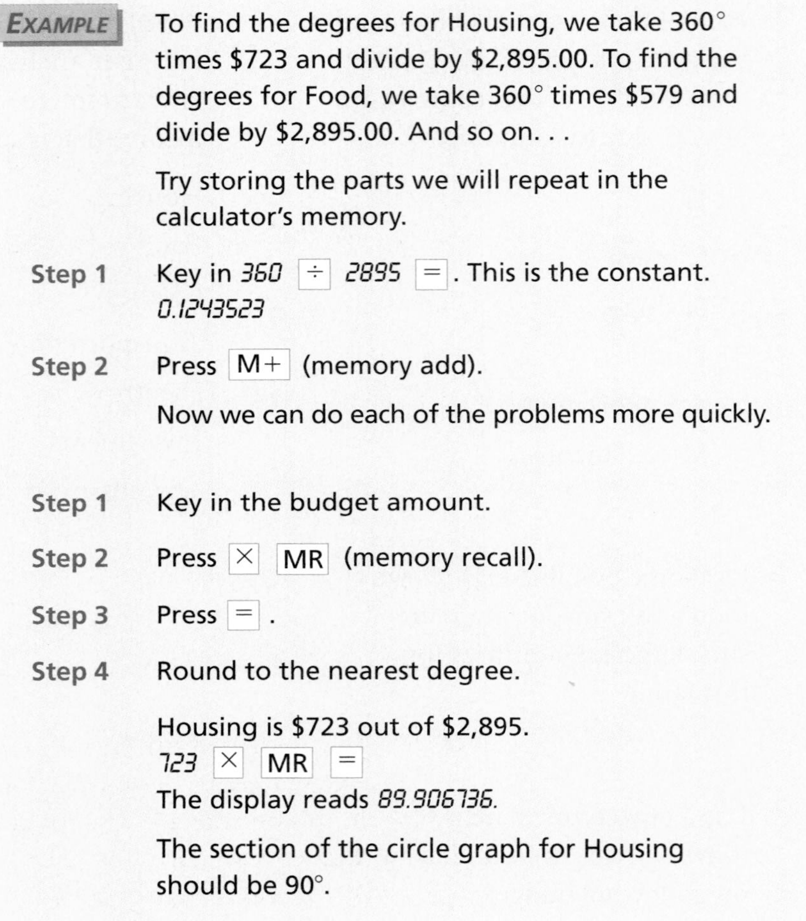

EXAMPLE To find the degrees for Housing, we take 360° times $723 and divide by $2,895.00. To find the degrees for Food, we take 360° times $579 and divide by $2,895.00. And so on. . .

Try storing the parts we will repeat in the calculator's memory.

Step 1 Key in 360 [÷] 2895 [=]. This is the constant.
0.1243523

Step 2 Press [M+] (memory add).

Now we can do each of the problems more quickly.

Step 1 Key in the budget amount.

Step 2 Press [×] [MR] (memory recall).

Step 3 Press [=].

Step 4 Round to the nearest degree.

Housing is $723 out of $2,895.
723 [×] [MR] [=]
The display reads 89.906736.

The section of the circle graph for Housing should be 90°.

Check your answers for problem 4 in Exercise A with the aid of a calculator.

Lesson 5 Balancing a Budget

Balancing a budget
Determining whether there is money remaining or a debt.

Balancing a budget means determining the state of finances after a given budget period. A person can learn if there is money remaining or a debt. The amount allotted for a certain budget category may not be entirely spent during the month. Some money may be saved to spend the next month.

To balance your monthly budget, you should keep good records of your income and expenses.

EXAMPLE Alex budgets $392.50 per month for food. At the end of August, he has $9.41 left after expenses. To this he adds $392.50 for September. He has a total of $401.91 to spend on food in September. At the end of September, Alex adds up his expenses and finds he spent $395.43 on food. His September balance is $6.48.

Alex's Food Budget	
August Balance	$ 9.41
+ September Budget	+392.50
Funds Available	$ 401.91
− September Expenses	−395.43
September Balance	$6.48

Exercise A Use addition and subtraction to complete this budget record for July. Follow the example on page 239. The first column is done for you.

	Food	Rent	Clothes	Car
June Balance + July Budget	$4.10 + 175.65	0 310.50	13.50 25.00	3.15 70.00
Funds Available – July Expenses	179.75 – 176.50	____ 310.50	____ 18.00	____ 67.36
July Balance + August Budget	3.25 + 175.65	____ 310.50	____ 25.00	____ 70.00
Funds Available	178.90	____	____	____

	Gifts	Savings	Miscellaneous
June Balance +July Budget	$36.50 + 20.00	0 45.00	176.10 57.50
Funds Available – July Expenses	____ – 10.99	____ 45.00	____ 65.60
July Balance +August Budget	____ + ____	____ ____	____ ____
Funds Available	____	____	____

Exercise B Answer these questions about the budget shown in Exercise A.

1) What is the total amount budgeted for July?

2) What is the total amount spent in July?

3) What percent of the income is actually spent in July?

When you plan budget categories based on percent of income, you want to check to be sure that the percents total 100%. Then calculate the amount that goes in each category by multiplying the percent times the monthly income.

Exercise C Copy and complete this budget record for an income of $975.35.

	Food 25%	Housing 30%	Clothes 20%
January Balance + February Budget	$1.15 + ____	11.65 ____	0 ____
Funds Available − February Expenses	____ − 236.36	____ 303.50	____ 86.58
February Balance			

	Car 18%	Savings 5%	Miscellaneous 2%
January Balance + February Budget	$36.09 + ____	0 ____	82.74 ____
Funds Available − February Expenses	____ − 111.06	____ 48.77	____ 97.36
February Balance	____	____	____

Exercise D Look at the completed budget record shown in Exercise C. Find the total amount spent in January.

EXAMPLE Mr. Coleman has an opportunity to buy some new clothes at a January sale. His monthly clothes budget is $24.00, and he has $5.10 left from December. He decides to spend $36.00 at the sale. How should he record this?

Step 1 List the December balance.

Step 2 Add the January budget allotment for clothes.

$$\begin{array}{r} \$\ 5.10 \\ +24.00 \\ \hline \$\ 29.10 \\ -36.00 \\ \hline \blacksquare \end{array}$$

Step 3 Subtract the expenses. $36.00 is too large to subtract from $29.10. To find how much greater his expenses are, reverse the numbers and subtract.

$$\begin{array}{r} \$\ 36.00 \\ -29.10 \\ \hline \$\ 6.90 \end{array}$$

Mr. Coleman has overspent his budget by $6.90.

Step 4 There are two ways to record this overspending. One is to write the new balance as −$6.90. Another is to write the number $6.90 in red, to indicate a debt.

Step 5 In February, Mr. Coleman will have to repay his debt to the clothes allotment.

January Balance	− $6.90
+ February Budget	$24.00
Funds Available in February	$17.10

$$\begin{array}{r} \$\ 24.00 \\ -\ \ 6.90 \\ \hline \$\ 17.10 \end{array}$$

PROBLEM SOLVING

Exercise E Answer these questions.

1) In the example on page 242, when Mr. Coleman overspends his budget, where can he get the extra money?

2) Anita has a balance of $32.50 at the beginning of May for gifts. Her allotment for the month is $17.60. She is invited to two bridal showers, two weddings, and a birthday party. The gifts she purchases amount to $63.95. What is the balance for this category at the end of May?

3) What is Anita's balance for gifts at the beginning of June?

4) Lars plans a barbecue party for some friends. His entertainment budget is $25.86, and his food budget has an extra $10.57. How much money is available to spend on the party?

5) Lars spent $52.75. He split this expense debt evenly between food and entertainment. How much "in debt" are food and entertainment?

6) Eileen borrowed $3.58 from her friend to purchase shampoo last month. Her new allotment in miscellaneous is $30.00. How much will she have after repaying her friend?

7) Micah overspent his transportation allotment because he replaced his brake shoes. He spent $17.84 more than he budgeted. How much is available next month if 17% of his $656.10 is for transportation?

Chapter 9 Review

Solve these problems.

1) Find the average monthly income for these weekly incomes: \$157.10, \$356.48, \$216.90, and \$257.03

2) How much of a \$2,376.80 monthly net income is allotted for food if 23% is budgeted?

3) What percent of \$2,376.80 is budgeted for housing and repairs if \$713.04 is allotted?

4) Draw a circle graph to represent this budget.

Housing	27%
Food	24%
Cars	19%
Clothes	15%
Health	8%
Savings	5%
Miscellaneous	2%

5) Balance this budget for a monthly income of $1,700.

	Housing 28%	Food 25%	Clothes 10%
Old Balance + New Budget	$16.76 + ______	−$10.50 ______	−$3.94 ______
Funds Available − Expenses	______ −450.00	______ 386.40	______ 157.87
New Balance	______	______	______

	Car 15%	Health 2%	Savings and Miscellaneous 20%
Old Balance + New Budget	$111.50 + ______	$36.88 ______	$47.89 ______
Funds Available − Expenses	______ − 235.84	______ 110.94	______ 375.00
New Balance	______	______	______

Test Taking Tip

Read a problem thoroughly before you begin to solve it. After you have completed your answer, read the problem again to be sure your answer makes sense.

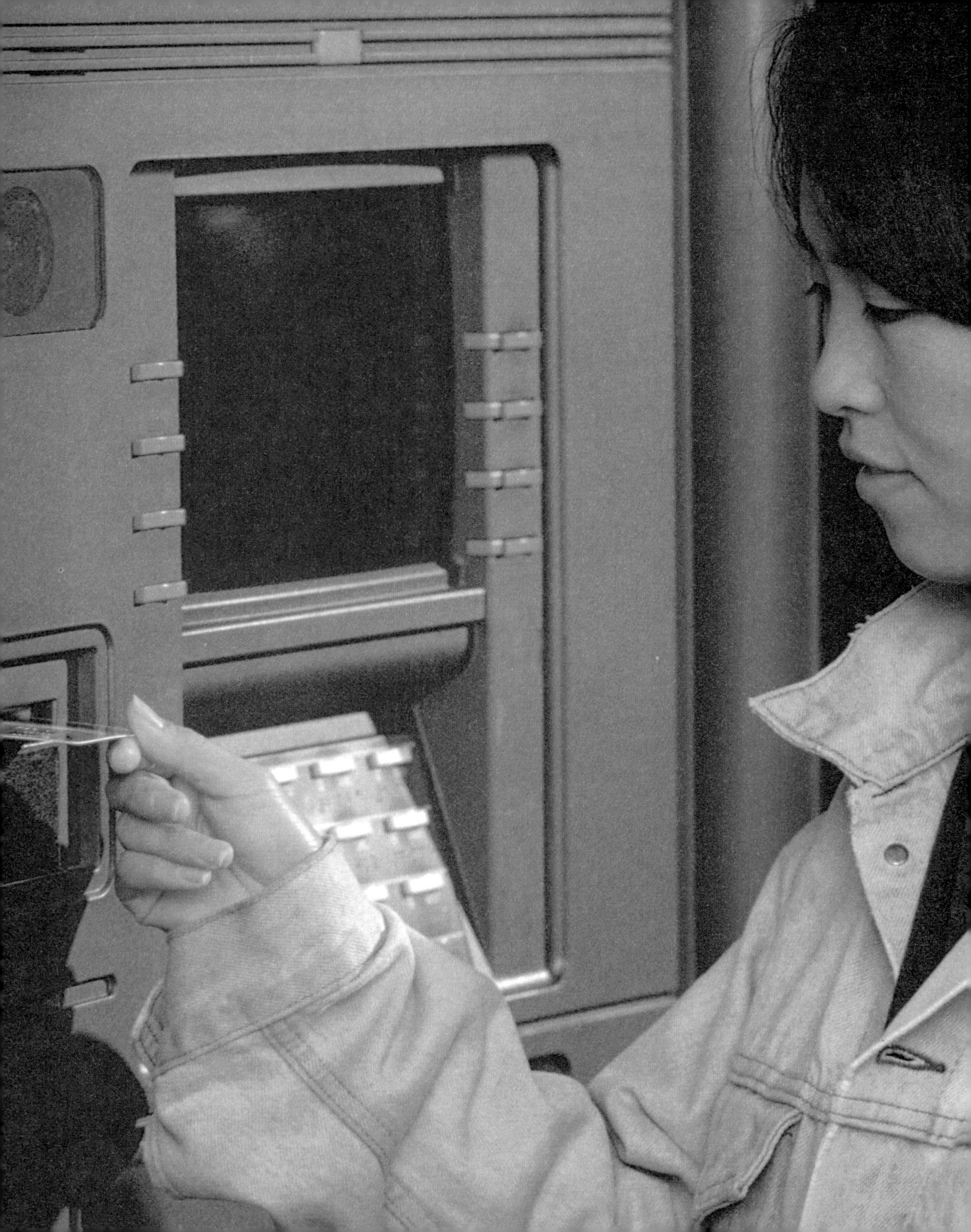

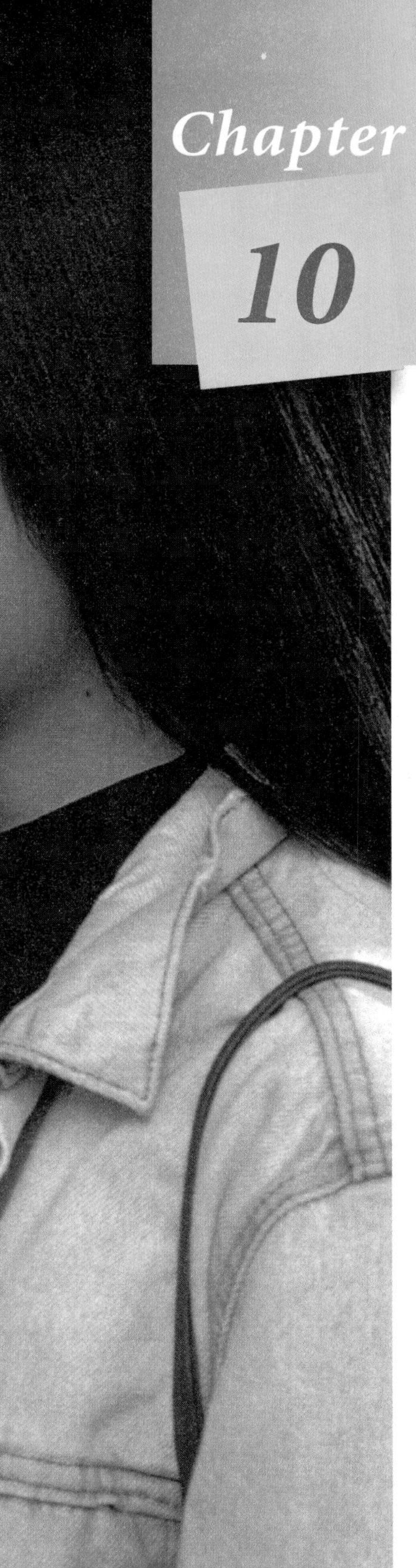

Chapter 10

Banking and Investing

People visit banks for a variety of reasons—to make a deposit in savings or checking accounts, cash checks, make payments, or borrow money. The earning of interest is an important part of the banking business. Here is how it works. People deposit money in their bank. The bank lends that money to individuals or businesses and charges them interest. The bank keeps some of the interest it earns and pays the rest to its depositors.

In Chapter 10, you will learn some of the mathematical skills required to understand banking and investing. You will also learn how to keep track of investment accounts and reports.

Goals for Learning

- To compute and compare earnings from simple and compound interest
- To compute the value of investments over time
- To use and maintain a checking account
- To determine the value of stocks and compute gains and losses
- To evaluate profits and losses from investments

Lesson 1 Simple Interest

Simple interest

A one-time payment or fee charged for the use of money loaned.

Rate

The percent of interest charged for money loaned.

Time

The period of time for which money is loaned.

The fees on some loans are computed by simple interest. **Simple interest** is a one-time payment or fee charged for the use of the money loaned.

Rule I = PRT. Interest is equal to the Principal (amount loaned) times the **Rate** (percent of interest charged) times the **Time** (number of years the money is loaned).

EXAMPLE Richard lends \$500 to his cousin, who pays him 7% simple interest each year. At the end of three years, the cousin pays back the loan. What is the total amount that Richard collects?

Step 1 Find the interest.

I = PRT

I = \$500 × 7% × 3

I = \$500 × .07 × 3

\$ 5 00	Principal
× .07	Rate
\$ 35.00	
× 3	Time in years
\$105.00	Interest

Step 2 Add the interest to the principal to find the total amount.

\$500	Principal
+105	Interest
\$605	Total amount

Exercise A Find the simple interest earned and the total amount in each case.

	Principal	Rate	Time	Interest	Total Amount
1)	\$300	5%	2 years	_______	_______
2)	\$150	6%	3 years	_______	_______
3)	\$658	10%	1 year	_______	_______
4)	\$22	5%	4 years	_______	_______
5)	\$128	$6\frac{1}{2}$% (.065)	10 years	_______	_______
6)	\$1,000	$5\frac{1}{4}$%	5 years	_______	_______
7)	\$10	$7\frac{3}{4}$%	2 years	_______	_______
8)	\$98	$8\frac{1}{2}$%	1.5 years	_______	_______
9)	\$1,527	$10\frac{1}{4}$%	3.5 years	_______	_______
10)	\$43	$12\frac{3}{4}$%	6.25 years	_______	_______

EXAMPLE Monique lends money to her brother for 3 months. How much interest does she earn on \$100 at $5\frac{3}{8}\%$ simple interest?

Step 1 Change the rate to a decimal.

$5\frac{3}{8}\% = .05\frac{3}{8}$

$.05\frac{3}{8} = .05375$ → $\frac{3}{8} = 8\overline{)3.000}$ = .375

Step 2 Time must be expressed in years, not months. Change 3 months to a decimal part of a year. To convert months to years, divide by 12.

3 months = .25 year

$$\frac{3}{12} = 12\overline{)3.000} = .25$$

```
    .25
12 )3.000
   -24
     60
    -60
```

Step 3 Multiply.

$I = P \times R \times T$

$I = \$100 \times .05375 \times .25$

```
    .053 75   Rate
 ×  $1 00     Principal
$  5.375 00
 ×      .25   Time in years
$1.34 375 00  Interest
```

Monique earns \$1.34 interest.

Exercise B Find the simple interest earned and the total amount in each case.

	Principal	Rate	Time	Interest	Total Amount
1)	\$100	$5\frac{1}{2}\%$	6 months	________	________
2)	\$500	$6\frac{1}{8}\%$	9 months	________	________
3)	\$600	$7\frac{1}{2}\%$	3 months	________	________
4)	\$900	18%	12 months	________	________
5)	\$1,500	$8\frac{1}{2}\%$	18 months	________	________
6)	\$7,000	$7\frac{3}{8}\%$	15 months	________	________
7)	\$8,796	12%	24 months	________	________
8)	\$4,023	$5\frac{5}{8}\%$	33 months	________	________
9)	\$10,000	$6\frac{1}{4}\%$	21 months	________	________
10)	\$20,000	$7\frac{1}{4}\%$	45 months	________	________

Lesson 2 Compound Interest

Savings accounts

Bank accounts in which depositors can earn interest on money deposited.

Compound interest

Interest paid on the principal plus interest added to date.

Many people deposit their money into **savings accounts** in the bank. These accounts earn interest for the depositor. Banks usually compute this amount as compound interest. When figuring compound interest on savings accounts, the principal is the amount deposited into the account. The rate is the percent of interest earned by the depositor. The time is the number of years that the money is kept in the account. A depositor earns **compound interest** on both the original principal and any interest added to the account.

EXAMPLE Kim Lee deposits \$100 into an account that earns 5% interest, compounded twice a year. Calculate the amount in the account after one year.

Step 1 Compute the interest for the first 6 months.

$I = PRT$

$I = \$100 \times 5\% \times \frac{6}{12}$

$= \$100 \times .05 \times .5$

\$ 100	Principal
× .05	Rate
\$ 5.00	
× .5	Time in years
\$2.500	Interest

Step 2 Add the interest to the original deposit, or principal, to find the new principal.

\$100.00	Principal
+ 2.50	Interest
\$102.50	New principal

Step 3 Compute the interest for the second 6 months.

$I = PRT$

$I = \$102.50 \times 5\% \times \frac{6}{12}$

$= \$102.50 \times .05 \times .5$

\$ 102.50	Step 2 principal
× .05	Rate
\$ 5.1250	
× .5	Time in years
\$2.56250	≈ \$2.56 Interest

Step 4 Add interest to the principal to find the new principal.

\$102.50	Step 2 principal
+ 2.56	Interest
\$105.06	New principal

At the end of one year, Kim has \$105.06 in her account.

Interest that is compounded twice a year is said to be compounded semiannually.

At the right is a table showing the number of times per year interest is compounded.

Compounded	Times per Year
Annually	1
Semiannually	2
Quarterly	4
Monthly	12
Daily	365

Exercise A Compute the new principal at the end of one year when the interest is compounded *semiannually.*

	Principal	Rate of Interest	New Principal
1)	$100	6%	________
2)	$100	7%	________
3)	$100	$5\frac{1}{2}\%$	________
4)	$100	$6\frac{1}{4}\%$	________
5)	$100	$7\frac{1}{2}\%$	________

Exercise B Compute the new principal at the end of one year when the interest is compounded *quarterly.*

	Principal	Rate of Interest	New Principal
1)	$100	$5\frac{1}{2}\%$	________
2)	$200	$5\frac{1}{2}\%$	________
3)	$300	$5\frac{1}{2}\%$	________
4)	$400	$5\frac{1}{2}\%$	________
5)	$500	$5\frac{1}{2}\%$	________

Exercise C Compute the new principal at the end of four months when the interest is compounded *monthly.* ($\frac{1}{12} = .083$)

	Principal	Rate of Interest	New Principal
1)	$1,000	6%	________
2)	$5,000	$5\frac{3}{4}\%$	________
3)	$1,500	8%	________

Amounts for $1.00 Compounded Daily

Years	5.00%	5.25%	5.50%	5.75%	6.00%	6.25%	6.50%
1	1.051	1.054	1.057	1.059	1.062	1.064	1.067
2	1.105	1.111	1.116	1.122	1.127	1.133	1.139
3	1.162	1.171	1.179	1.188	1.197	1.206	1.215
4	1.221	1.234	1.246	1.259	1.271	1.284	1.297
5	1.284	1.300	1.317	1.333	1.350	1.367	1.384
6	1.350	1.370	1.391	1.412	1.433	1.455	1.477
7	1.419	1.444	1.470	1.496	1.522	1.549	1.576
8	1.492	1.522	1.553	1.584	1.616	1.649	1.682
9	1.568	1.604	1.640	1.678	1.716	1.755	1.795
10	1.649	1.690	1.733	1.777	1.822	1.868	1.915
11	1.733	1.782	1.831	1.882	1.935	1.989	2.044
12	1.822	1.878	1.935	1.994	2.054	2.117	2.181
13	1.915	1.979	2.044	2.112	2.181	2.253	2.328
14	2.014	2.085	2.160	2.237	2.316	2.399	2.484
15	2.117	2.198	2.282	2.369	2.459	2.553	2.651
16	2.225	2.316	2.411	2.509	2.611	2.718	2.829
17	2.340	2.441	2.547	2.658	2.773	2.893	3.019
18	2.459	2.573	2.691	2.815	2.944	3.080	3.222
19	2.586	2.711	2.843	2.981	3.126	3.279	3.438
20	2.718	2.857	3.004	3.158	3.320	3.490	3.669
21	2.857	3.011	3.174	3.345	3.525	3.715	3.915
22	3.004	3.174	3.353	3.543	3.743	3.955	4.178
23	3.158	3.345	3.543	3.752	3.974	4.210	4.459
24	3.320	3.525	3.743	3.974	4.220	4.481	4.758
25	3.490	3.715	3.955	4.210	4.481	4.770	5.078

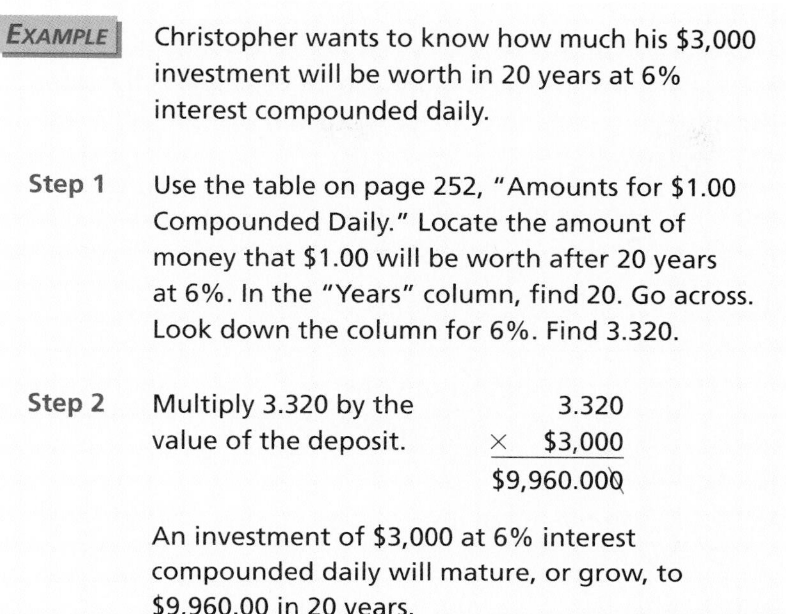

EXAMPLE Christopher wants to know how much his $3,000 investment will be worth in 20 years at 6% interest compounded daily.

Step 1 Use the table on page 252, "Amounts for $1.00 Compounded Daily." Locate the amount of money that $1.00 will be worth after 20 years at 6%. In the "Years" column, find 20. Go across. Look down the column for 6%. Find 3.320.

Step 2 Multiply 3.320 by the value of the deposit.

$$\begin{array}{r} 3.320 \\ \times \quad \$3{,}000 \\ \hline \$9{,}960.000 \end{array}$$

An investment of $3,000 at 6% interest compounded daily will mature, or grow, to $9,960.00 in 20 years.

Exercise D Calculate the value at maturity for each investment with compound interest. Use the table on page 252 to help you.

	Initial Investment	Rate of Interest	Number of Years	Value at Maturity
1)	$2,500	5.5%	10	________
2)	$2,500	5.5%	20	________
3)	$2,500	5.5%	25	________
4)	$7,000	5.0%	25	________
5)	$7,000	6.5%	25	________
6)	$6,850	5.25%	8	________
7)	$3,940	5.75%	11	________
8)	$20,000	6.0%	23	________
9)	$46,800	6.25%	12	________
10)	$54,960	6.5%	15	________

Calculator Practice

Use a calculator to find the value of an investment with simple interest. Use the formula I = PRT, where Principal is the same as the initial investment. Remember to add the interest to the initial investment.

Step 1 Key in the initial investment.

Step 2 Press ×.

Step 3 Key in the rate of interest as a decimal.

Step 4 Press ×.

Step 5 Key in the number of years.

Step 6 Press =. This is the interest earned.

Step 7 Press +.

Step 8 Key in the initial investment.

Step 9 Press =.

Step 10 Affix the dollar sign and insert commas.

Calculate how much Christopher's $3,000 investment will be worth in 20 years at 6% simple interest.

3000 × *.06* × *20* =

The display reads *3600*. $3,600 in simple interest is earned after 20 years.

3600 + *3000* =

The display reads *6600*. Christopher's $3,000 investment is worth $6,600 after 20 years at 6% simple interest.

Exercise E Calculate the value at maturity for each investment in Exercise D on page 253. Compare these values with those earned with compound interest in Exercise D.

Lesson 3 Doubling Your Money

U.S. savings bonds are one way to double your money.

Investors double their money when the amount of simple interest earned equals the amount invested, or the principal. How long does it take?

$$I = PRT$$

EXAMPLES

P = \$100	\$ 100
R = 5%	× .05
T = 20 years	\$ 5.00
I = \$100 × .05 × 20 = \$100.00	× 20
	\$100.00

P = \$300	\$ 3 00
R = 10%	× .10
T = 10 years	\$ 30.00
I = \$300 × .10 × 10 = \$300.00	× 10
	\$300.00

P = \$200	\$ 2 00
R = 4%	× .04
T = 25 years	\$ 8.00
I = \$200 × .04 × 25 = \$200.00	× 25
	\$200.00

In each example shown above, the interest equals the principal. The investor has "doubled" his or her money.

Rule To find the number of years it takes to double money at a given rate of simple interest, divide 100 by the rate of interest.

EXAMPLE How many years are necessary to double money at 20% simple interest?

$$20\overline{)100} = 5 \text{ years}$$

It will take five years for the money to double.

Exercise A Find the number of years necessary for an investment to double at each of these rates of simple interest. Round to the nearest tenth, if necessary.

1) 5%
2) 25%
3) 2%
4) 50%
5) 15%
6) 12%
7) 10%
8) 4%
9) 1%
10) 40%
11) 8%
12) 11%

Money doubles faster with compound interest than with simple interest. Instead of dividing into 100, you divide into 72.

Rule To find the approximate number of years necessary to double money at a given rate of yearly compounded interest, divide 72 by the rate of interest.

Exercise B Find the number of years necessary for an investment to double at each of these rates of compound interest. Round to the nearest tenth, if necessary. Compare rates and times to those found in Exercise A.

1) 5%
2) 25%
3) 2%
4) 50%
5) 15%
6) 12%
7) 10%
8) 4%
9) 1%
10) 40%
11) 8%
12) 11%

Lesson 4 Checking Accounts

> ***Checking account***
>
> *A bank account against which a depositor can draw checks.*

> ***Automated teller machine (ATM)***
>
> *A computer terminal that allows 24-hour access to bank accounts.*

> ***Check***
>
> *A written order that is considered as cash.*

A **checking account** allows depositors to withdraw cash from an **automated teller machine (ATM)** or write checks against money deposited in the account. An ATM card is used to withdraw cash or make a deposit at an ATM. Checks are a convenient and safe means of payment when you don't want to use cash. A **check** is a written order directing a bank to pay money as instructed. It may be cashed only by the person to whom it is written, unless that person signs the check over to a second party. It is safer to mail a check than to mail cash. After the check is returned to you or the bank, you have proof of payment.

Karen L. Phillips
10 Overland Rd.
Barker, TX 75001
February 14 20 01
NO. 742
7-89
520
PAY TO THE ORDER OF Ace Stereo Company $ 10.52
Ten and 52/100 DOLLARS
RIVER BANK OF COLUMBUS
FOR Stereo
Karen Lee Phillips
⑆052000896⑆0772⑈752 0742

When you write a check, you must fill in five items. Notice the placement of each item on the checks shown on this page.

1. The date
2. The name of the person or company who is to receive payment (the payee)
3. The amount written in digits
4. The amount written in words
5. Your signature

It is important to write amounts in words correctly on checks. The words for numbers between 20 and 100 are hyphenated when the number has two words.

EXAMPLES

85 is written as "Eighty-five."
24 is written as "Twenty-four."
99 is written as "Ninety-nine."

The word "and" is reserved for the decimal point. The cents are written as a fraction of a dollar, since the word "Dollars" appears at the end of the line.

EXAMPLES

$444.44 is written:	Four hundred forty-four and 44/100.
$306.10 is written:	Three hundred six and 10/100.
$17.36 is written:	Seventeen and 36/100.

When there are no cents, the fraction is usually written in zeros. Some people write the word "No" or letters "xx" instead of zeros.

EXAMPLES

$97.00 is written:	Ninety-seven and 00/100
or	Ninety-seven and no/100
or	Ninety-seven and xx/100

Exercise A Write each of these amounts in words as you would on a check.

1) $25.86	**4)** $18.18	**7)** $1,327.56	**10)** $87.72	**13)** $57.49
2) $905.15	**5)** $45.76	**8)** $449.37	**11)** $143.00	**14)** $70.61
3) $296.75	**6)** $37.16	**9)** $61.60	**12)** $48.18	**15)** $384.48

Lesson 5 Keeping the Account Up to Date

Stub

The part of a checkbook that serves as a record for the information written on the check.

Checkbooks include forms so check writers can keep a record of money in the checking account. Some checks have a **stub,** a part of the checkbook that remains after the check has been removed.

On the stub you write the previous balance of the account, the amount of the check, and subtract to find the new balance remaining. If you make a deposit, you write the amount and add it to find the new balance.

Some checking accounts charge a fee for processing each check that is written. Such a fee is written on the check stub as a deduction. Subtract any deductions to find the new balance brought forward.

Study the example of a check stub shown below. Notice how the numbers on each line are computed.

No. 742
Feb. 14 20 01
To Ace Stereo

	Dollars	Cents	
Bal. Fwd.	75	00	← previous balance
Deposits			
Total	75	00	
This check	10	52	← amount of the check
Balance	64	48	← new balance
Deductions		15	← processing fee
Bal. Fwd.	64	33	← new balance

Register

A form on which transactions and balances are recorded.

Transaction

The act of depositing to or withdrawing from a bank account.

Some checkbooks have a check **register** instead of stubs. Each **transaction** (deposit or withdrawal) is recorded on this form. A deposit is added to the previous balance. A payment (written check or ATM cash withdrawal) is subtracted from the previous balance. The resulting answer is called the new balance.

Notice the example of a check register shown on the next page.

EXAMPLE Peggy Jones' checking account balance is $345.79 on January 15. During the rest of January, Peggy writes six checks and makes two deposits. Shown below is a copy of her check register. Notice how the figures on each line are computed.

CHECK = CK DEPOSIT = D ELECTRONIC FUNDS TRANSFER = EFT AUTOMATED TELLER MACHINE = ATM PHONE = PH

DATE	TRANS NO.	TYPE OF TRANS	DESCRIPTION	AMOUNT OF TRANS (–)	AMOUNT OF DEPOSIT (+)	FEE (–)	TAX ITEM	BAL. FWD.	
								345	79
1-15	301	CK	A-1 Drug Store	7.27				–7	27
								338	52
1-16	302	CK	Telephone Co.	15.38				–15	38
								323	14
1-18		EFT	Paycheck		200.00			+200	00
								523	14
1-21	303	CK	River Bank,	159.25				–159	25
			mortgage					363	89
1-21	304	CK	LaHem Clothing,	84.60				–84	60
			dress					279	29
1-25		EFT	Paycheck		200.00			+200	00
								479	29
1-28	305	CK	Food World	35.72				–35	72
								443	57
1-30	306	CK	Bank Charge Card,	257.00				–257	00
			monthly payment					186	57

Exercise A This account begins with a balance of $297.15. Find the new balance after each transaction.

CHECK = CK DEPOSIT = D ELECTRONIC FUNDS TRANSFER = EFT AUTOMATED TELLER MACHINE = ATM PHONE = PH

	DATE	TRANS NO.	TYPE OF TRANS	DESCRIPTION	AMOUNT OF TRANS (–)	AMOUNT OF DEPOSIT (+)	FEE (–)	TAX ITEM	BAL. FWD.	
									297	15
1)	10-15		D	Paycheck		155.10			155	10
2)	10-16	401	CK	Food Farm	84.12				84	12
3)	10-18	402	CK	City Power Co.	37.45				37	45
4)	10-21	403	CK	Sally About	10.00				10	00
5)	10-22		D	Paycheck		155.10			155	10
6)	10-23	404	CK	Big Oil Co.	97.39				97	39
7)	10-28	405	CK	River Bank	150.79				150	79
8)	10-29		D	Paycheck		155.10			155	10
9)	11-1	406	CK	Tell E. Phone Co.	28.98				28	98
10)	11-2		ATM	Cash	40.00				40	00
11)	11-3	407	CK	Charge-A-Lot Card	210.89				210	89
12)	11-4		D	Paycheck		155.10			155	10
13)	11-5	408	CK	Food Farm	96.78				96	78
14)	11-5	409	CK	Sue's News	31.10				31	10
15)	11-6	410	CK	Manny Dept. Store	12.56				12	56
16)	11-6		D	Birthday Present		10.00			10	00
17)	11-8	411	CK	Prime Plumbers	36.50				36	50
18)	11-11		D	Paycheck		155.10			155	10
19)	11-14	412	CK	Ace Insurance	5.48				5	48
20)	11-14		ATM	Christmas Club	20.00				20	00

Lesson 6 Reconciling a Checking Account

Monthly statement
A summary that shows recent transactions.

Reconcile
To compare and check the accuracy of information in a checkbook.

When you have a checking account you receive a **monthly statement** or summary from your bank. Each statement shows recent transactions plus the current balance of the account. Some banks also return the canceled checks. You can then compare, or **reconcile** the information in the checkbook with the bank statement to make sure that no mistakes were made.

Reconciling your checking account monthly is the best way to keep your records up to date.

The balance on the bank statement seldom equals the one in a person's checkbook. There are several reasons why the bank balance and the checkbook balance may not agree.

Processed
Describes a check or deposit that has been handled by the bank.

EXAMPLES

Some checks that were written may not have been returned by the bank yet.

Some deposits may have been made, but they have not been **processed** yet or been through all the steps of being handled by the bank.

The person or the bank made an error.

To reconcile a checking account, follow these four steps:

Step 1 Add all the amounts of unprocessed deposits.
Step 2 Add that sum to the bank balance.
Step 3 Add all the amounts of unreturned checks.
Step 4 Subtract that sum from the bank balance.

Once those steps have been done, the checkbook balance should match the adjusted bank balance. If it does not, someone has made an error.

EXAMPLE Follow these steps to reconcile this checking account.

Bank balance:	\$476.15	
Unprocessed deposits:	\$10.56	\$15.00
Unreturned checks:	\$65.00	\$25.13
	\$146.10	\$210.59
Checkbook balance:	\$54.89	

Step 1 Add the deposits.

\$ 10.56	
+ 15.00	
\$ 25.56	Deposits

Step 2 Add the total deposits to the bank balance.

\$476.15	Bank balance
+ 25.56	Deposits
\$501.71	Balance after Step 2

Step 3 Add unreturned checks.

\$ 65.00	
25.13	
146.10	
+210.59	
\$446.82	Checks

Step 4 Subtract the total of unreturned checks from the bank balance figured after Step 2.

\$501.71	Balance after Step 2
−446.82	Unreturned checks
\$ 54.89	Adjusted bank balance

The adjusted bank balance agrees with the checkbook balance of \$54.89.

Consumer Humor

The bank says that your checking account is overdrawn by \$10.00.

No problem. I'll just write the bank a check for \$10.00.

Exercise A Reconcile each account. Find out whether the adjusted bank balance agrees with the checkbook balance. List the differences, if any.

	Bank Balance	Unprocessed Deposits	Unreturned Checks		Checkbook Balance
1)	$1,253.09	None	$9.40 $26.51 $19.05 $113.40	$158.23 $71.23 $98.92 $32.99	$723.26
2)	$2,582.20	$143.00	$8.40 $46.00 $26.85 $1,519.37 $87.15	$73.93 $33.32 $27.75 $19.75 $189.13	$694.05
3)	$856.43	$400.00	$29.95 $23.13 $25.37 $122.50	$95.35 $49.60 $72.79 $300.00	$533.28
4)	$3,065.96	$171.53	$77.36 $29.23 $117.51 $166.56	$527.98 $62.10 $188.58 $218.12	$1,850.05
5)	$3,747.50	None	$60.00 $1,000.00 $96.86 $36.95 $19.95	$22.99 $72.85 $27.09 $99.54 $63.18	$2,250.08

	Bank Balance	Unprocessed Deposits	Unreturned Checks		Checkbook Balance
6)	$613.23	$60.00 $20.00	$8.00 $5.00 $400.00	$5.00 $92.00 $1.25	$181.98
7)	$2,291.63	$798.90	$73.00 $29.61 $238.00 $47.20 $30.00	$44.09 $40.99 $131.90 $67.92	$2,387.74
8)	$2,876.75	$16.56	$26.94 $532.00 $144.84	$1,008.00 $16.98 $33.74	$1,114.25
9)	$774.19	None	$44.00 $52.86	$46.20 $23.67	$617.56
10)	$2,201.39	$629.88	$29.94 $1,005.00 $370.00	$235.00 $60.02 $29.31	$1,101.72

Lesson 7 Stock Market Mathematics

Stock

The element in a corporation that is divided into shares.

Shares

Parts into which capital stock of a corporation is divided.

The capital or money a corporation raises comes from stocks and bonds. Bonds are loans to the corporation. **Stock** is divided into equal **shares** that are actually part of the corporation. A buyer of shares of stock becomes part owner of the corporation issuing the stock.

Stocks are priced in eighths of a dollar. When you see a stock price listed as $19\frac{7}{8}$, each share will cost \$19.875. Many people purchase stock in multiples of 100 shares, so no one worries about needing a half of a cent.

EXAMPLE \$19.875 × 100 = \$1,987.50

Table of Eighths	Value in Cents	Table of Eighths	Value in Cents
$\frac{1}{8}$	$12\frac{1}{2}$¢	$\frac{5}{8}$	$62\frac{1}{2}$¢
$\frac{2}{8} = \frac{1}{4}$	25¢	$\frac{6}{8} = \frac{3}{4}$	75¢
$\frac{3}{8}$	$37\frac{1}{2}$¢	$\frac{7}{8}$	$87\frac{1}{2}$¢
$\frac{4}{8} = \frac{2}{4} = \frac{1}{2}$	50¢	$\frac{8}{8} = \frac{4}{4} = \frac{2}{2} = 1$	100¢

EXAMPLE Builder Company stock closes at $24\frac{1}{4}$. The next day the stock goes "up" $3\frac{3}{8}$. What is the new price?

Add the numbers. Use the eighths chart to find the common denominator.

$$\begin{array}{rcr} 24\frac{1}{4} & = & 24\frac{2}{8} \\ +3\frac{3}{8} & = & 3\frac{3}{8} \\ \hline & & 27\frac{5}{8} \end{array}$$

The new price of Builder Company stock is $27\frac{5}{8}$, or \$27.625 per share.

EXAMPLE Shares of Radio, Inc. are being sold for $48\frac{7}{8}$. The price increases $2\frac{3}{8}$. What is the new price?

Add the numbers.

$$\begin{array}{l} 48\frac{7}{8} \\ +2\frac{3}{8} \\ \hline 50\frac{10}{8} \end{array}$$

Simplify. $\frac{10}{8} = 1\frac{2}{8}$ or $1\frac{1}{4}$

$50 + 1\frac{1}{4} = 51\frac{1}{4}$.

The new price of Radio, Inc., is $51\frac{1}{4}$ or $51.25 per share.

Exercise A Find the new price of each stock after its increase.

	Stock	Price	Up	New Price
1)	Signal, Inc.	$91\frac{3}{4}$	$4\frac{3}{8}$	_____
2)	Green Co.	$25\frac{7}{8}$	$2\frac{1}{2}$	_____
3)	Videos Ltd.	$7\frac{3}{8}$	$\frac{3}{4}$	_____
4)	Crystal Corp.	$10\frac{1}{2}$	$1\frac{1}{8}$	_____
5)	Techno A	$18\frac{5}{8}$	$\frac{3}{8}$	_____
6)	Mast Assn.	$39\frac{1}{2}$	$1\frac{1}{4}$	_____
7)	United Works	$22\frac{1}{2}$	$\frac{1}{8}$	_____
8)	General CD	$18\frac{3}{4}$	$1\frac{5}{8}$	_____
9)	Parker Supply	$93\frac{1}{2}$	$1\frac{1}{4}$	_____
10)	Tri Co.	$25\frac{7}{8}$	$\frac{5}{8}$	_____
11)	Techno B	$25\frac{3}{8}$	$1\frac{7}{8}$	_____

When the selling price of stock is more than the purchase price, the stockholder makes a **profit**. When the purchase price is more than the selling price, the stockholder has a **loss**.

Profit
A gain or increase in value.

Loss
A decrease in value.

EXAMPLES Ms. Nunez buys a stock at $14\frac{5}{8}$ and sells it for $18\frac{3}{4}$. What is her profit?

Subtract.
Find the common denominators.

$$\begin{array}{rcr} 18\frac{3}{4} & = & 18\frac{6}{8} \\ -14\frac{5}{8} & = & -14\frac{5}{8} \\ \hline & & 4\frac{1}{8} \end{array}$$

The profit per share is $4\frac{1}{8}$.

Mr. Hastings buys a stock at $32\frac{1}{4}$ and sells it for $25\frac{5}{8}$. What is his loss per share?

Subtract.
Find the common denominators.

$$\begin{array}{rcrcr} 32\frac{1}{4} & = & 32\frac{2}{8} & = & 31\frac{10}{8} \\ -25\frac{5}{8} & = & -25\frac{5}{8} & = & -25\frac{5}{8} \\ \hline & & & & 6\frac{5}{8} \end{array}$$

Mr. Hastings' loss per share is $6\frac{5}{8}$.

Exercise B Compute the profit per share.

	Bought	Sold	Profit		Bought	Sold	Profit
1)	$59\frac{7}{8}$	$65\frac{1}{2}$	____	**5)**	$33\frac{5}{8}$	$38\frac{1}{8}$	____
2)	$12\frac{7}{8}$	$13\frac{5}{8}$	____	**6)**	$14\frac{1}{2}$	$18\frac{3}{8}$	____
3)	$28\frac{3}{8}$	$29\frac{5}{8}$	____	**7)**	$26\frac{7}{8}$	$30\frac{1}{2}$	____
4)	$48\frac{3}{4}$	$59\frac{5}{8}$	____	**8)**	$35\frac{1}{4}$	$39\frac{3}{4}$	____

Exercise C Compute the loss per share.

	Bought	Sold	Loss
1)	$45\frac{1}{2}$	$39\frac{7}{8}$	____
2)	$22\frac{7}{8}$	$21\frac{5}{8}$	____
3)	$19\frac{5}{8}$	$18\frac{3}{8}$	____
4)	$16\frac{1}{8}$	$13\frac{5}{8}$	____
5)	$14\frac{1}{2}$	$12\frac{3}{8}$	____
6)	$40\frac{1}{4}$	$36\frac{3}{8}$	____
7)	28	$23\frac{7}{8}$	____
8)	$48\frac{3}{8}$	$44\frac{1}{2}$	____
9)	$39\frac{1}{8}$	$34\frac{5}{8}$	____
10)	$72\frac{3}{8}$	$68\frac{3}{4}$	____

Exercise D Compute the profit or loss per share.

	Bought	Sold	Profit or Loss
1)	$18\frac{3}{8}$	$16\frac{1}{8}$	____
2)	$39\frac{1}{4}$	$38\frac{1}{4}$	____
3)	$46\frac{1}{8}$	$45\frac{5}{8}$	____
4)	$35\frac{3}{4}$	37	____
5)	$82\frac{3}{8}$	83	____
6)	$51\frac{1}{2}$	$50\frac{1}{4}$	____
7)	$103\frac{1}{2}$	$65\frac{1}{8}$	____
8)	$19\frac{3}{8}$	$18\frac{7}{8}$	____
9)	$40\frac{1}{2}$	$29\frac{5}{8}$	____
10)	$5\frac{3}{8}$	$10\frac{3}{4}$	____

EXAMPLE Find the cost of 100 shares of stock priced at $20\frac{5}{8}$.

Step 1 Convert the fraction to a decimal.

$$\frac{5}{8} = \quad 8\overline{)5.000}^{\;.625}$$

Step 2 Add the decimal to the whole number. Write the number as dollars and cents.

$20.625

Step 3 Multiply the price by the number of shares.

$	20.625	Price per share
×	100	Number of shares
$2,062.500		Cost

The cost of 100 shares of stock is $2,062.50

Exercise E Find the cost of these shares of stock.

1) 100 shares at $12\frac{3}{8}$
2) 200 shares at $52\frac{1}{4}$
3) 150 shares at $28\frac{1}{2}$
4) 100 shares at $16\frac{7}{8}$
5) 300 shares at $7\frac{3}{4}$
6) 200 shares at $37\frac{1}{4}$
7) 700 shares at $56\frac{7}{8}$
8) 900 shares at $36\frac{5}{8}$
9) 800 shares at $32\frac{1}{4}$
10) 500 shares at $29\frac{1}{2}$
11) 850 shares at $9\frac{5}{8}$
12) 200 shares at $6\frac{3}{4}$
13) 900 shares at $15\frac{5}{8}$
14) 600 shares at $7\frac{1}{8}$
15) 400 shares at 31
16) 950 shares at $47\frac{5}{8}$
17) 400 shares at $4\frac{3}{8}$
18) 900 shares at $48\frac{7}{8}$
19) 1,000 shares at 18
20) 1,500 shares at $15\frac{1}{2}$

EXAMPLE Nicole has $1,000 to invest. She likes a stock selling for $52\frac{1}{2}$. How many shares could she purchase? Find the cost.

Step 1 Divide $1,000 by the cost per share. Discard the remainder.

$$
\begin{array}{r}
19. \\
52.5\overline{)1000.0} \\
-525 \\
\hline
4750 \\
-4725 \\
\hline
25
\end{array}
$$

Step 2 Multiply the cost per share times the number of shares purchased.

$ 52.50	Cost per share
× 19	Number of shares
$997.50	Total cost

Exercise F For each amount available, compute the number of shares that can be purchased. Then compute the total cost.

	Money Available	Cost per Share	No. of Shares	Total Cost
1)	$1,000	$20\frac{1}{4}$	______	______
2)	$1,500	$12\frac{3}{4}$	______	______
3)	$800	$9\frac{3}{4}$	______	______
4)	$600	$1\frac{5}{8}$	______	______
5)	$3,000	$3\frac{1}{4}$	______	______
6)	$1,800	$16\frac{3}{4}$	______	______
7)	$4,000	$26\frac{1}{8}$	______	______
8)	$100	$4\frac{1}{4}$	______	______
9)	$75	$\frac{5}{8}$	______	______
10)	$1,200	$20\frac{1}{2}$	______	______
11)	$900	$4\frac{1}{2}$	______	______
12)	$10,000	$87\frac{1}{2}$	______	______
13)	$7,500	$16\frac{1}{8}$	______	______

Lesson 8 Evaluating Profits and Losses

Investors are concerned about the "return on their money." They compute the percent of increase in a stock's price. The higher the percent of increase, the better the return on the money.

EXAMPLE Cy invests in an environmental company. He buys the stock at $11\frac{1}{4}$ and sells it at 17. Find the percent of increase.

Step 1 Subtract to find the increase, or profit.

$$\begin{array}{rcrl} 17 & = & 16\frac{4}{4} & \text{Selling price} \\ -11\frac{1}{4} & = & 11\frac{1}{4} & \text{Purchase price} \\ \hline & & 5\frac{3}{4} & \text{Profit} \end{array}$$

Step 2 Write both the purchase price and the profit as decimals.

$11\frac{1}{4} = 11.25$ Purchase price

$5\frac{3}{4} = 5.75$ Profit

Step 3 Divide the profit by the purchase price. Round the answer to two decimal places.

$$\begin{array}{r} .511 \approx .51 \\ 11.25.\overline{)5.75.000} \\ -5\,62\,5 \\ \hline 12\,50 \\ -11\,25 \\ \hline 1\,250 \\ -1\,125 \\ \hline \end{array}$$

Step 4 Write this decimal as a percent.

$.51 = 51\%$

The price of Cy's stock increased 51%.

EXAMPLE Ms. Smart invests in a tube company. She buys the stock at $47\frac{3}{8}$ and sells it for $32\frac{7}{8}$. What is the percent of decrease?

Step 1 Subtract to find the decrease, or loss.

$$\begin{array}{rcrl} 47\frac{3}{8} & = & 46\frac{11}{8} & \text{Purchase price} \\ -32\frac{7}{8} & = & -32\frac{7}{8} & \text{Selling price} \\ \hline & & 14\frac{4}{8} & = 14\frac{1}{2}\ \text{Loss} \end{array}$$

Step 2 Write both the purchase price and the loss as decimals.

$47\frac{3}{8} = 47.375$ Purchase price

$14\frac{1}{2} = 14.5$ Loss

Step 3 Divide the loss by the purchase price. Round the answer to two decimal places.

$$\begin{array}{r} .306 \approx .31 \\ 47.375.\overline{)14.500.000} \\ -14\ 212\ 5 \\ \hline 287\ 500 \\ -284\ 250 \\ \hline 3\ 250 \end{array}$$

Step 4 Write this decimal as a percent. $.31 = 31\%$
Ms. Smart's stock decreases 31%.

Exercise A State whether each investment below realized a profit or loss. Compute the percent of increase or decrease.

	Purchase Price	Selling Price		Purchase Price	Selling Price		Purchase Price	Selling Price
1)	12	$8\frac{1}{4}$	**7)**	9	$11\frac{1}{4}$	**12)**	$70\frac{1}{2}$	$54\frac{1}{4}$
2)	25	$17\frac{3}{8}$	**8)**	7	$10\frac{1}{4}$	**13)**	$7\frac{5}{8}$	$10\frac{7}{8}$
3)	21	$16\frac{3}{4}$	**9)**	$17\frac{1}{2}$	$28\frac{1}{2}$	**14)**	$11\frac{5}{8}$	$8\frac{5}{8}$
4)	8	$9\frac{3}{4}$	**10)**	$19\frac{3}{4}$	$30\frac{1}{4}$	**15)**	30	$22\frac{1}{8}$
5)	20	27	**11)**	$15\frac{1}{2}$	$23\frac{1}{4}$	**16)**	$50\frac{1}{4}$	$57\frac{1}{2}$
6)	$9\frac{7}{8}$	$3\frac{5}{8}$						

Lesson 9 Earning Dividends

Shareholders

The people who own the stock of a corporation.

Dividend

Profit from stock.

Income stock

Stock that makes a profit.

Corporations divide their profits among their **shareholders**, the people who own the stock. A **dividend** is the amount of profit that a shareholder earns for each share of stock. The term comes from *divid*ing profits at the *end* of an earning period. Stock that pays dividends is called **income stock**.

Many companies that offer dividends to their shareholders sell their stock on Wall Street at the New York Stock Exchange.

EXAMPLE

Harold buys 425 shares of an income stock. The company pays a dividend of $1.30 per share. What is his total dividend?

Multiply the dividend by the number of shares held.

	4 25	Shares
	× $1.30	Dividend per share
	127 50	
	+425	
	$ 552.50	Total dividends

Harold's dividend is $552.50.

Exercise A Compute the total dividend for each investment.

	Dividend per Share	Number of Shares
1)	$ .80	300
2)	$8.38	150
3)	$ .72	273
4)	$2.48	50
5)	$5.24	335
6)	$7.85	900
7)	$5.87	1,438
8)	$1.60	768
9)	$2.67	958
10)	$7.68	1,392

PROBLEM SOLVING

Exercise B Compute the number of shares that can be purchased in each case.

1) Amber wants to use her dividends to purchase more stock. She owns 1,376 shares. The dividend is $1.72 per share. How many shares of stock priced at $71 can she purchase?

2) Mark owns 153 shares of stock selling for $14\frac{3}{4}$. How many more shares can he purchase after receiving a dividend of $.80 per share?

3) Val receives a dividend of $1.36 on each of her 398 shares. How many shares can she buy at $15\frac{7}{8}$?

Chapter 10 Review

Solve these problems.

1) Compute the simple interest on a $1,000 loan at $16\frac{3}{4}$% for 5 years.

2) Calculate the amount of money in the savings account at the end of six months. The principal is $100, the rate is 10%, and the interest is compounded quarterly.

3) If you were to loan a friend $100, what interest rate would you ask for? Explain your answer and compute what your return will be.

4) Estimate the length of time that it would take to double your money at 15.86% with compound interest.

5) Would you double your money sooner with a compound interest rate of 5% or a simple interest rate of 6%? Explain your reasoning.

6) Write this amount in words for a check: $3,476.89.

7) Compute the new checkbook balance.

Previous balance:	$465.98
Checks written:	$10.00, $14.95, $6.07, and $109.10
Deposits made:	$30.00

8) Reconcile the following account. Does this checkbook balance agree with the adjusted bank balance?

Bank balance:	\$304.79
Checkbook balance:	\$206.19
Unreturned checks:	\$110.17
Unprocessed deposits:	\$12.58

9) Find the cost of 900 shares of stock selling for $57\frac{5}{8}$.

10) Compute the percent of loss on shares of stock that are purchased at $27\frac{5}{8}$ and sold at $15\frac{3}{8}$.

Test Taking Tip

When you are given a mathematical problem, try to consider it in a way that is similar to what you encounter in your daily life. That will help you to make sense of what the question is asking.

Tax Guide

Chapter 11

Paying Taxes

In Chapter 1, it was mentioned that paychecks are usually smaller than most people expect. This is because a certain percentage of your earnings are deducted to pay taxes. State and federal agencies collect taxes in order to pay for public services. Fire and police protection, schools, roads, and street lights are just a few examples of things that are paid for with tax dollars.

In Chapter 11, you will learn how the amount of taxes that people pay is determined. You will also learn about property taxes that are paid on homes and businesses.

Goals for Learning

- To calculate exemptions, deductions, and taxable income
- To read and use tax tables to estimate taxes
- To compute assessed values and property taxes
- To express property tax rates as percents
- To determine the effective tax rate

Lesson 1 The Key to Large Numbers

Large numbers can be difficult to read quickly. To help you read large numbers, writers often use words in place of extra digits. Large numbers can be written both in digits and in words. Study these examples of large numbers.

EXAMPLES You can write three million dollars in words as \$3 million. You can write three million dollars in digits as \$3,000,000.

Recall	1 thousand	=	1,000
	1 million	=	1,000,000
	1 billion	=	1,000,000,000
	1 trillion	=	1,000,000,000,000

Write the following amount in digits: \$1.25 million.

Step 1	Locate the decimal point in the number.	\$1.25 million
Step 2	Recall that a *million* has 6 zeros in the number.	1,000,000
Step 3	Move the decimal point as many places as the number of zeros in the figure named by the word.	1.25 .
Step 4	Write a zero in each empty place.	1 250 000.
Step 5	Begin at the decimal point. Put a comma after each group of 3 digits.	1,250,000.
Step 6	If the number represents money, then place the dollar sign in front of the number.	\$1,250,000.

Exercise A Write the following amounts in digits.

1) 1.6 million

2) 72.5 trillion

3) $416 million

4) 605.6 billion

5) 250 thousand

6) $260.408 billion

Exercise B The following problems contain pairs of numbers. Write each number in digits. Decide which number is larger in each case.

1) 200 million or 1 trillion

2) 64 billion or 6.4 million

3) 500 thousand or .5 million

4) 18.8 million or 10 billion

5) 32 thousand or 32 million

6) 10 billion or 1 trillion

PROBLEM SOLVING

Exercise C Look in a newspaper and find five amounts written in words. Write each number in digits.

Lesson 2 The Federal Budget

Revenue

The money that federal or state agencies collect and use.

Each year the President of the United States submits a budget to Congress. This budget shows where the tax money will come from and how this **revenue** or income, will be spent.

EXAMPLE This circle graph shows possible sources of federal money for a typical year. According to this graph, 43¢ of every dollar received comes from individual income taxes.

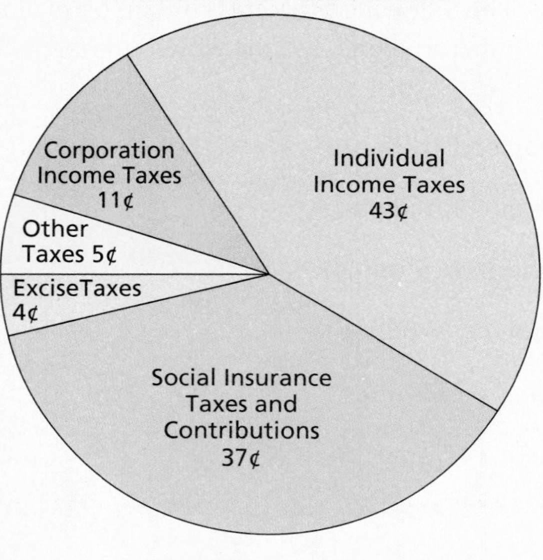

$$\frac{43¢}{\$1} = \frac{43¢}{100¢} \quad 43\%$$

Receipts

Income.

This figure means that 43% of the total **receipts**, or money received, comes from individual income taxes.

EXAMPLE In one year the federal income is $1.257 trillion. How much of that comes from individual income taxes? Use the circle graph on page 282.

43% of federal income comes from individual income taxes.

To find 43% of $1.257 trillion, you multiply.

```
$   1.2 57
×      .43
----------
    3 7 71
+50 2 8
----------
$.54 0 51  trillion
```

For this year, the federal government receives $.54051 trillion from individual income taxes. Since .5 trillion equals 500 billion, move the decimal three places to the right to find out how many billions were received from individual income taxes.

$.54051 trillion = $540.51 billion

Exercise A Tell what percent of the receipts came from each source of federal revenue. Then calculate the amount in billions of dollars. Use information from the graph on page 282 to help you find your answers. The first answer has been completed as an example.

Source	Percent	Amount in Billions
1) Individual Income Taxes	43%	$540.51
2) Social Insurance Taxes and Contributions	____	______
3) Corporation Income Taxes	____	______
4) Other Taxes	____	______
5) Excise Taxes	____	______

EXAMPLE In the same year, the federal expenditures are $1.46 trillion. This circle graph shows how this money is spent during that year.

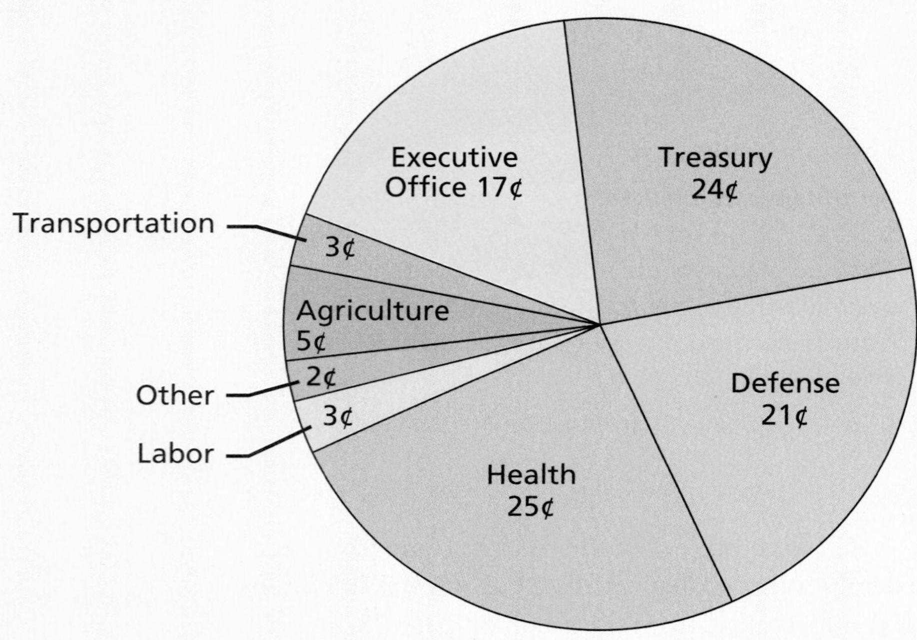

For every dollar that is spent,

25¢ goes to Health
24¢ goes to the Treasury
21¢ goes to Defense
17¢ goes to the Executive Office
5¢ goes to Agriculture
3¢ goes to Labor
3¢ goes to Transportation
2¢ goes to Other Categories

100¢ or $1.00

Exercise B Tell what percent of the expenditures are for each item. Then calculate the amount in billions of dollars. Use information from the graph on page 284 to help you find your answers.

Source	Percent	Amount in Billions
1) Health	______	________
2) Treasury	______	________
3) Defense	______	________
4) Executive office	______	________
5) Agriculture	______	________
6) Labor	______	________
7) Transportation	______	________
8) Other	______	________

PROBLEM SOLVING

Exercise C The sample federal budget shown in Exercises A and B does not balance. Explain the reason(s) why.

Lesson 3 Paying Taxes

Deductions and exemptions
Money you deduct from your income.

Dependent
A person who is supported financially by another person.

Income
The amount of money you earn.

Taxable income
The total income on which taxes are paid.

Federal taxes are determined by two facts: how much money you earn and how many deductions and exemptions you have. The total money you make is called your **income**. **Deductions and exemptions** are amounts of money you may subtract from your income before you figure your taxes.

For example, you may subtract as an exemption an amount of money for each person who depends on you for support. Such a person is called a **dependent**.

Deductions can also be subtracted from total income. In some cases, deductions are allowed for:

- interest you pay on your mortgage,
- money you spend on medical bills,
- losses not covered by insurance,
- and many others.

There are a large number of such deductions. We will study some of them.

After you subtract all of the exemptions and deductions from your income, the remainder is called **taxable income**. This amount is used to figure how much federal income tax you owe.

EXAMPLE Dee Jackson had exemptions of $5,000 for dependents. Her deductions include $2,500 for damage caused to her house by a lightning storm and $500 for charitable contributions. What is her taxable income if she has an income of $62,500?

Step 1 Total exemptions and deductions.

$5,000	Exemptions for dependents
2,500	Uninsured losses
+ 500	Charitable contributions
$8,000	Total exemptions and deductions

EXAMPLE *(continued)*

Step 2 Subtract the total exemptions and deductions from her total income.

$62,500	Total income
− 8,000	Total exemptions and deductions
$54,500	Taxable income

Her taxable income is $54,500.

Exercise A The following four taxpayers have listed their allowable exemptions and deductions. Calculate the total exemptions and deductions. Then find the taxable income in each case.

	Item	Exemptions and Deductions	Total Exemptions and Deductions	Total Income	Taxable Income
1)	Exemptions for dependents Allowable medical expenses	$2,500 1,600	______	$42,586	______
2)	Exemptions for dependents Interest paid Business travel costs	$7,500 856 939	______	$79,421	______
3)	Business loss State taxes Rentals loss	$14,987 1,234 658	______	$125,890	______
4)	Exemptions for dependents Charitable contributions Business costs	$5,000 87 358	______	$36,941	______

Lesson 4 Reading the Tax Table

Some taxpayers with taxable incomes of less than $100,000 can use a tax table to find the amount of tax that they should pay. This table comes with their federal income tax forms.

EXAMPLE

Mr. and Mrs. Brown are filing a joint return. Their taxable income (the amount on which taxes are paid) is $23,270.

In the tax table, they find the $23,250-$23,300 income line. Next, they find the column for Married filing jointly and read down this column. The amount shown where the income line and filing status column meet is $3,491. This amount is their tax.

At least	But less than	Single	Married filing jointly	Married filing sepa-rately	Head of a house-hold
			Your tax is—		
23,200	23,250	3,484	3,484	3,968	3,484
→ 23,250	23,300	3,491	**3,491**	3,982	3,491
23,300	23,350	3,499	3,499	3,996	3,499

If line 37 (taxable income) is —		And you are —				If line 37 (taxable income) is—		And you are —			
At least	But less than	Single	Married filing jointly *	Married filing sepa-rately	Head of a house-hold	At least	But less than	Single	Married filing jointly *	Married filing sepa-rately	Head of a house-hold
		Your tax is —						Your tax is —			
20,000						**21,000**					
20,000	**20,050**	3,004	3,004	3,072	3,004	**21,000**	**21,050**	3,154	3,154	3,352	3,154
20,050	**20,100**	3,011	3,011	3,086	3,011	**21,050**	**21,100**	3,161	3,161	3,366	3,161
20,100	**20,150**	3,019	3,019	3,100	3,019	**21,100**	**21,150**	3,169	3,169	3,380	3,169
20,150	**20,200**	3,026	3,026	3,114	3,026	**21,150**	**21,200**	3,176	3,176	3,394	3,176
20,200	**20,250**	3,034	3,034	3,128	3,034	**21,200**	**21,250**	3,184	3,184	3,408	3,184
20,250	**20,300**	3,041	3,041	3,142	3,041	**21,250**	**21,300**	3,191	3,191	3,422	3,191
20,300	**20,350**	3,049	3,049	3,156	3,049	**21,300**	**21,350**	3,199	3,199	3,436	3,199
20,350	**20,400**	3,056	3,056	3,170	3,056	**21,350**	**21,400**	3,206	3,206	3,450	3,206
20,400	**20,450**	3,064	3,064	3,184	3,064	**21,400**	**21,450**	3,214	3,214	3,464	3,214
20,450	**20,500**	3,071	3,071	3,198	3,071	**21,450**	**21,500**	3,221	3,221	3,478	3,221
20,500	**20,550**	3,079	3,079	3,212	3,079	**21,500**	**21,550**	3,229	3,229	3,492	3,229
20,550	**20,600**	3,086	3,086	3,226	3,086	**21,550**	**21,600**	3,236	3,236	3,506	3,236
20,600	**20,650**	3,094	3,094	3,240	3,094	**21,600**	**21,650**	3,244	3,244	3,520	3,244
20,650	**20,700**	3,101	3,101	3,254	3,101	**21,650**	**21,700**	3,251	3,251	3,534	3,251
20,700	**20,750**	3,109	3,109	3,268	3,109	**21,700**	**21,750**	3,259	3,259	3,548	3,259
20,750	**20,800**	3,116	3,116	3,282	3,116	**21,750**	**21,800**	3,266	3,266	3,562	3,266
20,800	**20,850**	3,124	3,124	3,296	3,124	**21,800**	**21,850**	3,274	3,274	3,576	3,274
20,850	**20,900**	3,131	3,131	3,310	3,131	**21,850**	**21,900**	3,281	3,281	3,590	3,281
20,900	**20,950**	3,139	3,139	3,324	3,139	**21,900**	**21,950**	3,289	3,289	3,604	3,289
20,950	**21,000**	3,146	3,146	3,338	3,146	**21,950**	**22,000**	3,296	3,296	3,618	3,296

Exercise A Use the tax table on page 288 to determine the tax due in each case.

	Filing Status	Taxable Income
1)	Single	$20,525
2)	Single	$20,400
3)	Married filing jointly	$21,125
4)	Single	$20,000
5)	Married filing separately	$20,169
6)	Head of household	$21,042
7)	Single	$21,054
8)	Married filing jointly	$21,508
9)	Head of household	$21,640
10)	Married filing separately	$21,525
11)	Single	$21,826
12)	Married filing separately	$21,296
13)	Married filing jointly	$21,440
14)	Head of household	$21,724
15)	Single	$20,604
16)	Married filing jointly	$21,152
17)	Head of household	$20,979
18)	Single	$20,543
19)	Married filing separately	$20,572
20)	Married filing jointly	$20,295

Lesson 5 Using a Tax Schedule

The instruction booklet that accompanies income tax forms contains several tax rate schedules.

Schedule Y is used by certain married persons. Those filing joint returns use Schedule Y-1 on the left. Those filing separate returns use Schedule Y-2 on the right.

Tax Rate Schedules

Caution! *Use* ***only*** *if your taxable income (Form 1040, line 37) is $100,000 or more. If less, use the* ***Tax Table.*** *Even though you cannot use the tax rate schedules below if your taxable income is less than $100,000, all levels of taxable income are shown so taxpayers can see the tax rate that applies to each level.*

Schedule Y-1—Use if your filing status is **Married filing jointly or Qualifying widow(er)**

If the amount on Form 1040, line 37, is: Over—	*But not over*—	Enter on Form 1040, line 38	*of the amount over*—
$0	$39,000	.... **15%**	**$0**
39,000	94,250	**$5,850.00 + 28%**	**39,000**
94,250	143,600	**21,320.00 + 31%**	**94,250**
143,600	256,500	**36,618.50 + 36%**	**143,600**
256,500	....	**77,262.50 +39.6%**	**256,500**

Schedule Y-2—Use if your filing status is **Married filing separately**

If the amount on Form 1040, line 37, is: Over—	*But not over*—	Enter on Form 1040, line 38	*of the amount over*—
$0	$19,500	.... **15%**	**$0**
19,500	47,125	**$2,925.00 + 28%**	**19,500**
47,125	71,800	**10,660.00 + 31%**	**47,125**
71,800	128,250	**18,309.25 + 36%**	**71,800**
128,250	....	**38,631.25 +39.6%**	**128,250**

EXAMPLE Anita and Mark Hammer have a taxable income of $118,673. Compute their tax by using Schedule Y-1. They are filing a joint return.

Step 1 Locate the tax bracket in Schedule Y-1.
$118,673 is:

Over—	But not over—	The tax is—	of the amount over—
$94,250	$143,600	$21,320.00 + 31%	$94,250

Step 2 Subtract $94,250 from the taxable income.

$$\begin{array}{r} \$118{,}673 \\ -\ 94{,}250 \\ \hline \$\ 24{,}423 \end{array}$$

Step 3 Multiply the amount over $94,250 by 31%.
31% = .31

$$\begin{array}{r} \$\ 24{,}423 \\ \times\ \ .31 \\ \hline \$7{,}571.13 \end{array}$$

Step 4 Add this amount to $21,320.00.

$$\begin{array}{r} \$21{,}320.00 \\ +\ 7{,}571.13 \\ \hline \$28{,}891.13 \end{array}$$

The Hammers' tax is $28,891.13.

Exercise A Compute the tax on each of these incomes. Use Schedules Y-1 and Y-2 on page 290.

1) $154,000 joint
2) $107,123 separate
3) $153,200 joint
4) $162,000 joint
5) $106,762 separate
6) $167,200 separate
7) $122,462 separate
8) $275,150 joint
9) $285,243 joint
10) $174,754 separate

Lesson 6 Refund or Balance Due

> ***Refund***
> *A payment returned to the taxpayer.*

> ***Balance due***
> *A payment owed by the taxpayer.*

Federal income tax is withheld from employees' wages each payday. By the end of the year, it is possible that too much money was withheld. If that happens, the employee will get a **refund** of the extra money. However, if not enough money was withheld, the person then has a **balance due** on his or her tax return and must pay additional taxes.

EXAMPLE Pedro Sanchez, the head of a household, has a taxable income of \$20,359.72. During the year \$4,234.18 is withheld from his pay for federal income taxes. Does Pedro Sanchez receive a refund, or does he pay additional taxes?

Step 1 Read the amount of tax due from the Tax Table on page 293. \$3,056

Step 2 Compare the tax due with the amount withheld.
\$3,056.00 is less than \$4,234.18.
Too much money was withheld.
He receives a refund.

Step 3 Find the amount of the refund. Subtract the amount of tax due from the amount withheld.

\$ 4,234.18	Withheld
−3,056.00	Tax due
\$ 1,178.18	Refund

Pedro Sanchez receives a tax refund of \$1,178.18.

If line 37 (taxable income) is—		And you are—				If line 37 (taxable income) is—		And you are—			
At least	But less than	Single	Married filing jointly *	Married filing sepa-rately	Head of a house-hold	At least	But less than	Single	Married filing jointly *	Married filing sepa-rately	Head of a house-hold
		Your tax is—						Your tax is—			
20,000						**21,000**					
20,000	**20,050**	3,004	3,004	3,072	3,004	**21,000**	**21,050**	3,154	3,154	3,352	3,154
20,050	**20,100**	3,011	3,011	3,086	3,011	**21,050**	**21,100**	3,161	3,161	3,366	3,161
20,100	**20,150**	3,019	3,019	3,100	3,019	**21,100**	**21,150**	3,169	3,169	3,380	3,169
20,150	**20,200**	3,026	3,026	3,114	3,026	**21,150**	**21,200**	3,176	3,176	3,394	3,176
20,200	**20,250**	3,034	3,034	3,128	3,034	**21,200**	**21,250**	3,184	3,184	3,408	3,184
20,250	**20,300**	3,041	3,041	3,142	3,041	**21,250**	**21,300**	3,191	3,191	3,422	3,191
20,300	**20,350**	3,049	3,049	3,156	3,049	**21,300**	**21,350**	3,199	3,199	3,436	3,199
20,350	**20,400**	3,056	3,056	3,170	3,056	**21,350**	**21,400**	3,206	3,206	3,450	3,206
20,400	**20,450**	3,064	3,064	3,184	3,064	**21,400**	**21,450**	3,214	3,214	3,464	3,214
20,450	**20,500**	3,071	3,071	3,198	3,071	**21,450**	**21,500**	3,221	3,221	3,478	3,221
20,500	**20,550**	3,079	3,079	3,212	3,079	**21,500**	**21,550**	3,229	3,229	3,492	3,229
20,550	**20,600**	3,086	3,086	3,226	3,086	**21,550**	**21,600**	3,236	3,236	3,506	3,236
20,600	**20,650**	3,094	3,094	3,240	3,094	**21,600**	**21,650**	3,244	3,244	3,520	3,244
20,650	**20,700**	3,101	3,101	3,254	3,101	**21,650**	**21,700**	3,251	3,251	3,534	3,251
20,700	**20,750**	3,109	3,109	3,268	3,109	**21,700**	**21,750**	3,259	3,259	3,548	3,259
20,750	**20,800**	3,116	3,116	3,282	3,116	**21,750**	**21,800**	3,266	3,266	3,562	3,266
20,800	**20,850**	3,124	3,124	3,296	3,124	**21,800**	**21,850**	3,274	3,274	3,576	3,274
20,850	**20,900**	3,131	3,131	3,310	3,131	**21,850**	**21,900**	3,281	3,281	3,590	3,281
20,900	**20,950**	3,139	3,139	3,324	3,139	**21,900**	**21,950**	3,289	3,289	3,604	3,289
20,950	**21,000**	3,146	3,146	3,338	3,146	**21,950**	**22,000**	3,296	3,296	3,618	3,296

Exercise A Compute the amount to be refunded or the balance due in each case.

	Filing Status	Taxable Income	Amount of Tax Withheld	Amount of Tax Due
1)	Single	$20,525	$4,000	$3,079
2)	Single	$20,400	$5,000	$3,064
3)	Married filing jointly	$20,140	$2,764	$3,019
4)	Head of household	$21,315	$3,423	$3,199
5)	Married filing separately	$20,702	$4,700	$3,268
6)	Head of household	$21,105	$3,230	$3,169
7)	Single	$20,708	$3,100	$3,109
8)	Married filing jointly	$21,000	$4,300	$3,154
9)	Head of household	$20,750	$4,101	$3,116
10)	Married filing separately	$20,212	$5,000	$3,128
11)	Single	$20,826	$3,100	$3,124
12)	Married filing separately	$20,425	$4,123	$3,184

Calculator Practice

Use your calculator to help you determine how much of a refund or a balance is due. Subtract the Tax Due from the Amount Withheld. If the number is positive, then you get a refund. If it is negative, then you have a balance due.

EXAMPLES

Amount Withheld: $4,000.00

Tax Due: $4,356.78

Press *4,000* [−] *4,356.78* [=]

The display reads *− 356.78*

You have a balance due of $356.78.

Amount Withheld: $5,391.00

Tax Due: $4,877.45

Press *5,391* [−] *4,877.45* [=]

The display reads *513.55*

You get a refund of $513.55.

Check your answers in Exercise A by using this method.

Lesson 7 Property Tax

Assessed value

A figure based on a percent of the market value of property.

Market value

The selling price of property on the open market.

Property tax

A figure based on a percent of the assessed value.

Local governments raise revenues for local projects by taxing owners of property. Property tax is based on the value of the property.

The **assessed value** of a property is a percent of its **market value**, or selling price on the open market. The assessment rate is determined by the local government and is used for tax purposes.

The **property tax** is a percent of the assessed value. This rate is also set by local governments.

EXAMPLE Melissa wants to calculate her property tax. These are the facts:

a) The market value of the property is $75,500.

b) The assessment rate is 48%.

c) The property tax rate is $47.30 per $1,000 of assessed value.

Step 1 Multiply the market value by the assessment rate to find the assessed value.

$ 75,5 00	Market value
× .48	Assessment rate
$36,24 0.00	Assessed value

Step 2 Find the tax rate as a percent.

Write the fraction. Divide.

$47.30 per $1,000

$\frac{47.30}{1,000}$ $\qquad 1,000\overline{)47.30\ 00} = 04.73 = 4.73\%$

Step 3 Multiply the assessed value by the tax rate.

$ 3 6,240	Assessed value
× .0 473	Tax rate
$1,71 4.152	≈ $1,714.15

Melissa's property tax is $1,714.15.

Exercise A Compute the assessed value for each property.

	Market Value	Assessment Rate
1)	$60,000	45%
2)	$70,000	50%
3)	$75,000	40%
4)	$65,000	52%
5)	$67,250	47%
6)	$71,500	60%
7)	$80,240	42%
8)	$63,275	55%
9)	$60,005	43%
10)	$78,423	48%

Exercise B Express each of these tax rates as a percent.

1) $3.67 per $100 of assessed value

2) $42.10 per $1,000 of assessed value

3) $3.52 per $100 of assessed value

4) $4.01 per $100 of assessed value

5) $37.51 per $1,000 of assessed value

6) $50.09 per $1,000 of assessed value

7) $4.50 per $100 of assessed value

8) $500 per $10,000 of assessed value

9) $3.99 per $100 of assessed value

10) $4.11 per $100 of assessed value

Exercise C Calculate each of these property taxes.

	Assessed Value	Property Tax Rate
1)	$27,000	3.67%
2)	$35,000	4.21%
3)	$30,000	3.52%
4)	$33,800	4.01%
5)	$31,607	3.75%
6)	$42,900	5.01%
7)	$33,700	4.5%
8)	$34,801	5%
9)	$25,802	3.99%
10)	$37,643	4.11%

Appraisers assess the value of a home based on many factors.

Lesson 8 Effective Tax Rate

> ***Effective tax rate***
> *The assessment rate times property tax rate.*

Both the assessment rate and the property tax rate affect the amount of taxes due. The **effective tax rate** is the product of the assessment rate and the property tax rate.

EXAMPLE For Kate Hart's ranch, the assessment rate is 46%. The property tax rate is $32.56 per $1,000. What is the effective tax rate?

Step 1 Write the property tax rate as a decimal.

$$\frac{32.56}{1{,}000} = 1{,}000\overline{)32.56000}\quad .03256$$

Step 2 Write the assessment rate as a decimal.

46% = .46

Step 3 Then multiply the property tax rate by the assessment rate.

.032 56	Property tax rate
× .46	Assessment rate
195 36	
+1 302 4	
.01 497 76	Effective tax rate

Step 4 Round this answer to three places.

$.0149776 \approx .015$

Kate's effective tax rate is .015 or 1.5%.

Exercise A Kate's ranch has a market value of $450,000. Compute her property tax.

1) Assessment method: $450,000 × .46 × .03256 = ■

2) Effective rate method: $450,000 × .015 = ■

Exercise B Calculate the effective tax rate for each property. Then circle the lower effective rate in each pair.

	Assessment Rate	Property Tax Rate	Effective Tax Rate
1) a)	35%	$36.70 per $1,000	________
b)	50%	$2.50 per $100	________
2) a)	40%	$3.04 per $100	________
b)	35%	$3.26 per $100	________
3) a)	25%	$47.23 per $1,000	________
b)	30%	$42.16 per $1,000	________
4) a)	42%	$3.70 per $100	________
b)	37%	$4.20 per $100	________
5) a)	33%	$425 per $10,000	________
b)	39%	$3.70 per $100	________
6) a)	42%	$1.60 per $100	________
b)	36%	$22 per $1,000	________
7) a)	28%	$3.75 per $100	________
b)	35%	$2.87 per $100	________
8) a)	41%	$5 per $100	________
b)	37%	$53 per $1,000	________
9) a)	36%	$4.10 per $100	________
b)	45%	$3.50 per $100	________
10) a)	40%	$1.72 per $100	________
b)	31%	$2.35 per $100	________

Chapter 11 Review

Solve these problems.

1) Calculate 38% of $1.465 trillion.

2) Jerome has exemptions of $7,500 for dependents. His deductions include $2,400 in allowable medical expenses, and $450 for damage to his home caused by a hail storm. What is Jerome's taxable income if he has an income of $47,900?

3) What is the tax for a single person whose taxable income is $20,576? Use the income tax table below.

If line 37 (taxable income) is—		And you are—				If line 37 (taxable income) is—		And you are—			
At least	But less than	Single	Married filing jointly *	Married filing sepa-rately	Head of a house-hold	At least	But less than	Single	Married filing jointly *	Married filing sepa-rately	Head of a house-hold
		Your tax is—						Your tax is—			
20,000						**21,000**					
20,000	**20,050**	3,004	3,004	3,072	3,004	**21,000**	**21,050**	3,154	3,154	3,352	3,154
20,050	**20,100**	3,011	3,011	3,086	3,011	**21,050**	**21,100**	3,161	3,161	3,366	3,161
20,100	**20,150**	3,019	3,019	3,100	3,019	**21,100**	**21,150**	3,169	3,169	3,380	3,169
20,150	**20,200**	3,026	3,026	3,114	3,026	**21,150**	**21,200**	3,176	3,176	3,394	3,176
20,200	**20,250**	3,034	3,034	3,128	3,034	**21,200**	**21,250**	3,184	3,184	3,408	3,184
20,250	**20,300**	3,041	3,041	3,142	3,041	**21,250**	**21,300**	3,191	3,191	3,422	3,191
20,300	**20,350**	3,049	3,049	3,156	3,049	**21,300**	**21,350**	3,199	3,199	3,436	3,199
20,350	**20,400**	3,056	3,056	3,170	3,056	**21,350**	**21,400**	3,206	3,206	3,450	3,206
20,400	**20,450**	3,064	3,064	3,184	3,064	**21,400**	**21,450**	3,214	3,214	3,464	3,214
20,450	**20,500**	3,071	3,071	3,198	3,071	**21,450**	**21,500**	3,221	3,221	3,478	3,221
20,500	**20,550**	3,079	3,079	3,212	3,079	**21,500**	**21,550**	3,229	3,229	3,492	3,229
20,550	**20,600**	3,086	3,086	3,226	3,086	**21,550**	**21,600**	3,236	3,236	3,506	3,236
20,600	**20,650**	3,094	3,094	3,240	3,094	**21,600**	**21,650**	3,244	3,244	3,520	3,244
20,650	**20,700**	3,101	3,101	3,254	3,101	**21,650**	**21,700**	3,251	3,251	3,534	3,251
20,700	**20,750**	3,109	3,109	3,268	3,109	**21,700**	**21,750**	3,259	3,259	3,548	3,259
20,750	**20,800**	3,116	3,116	3,282	3,116	**21,750**	**21,800**	3,266	3,266	3,562	3,266
20,800	**20,850**	3,124	3,124	3,296	3,124	**21,800**	**21,850**	3,274	3,274	3,576	3,274
20,850	**20,900**	3,131	3,131	3,310	3,131	**21,850**	**21,900**	3,281	3,281	3,590	3,281
20,900	**20,950**	3,139	3,139	3,324	3,139	**21,900**	**21,950**	3,289	3,289	3,604	3,289
20,950	**21,000**	3,146	3,146	3,338	3,146	**21,950**	**22,000**	3,296	3,296	3,618	3,296

4) A married person filing a separate return has a taxable income of $20,327. During the year $3,243 is withheld from wages. Using the tax table above, does this person owe more taxes, or does he or she get a refund? What amount will this person owe or be refunded?

5) Compute the income tax on a taxable income of $165,872 for a couple who is filing a joint return. Use Schedule Y-1 below.

Tax Rate Schedules

Caution! *Use* ***only*** *if your taxable income (Form 1040, line 37) is $100,000 or more. If less, use the* ***Tax Table.*** *Even though you cannot use the tax rate schedules below if your taxable income is less than $100,000, all levels of taxable income are shown so taxpayers can see the tax rate that applies to each level.*

Schedule Y-1—Use if your filing status is **Married filing jointly or Qualifying widow(er)**

If the amount on Form 1040, line 37, is: Over—	But not over—	Enter on Form 1040, line 38	of the amount over—
$0	$39,000	.... 15%	$0
39,000	94,250	$5,850.00 + 28%	39,000
94,250	143,600	21,320.00 + 31%	94,250
143,600	256,500	36,618.50 + 36%	143,600
256,500	....	77,262.50 +39.6%	256,500

Schedule Y-2—Use if your filing status is **Married filing separately**

If the amount on Form 1040, line 37, is: Over—	But not over—	Enter on Form 1040, line 38	of the amount over—
$0	$19,500	.... 15%	$0
19,500	47,125	$2,925.00 + 28%	19,500
47,125	71,800	10,660.00 + 31%	47,125
71,800	128,250	18,309.25 + 36%	71,800
128,250	....	38,631.25 +39.6%	128,250

6) A married couple filing separately has a taxable income of $168,210. What is their tax? Use Schedule Y-2 above.

7) Compute the property tax on a house with a market value of $170,000.
   - The assessment rate is 46%.
   - The tax rate is $37.84 per $1,000 of assessed value.

8) Express $42.75 per $1,000.00 as a percent.

9) Explain the difference between the market value of a property and its assessed value.

10) Find the effective tax rate for an assessment rate of 47% and a tax rate of $3.89 per $100 of assessed value.

Test Taking Tip It is a good idea to double-check the location of numbers or other data that you identify in a table or chart.

INTERGRAPH

Chapter 12 Preparing for Careers

Practically every career requires some knowledge of mathematics. Mathematical skills such as computation, measurement, using formulas, and interpreting numerical data are extremely useful. Sound knowledge of these skills will help you prepare for your chosen field.

In Chapter 12, you will practice actual skills that are used by people in six career fields: salesclerks, electricians, auto mechanics, carpenters, drafters, and machine operators. You will see the importance of mathematics skills in each of these careers.

Goals for Learning

- To read a sales tax table and compute the value of purchases that include tax
- To determine correct change
- To apply electrical formulas to calculate watts, amps, ohms, or volts
- To order fractions from smallest to largest
- To practice making precise measurements
- To measure line segments and compute scale length for drawings
- To apply the rule for RPM plus number of teeth to problems about gears

Lesson 1 Salesclerks

Sales tax is computed on the sale of goods and services. It is figured as a percentage of the purchase price and is collected by the seller.

One job of a salesclerk is to find the correct amount of sales tax and then add it to customers' purchases. The rate of sales tax varies from state to state. A few states do not have a sales tax. Many cash registers are computerized and calculate the sales tax. It is still important to understand how to compute the tax.

EXAMPLE Jon Kirshner sells a customer $21.05 worth of merchandise. The sales tax rate is 5%. What is the tax? What is the total bill?

Step 1 Multiply the purchase price by the rate to find the sales tax.

$ 21.05 Purchase price
× .05 Rate (5%)
$1.0525 ≈ $1.05 Sales tax (Round to **nearest** cent.)

Step 2 Add the sales tax to the purchase price to find the total bill.

$21.05 Purchase price
+ 1.05 Sales tax
$22.10 Total bill

Exercise A Multiply to find the amount of sales tax for each purchase. Use a sales tax rate of 5%.

1) $11.30

2) $9.95

3) $24.85

4) $35.25

5) $52.98

6) $168.42

Another way to find the sales tax is to use the chart that many stores post for their clerks.

EXAMPLE Shown below is part of a state sales tax chart. Look in this chart for the sale bracket containing $21.05. Read the tax. Add the tax to the purchase price. $21.05 + $1.06 = $22.11.

5% State Sales Tax					
Amount of Sale	**Tax**	**Amount of Sale**	**Tax**	**Amount of Sale**	**Tax**
.01 – .20	.01	10.01 – 10.20	.51	20.01 – 20.20	1.01
.21 – .40	.02	10.21 – 10.40	.52	20.21 – 20.40	1.02
.41 – .60	.03	10.41 – 10.60	.53	20.41 – 20.60	1.03
.61 – .80	.04	10.61 – 10.80	.54	20.61 – 20.80	1.04
.81 – 1.00	.05	10.81 – 11.00	.55	20.81 – 21.00	1.05
1.01 – 1.20	.06	11.01 – 11.20	.56	21.01 – 21.20	1.06 ←
1.21 – 1.40	.07	11.21 – 11.40	.57	21.21 – 21.40	1.07
1.41 – 1.60	.08	11.41 – 11.60	.58	21.41 – 21.60	1.08
1.61 – 1.80	.09	11.61 – 11.80	.59	21.61 – 21.80	1.09
1.81 – 2.00	.10	11.81 – 12.00	.60	21.81 – 22.00	1.10

Exercise B Find the sales tax for each of these purchases. Then compute the total bill in each case. Use the 5% sales tax chart to help you.

	Purchase	Sales Tax	Total		Purchase	Sales Tax	Total
1)	$1.43	______	______	**11)**	$11.30	______	______
2)	$11.90	______	______	**12)**	$10.75	______	______
3)	$.85	______	______	**13)**	$21.50	______	______
4)	$10.90	______	______	**14)**	$10.45	______	______
5)	$1.20	______	______	**15)**	$21.00	______	______
6)	$20.90	______	______	**16)**	$11.00	______	______
7)	$21.35	______	______	**17)**	$10.17	______	______
8)	$20.39	______	______	**18)**	$.38	______	______
9)	$21.07	______	______	**19)**	$10.39	______	______
10)	$20.97	______	______	**20)**	$11.08	______	______

On rare occasions, customers actually have the correct change for a purchase. Most of the time a salesclerk will need to give change. One method for doing this is called "Counting Up." The salesclerk will start with the amount of the purchase and count the amount of money paid back to the customer, stopping at the amount the customer gave the clerk. When using this method, salesclerks follow one general rule: try to give the change in the fewest number of coins and bills possible.

EXAMPLE A purchase costs $37.58. A customer pays with two $20 dollar bills. Count up the change as it is given to the customer.

Step 1 The customer pays $40.00 (2 × $20.00). Make a mental note to stop at $40.00.

Step 2

	PAY	SAY
Say the amount of the sale.		"$37.58"
Start with pennies:	1 penny	"59"
	1 penny	"60"
Now change to dimes	1 dime	"70"
Now change to nickels	1 nickel	"75"
Now change to quarters	1 quarter	"$38.00"
Now change to dollars	1 dollar	"$39.00"
	1 dollar	"and $40.00"

Stop because you are at $40.00.

The salesclerk gives change using only 7 bills and coins. There are other ways to give this change. You can try to show another way.

Some people will try to avoid receiving pennies in change and may give you extra pennies. The customer in this example could give the clerk $40.03 to avoid getting an extra two pennies.

Exercise C Calculate the correct change for each purchase using the "Counting Up" method. Write PAY and SAY columns to describe the change given.

	Purchase	Amount Paid		Purchase	Amount Paid
1)	$9.00	$10.00	**6)**	$14.32	$14.00 and 2 quarters
2)	$4.75	$5.00	**7)**	$8.63	$10.00
3)	$13.85	$10.00 and $5.00	**8)**	$6.71	$7.00
4)	$23.50	$20.00 and $5.00	**9)**	$8.63	$10.00 and 3 pennies
5)	$22.34	three $10.00 bills	**10)**	$6.71	$7.00 and 1 penny

Many cash registers compute the amount of change due to a customer. Salesclerks are responsible for giving the correct change. Clerks are trained to give change with the smallest number of bills and coins. This method is called "Counting Down."

EXAMPLE Dmika Ho owes a customer $16.47 in change. How should she make change using the smallest number of bills and coins?

		PAY	SAY
Step 1	Start with the largest bill or coin that is not larger than the change due.		
		1 $10 bill	"$10.00"
		1 $5 bill	"$15.00"
Step 2	Repeat process, choosing smaller coins and bills.	1 $1 bill	"$16.00"
		1 quarter	"25"
		1 dime	"35"
Step 3	Repeat the total to the customer.	1 dime	"45"
		1 penny	"46"
		1 penny	"47"
	The change consists of a $10 bill, a $5 bill, a $1 bill, 1 quarter, 2 dimes and 2 pennies.		"$16.47"

Exercise D Use the "Counting Down" method to give change using the smallest number of bills and coins. Write PAY and SAY columns to describe the change given

1) 42¢

2) 89¢

3) $1.23

4) $3.62

5) $8.37

6) $11.01

7) $19.99

8) $24.32

9) $51.48

10) $78.43

Lesson 2 The Key to Square Root

Square root

An equal factor of a number.

The **square root** of a number is one of two equal factors of that number.

EXAMPLE

$4 \times 4 = 16$	4 is the square root of
$\sqrt{16} = 4$	16 because 4 is one of two equal factors of 16.
$2 \times 8 = 16$	2 is not the square root of 16. The factors 2 and 8 are not equal.

Exercise A Find the following square roots.

1) $\sqrt{4}$

2) $\sqrt{36}$

3) $\sqrt{100}$

4) $\sqrt{64}$

5) $\sqrt{49}$

6) $\sqrt{25}$

7) $\sqrt{81}$

8) $\sqrt{1}$

9) $\sqrt{144}$

10) $\sqrt{9}$

Rule To find the square root of a number when the factors are not known, you can divide and average.

EXAMPLE Find the square root of 56. $\sqrt{56} = ■$

Step 1 Choose any number and divide it into 56.
Let's try 7, since 7×7 is 49, and 49 is close to 56.

$$7\overline{)56}^{\,8}$$

Step 2 The square root is between 7 and 8. Average 7 and 8.

$$\begin{array}{r} 7 \\ +\ 8 \\ \hline 15 \end{array} \qquad 2\overline{)15.0}^{\,7.5}$$

EXAMPLE *(continued)*

Step 3 Divide 56 by the average. Round to the nearest tenth.

$\sqrt{56} \approx 7.5$

```
         7.46 ≈ 7.5
 7.5. ) 56.0.00
       -52 5
         3 5 0
        -3 0 0
           5 00
```

To check your work test 7.5 by squaring it.

```
    7.5
 ×  7.5
   3 7 5
 +52 5
  56.2 5 ≈ 56
```

7.5 is close to the square root. More decimal places may be found by averaging 7.5 and 7.46 and returning to step 3.

A calculator gives the square root of 56 as 7.483314. . . . This number rounded to the nearest tenth is 7.5.

Exercise B Use the "divide and average" method to find the following square roots. Round your answers to the nearest tenth.

1) $\sqrt{300}$
2) $\sqrt{38}$
3) $\sqrt{654}$
4) $\sqrt{128}$
5) $\sqrt{256}$
6) $\sqrt{21}$
7) $\sqrt{409}$
8) $\sqrt{345}$
9) $\sqrt{717}$
10) $\sqrt{1024}$

Lesson 3 Electricians

Amps
A measure of the intensity of electrical current.

Ohms
A measure of electrical resistance.

Volts
A measure of electromotive force.

Electricians use formulas in their work. These formulas yield information about electrical current. A handy way to remember the formulas is to use the word WIRE.

W = power measured in watts
I = intensity measured in **amps**
R = resistance measured in **ohms**
E = electromotive force measured in **volts**

Electricians must measure amps, ohms, watts, and volts when checking a wire assembly.

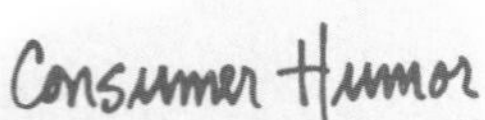

Did you hear that Joe, the electrician, opened a car lot?

Yes, he's selling mobile ohms and voltswagens.

Formulas for finding watts:

1) $W = EI$

2) $W = I^2R$

3) $W = \frac{E^2}{R}$

Formulas for finding amps:

4) $I = \frac{E}{R}$

5) $I = \sqrt{\frac{W}{R}}$

6) $I = \frac{W}{E}$

Formulas for finding ohms:

7) $R = \frac{E}{I}$

8) $R = \frac{W}{I^2}$

9) $R = \frac{E^2}{W}$

Formulas for finding volts:

10) $E = IR$

11) $E = \frac{W}{I}$

12) $E = \sqrt{WR}$

EXAMPLES Find the intensity of a current that supplies 250 watts of power and has 2.5 ohms of resistance.

Step 1 Choose the formula for intensity (I) that uses watts (W) and ohms (R). This is formula #5 on page 310.

$$I = \sqrt{\frac{W}{R}}$$

Step 2 Replace the letters with their values.

$$I = \sqrt{\frac{250}{2.5}}$$

Step 3 Simplify.

$I = \sqrt{100}$

Step 4 Find the square root.

$\sqrt{100} = 10$

The intensity is 10 amps.

Find the power in a circuit with 12 amps and 1.5 ohms.

Step 1 Choose the formula for power (W) that uses amps (I) and ohms (R). This is formula #2.

$W = I^2R$

Step 2 Replace the letters with their values.

$W = 12^2 \times 1.5$

Step 3 12^2 means 12×12.

$W = 12 \times 12 \times 1.5$

Step 4 Multiply the product of 12×12 by 1.5.

$12 \times 12 = 144$

$$\begin{array}{r} 144 \\ \times \quad 1.5 \\ \hline 720 \\ +144 \\ \hline 216.0 \end{array}$$

The power in the circuit is 216 watts.

EXAMPLE Find the force (E) in an electrical circuit that has 250 watts (W) and 4.9 ohms (R).

Step 1 Choose the formula for E that uses W and R. This is formula #12.

$E = \sqrt{WR}$ $\quad$ $E = \sqrt{250 \times 4.9}$

Step 2 Multiply $W \times R$.

$$\begin{array}{r} 25\,0 \\ \times \quad 4.9 \\ \hline 225\,0 \\ +1\,000 \\ \hline 1{,}225.0 \end{array} \qquad E = \sqrt{1{,}225}$$

Step 3 Find the square root.

a) Guess 30.

$30^2 = 30 \times 30 = 900$

$$30\,\overline{)1{,}225.0} = 40.8 \approx 41$$

b) Average 41 and 30.

$$\begin{array}{r} 30 \\ +\,41 \\ \hline 71 \end{array} \qquad 2\,\overline{)71.0} = 35.5$$

c) Divide by 35.5.

$$35.5.\,\overline{)1{,}225.0.0} = 34.5$$

d) Average 34.5 and 35.5.

$$\begin{array}{r} 34.5 \\ +\,35.5 \\ \hline 70.00 \end{array} \qquad 2\,\overline{)70} = 35$$

e) Divide by 35.

$$35\,\overline{)1{,}225} = 35$$

The force in the circuit is 35 volts.

$E = \sqrt{1{,}225}$ $\quad$ $E = 35$

Formulas for finding watts:

1) $W = EI$

2) $W = I^2R$

3) $W = \frac{E^2}{R}$

Formulas for finding amps:

4) $I = \frac{E}{R}$

5) $I = \sqrt{\frac{W}{R}}$

6) $I = \frac{W}{E}$

Formulas for finding ohms:

7) $R = \frac{E}{I}$

8) $R = \frac{W}{I^2}$

9) $R = \frac{E^2}{W}$

Formulas for finding volts:

10) $E = IR$

11) $E = \frac{W}{I}$

12) $E = \sqrt{WR}$

Exercise A Complete this chart by calculating the missing quantities. Use the formulas on page 312 to help you. Round your answer to the nearest hundredth.

	W (in watts)	I (in amps)	R (in ohms)	E (in volts)
1)	128 W	______	2 ohms	______
2)	100 W	5 amps	______	______
3)	______	7 amps	______	120 volts
4)	7,280 W	______	______	1,000 volts
5)	______	10 amps	16 ohms	______
6)	______	______	2 ohms	240 volts

PROBLEM SOLVING

Exercise B Solve the following problems. Use the formulas to help you.

1) A toaster uses 1,200 watts. It is plugged into a 120-volt outlet. How many amps will the toaster draw?

2) A waffle iron uses 1,300 watts. It is also plugged into a 120-volt outlet. How many amps will the waffle iron draw?

3) Find the total number of amps drawn by both appliances in problems #1 and #2.

4) Most household wiring supplies 15 amps to an outlet. Should you run both the waffle iron and the toaster at the same time from the same outlet?

5) What might be the result of overloading an electrical outlet?

Calculator Practice

Use the $\sqrt{\ }$ key to find square roots on a calculator. Remember to do any calculations under the square root symbol first, then press =, then press $\sqrt{\ }$.

EXAMPLE Find the value $\sqrt{250 \times 4.9}$

Press 250 × 4.9 = $\sqrt{\ }$. The display reads 35.

The square root of 250 × 4.9 is 35.

Check your answers in Exercise A and B using a calculator.

Lesson 4 Auto Mechanics

Auto mechanics need tools of many sizes to work on different parts of an engine.

Mechanics' tools come in two sets of standard sizes. There are metric tools that use decimal measurements, and there are customary tools that use fractional inch measurements.

EXAMPLE Pat is tightening a fitting. She finds that the $\frac{3}{8}''$ wrench is too loose. She asks Andy to pass her the next size smaller wrench. These 15 wrenches are in the tool box.

$\frac{1}{16}''$ $\frac{3}{16}''$ $\frac{5}{16}''$ $\frac{7}{16}''$ $\frac{9}{16}''$ $\frac{11}{16}''$ $\frac{13}{16}''$

$\frac{15}{16}''$ $\frac{1}{8}''$ $\frac{5}{8}''$ $\frac{7}{8}''$ $\frac{1}{4}''$ $\frac{3}{4}''$ $\frac{1}{2}''$ 1″

Which one does Andy select? He puts the wrenches in order to select more easily the next smaller wrench.

Step 1 To compare fractions, use a common denominator. Use 16 since all of the denominators are factors of 16.

$\frac{1}{8} = \frac{\blacksquare}{16}$

Divide. $8\overline{)16}$ = 2

Multiply the numerator 1 by 2.

$1 \times 2 = 2$

$\frac{1}{8} = \frac{2}{16}$

Pat's wrench → $\frac{3}{8} = \frac{6}{16}$

$\frac{1}{8} = \frac{2}{16}$

$\frac{5}{8} = \frac{10}{16}$

$\frac{7}{8} = \frac{14}{16}$

$\frac{1}{4} = \frac{4}{16}$

$\frac{3}{4} = \frac{12}{16}$

$\frac{1}{2} = \frac{8}{16}$

$1 = \frac{16}{16}$

EXAMPLE *(continued)*

Step 2 Arrange the sizes from the smallest to the largest. Look at the numerators.

$\frac{1}{16}''$ Smallest wrench	$\frac{9}{16}''$
$\frac{2}{16}'' = \frac{1}{8}''$	$\frac{10}{16}'' = \frac{5}{8}''$
$\frac{3}{16}''$	$\frac{11}{16}''$
$\frac{4}{16}'' = \frac{1}{4}''$	$\frac{12}{16}'' = \frac{3}{4}''$
$\boxed{\frac{5}{16}''}$	$\frac{13}{16}''$
$\frac{6}{16}'' = \frac{3}{8}''$ ← Pat has this wrench.	$\frac{14}{16}'' = \frac{7}{8}''$
$\frac{7}{16}''$	$\frac{15}{16}''$
$\frac{8}{16}'' = \frac{1}{2}''$	$\frac{16}{16}'' = 1''$ Largest wrench

The $\frac{5}{16}''$ wrench is the one that Andy selects.

Exercise A Arrange each set of tool sizes from the smallest to the largest.

1) $\frac{3}{8}$ $\frac{5}{8}$ $\frac{7}{16}$ $\frac{1}{2}$ $\frac{5}{16}$

2) $1\frac{1}{2}$ $1\frac{1}{8}$ $1\frac{3}{16}$ $1\frac{5}{8}$ $1\frac{7}{16}$

3) $2\frac{5}{8}$ $2\frac{3}{4}$ $2\frac{9}{16}$ $2\frac{7}{8}$ $2\frac{11}{16}$

4) $\frac{11}{16}$ $\frac{5}{8}$ $\frac{13}{16}$ $\frac{3}{4}$ $\frac{9}{16}$

5) $1\frac{1}{16}$ $1\frac{1}{32}$ $1\frac{1}{8}$ 1 $1\frac{1}{4}$

Lesson 5 Carpenters

Carpenters must often make precise measurements. The building industry continues to use the customary system of measurement. Carpenters need to develop the skill of making exact customary measurements.

EXAMPLES Measure these line segments.

1) To the nearest inch: 4″

2) To the nearest half inch: 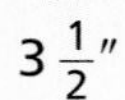

$3\frac{1}{2}''$

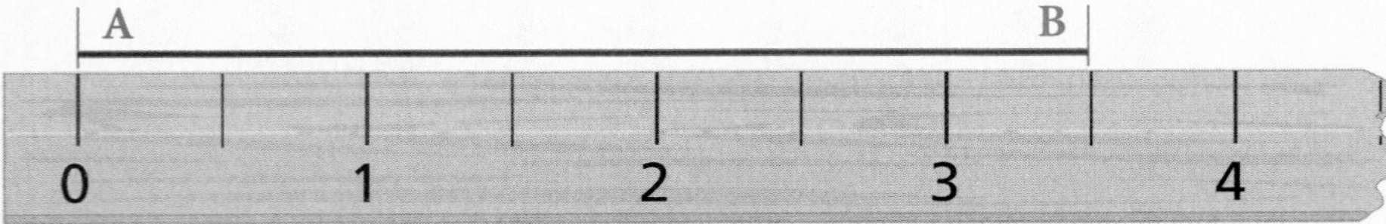

3) To the nearest quarter inch: $3\frac{3}{4}''$

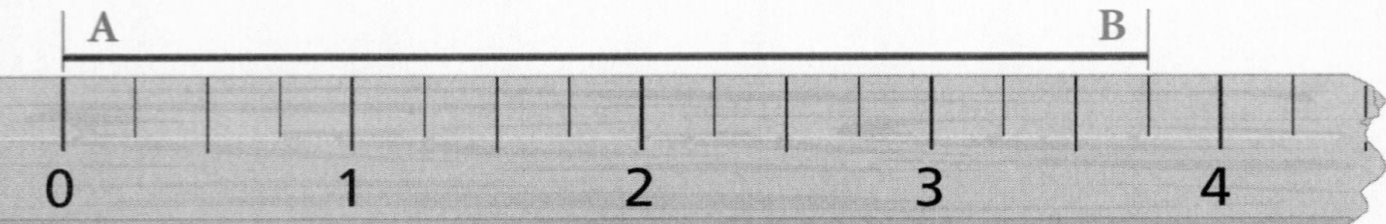

4) To the nearest eighth inch: $3\frac{6}{8}'' = 3\frac{3}{4}''$

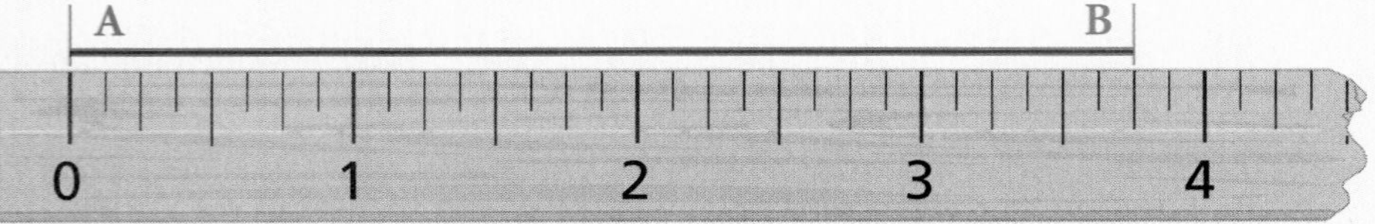

5) To the nearest sixteenth inch: $3\frac{12}{16}'' = 3\frac{3}{4}''$

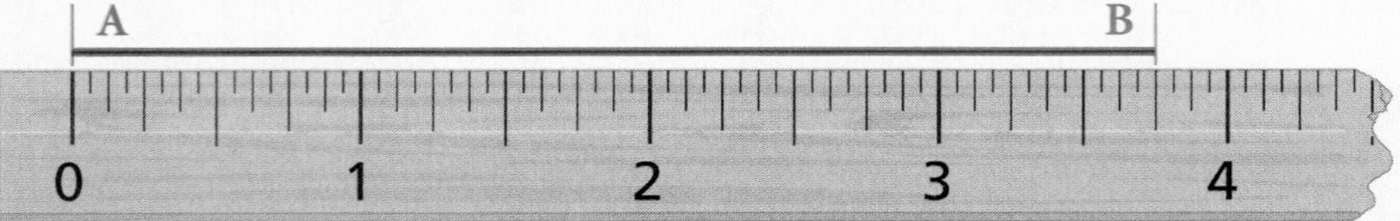

Exercise A Measure each line segment to the nearest quarter inch.

1) ____________

2) ________________________

3) _________________

4) __________________________________

5) ______________

6) ___________________________

7) ____

Exercise B Measure each line segment to the nearest eighth inch.

1) ___________

2) _______________________

3) ___________________________________

4) ________________________

5) ____________________________________

6) ______________________

7) ____________________________

Exercise C Measure each line segment to the nearest sixteenth inch.

1) _____

2) ______________________

3) ________________________________

4) __________________________

5) ______________________________________

6) ____

7) _______________________________________

Lesson 6 Drafters

Drafters
People who draw plans for projects.

Blueprints
Maps, mechanical drawings, or architectural plans.

Scale drawing
A picture that shows the relative sizes of actual objects.

Drafters are people who draw **blueprints**, plans, and sketches for construction and manufacturing projects. They must make a **scale drawing** of a finished product that is being planned. Most drawings are smaller than the actual product. A scale gives the ratio of the size on a drawing, map, or model to the original size.

For example, a $\frac{1}{12}$ scale drawing means that a line one inch long on the drawing represents a 12-inch line on the finished product.

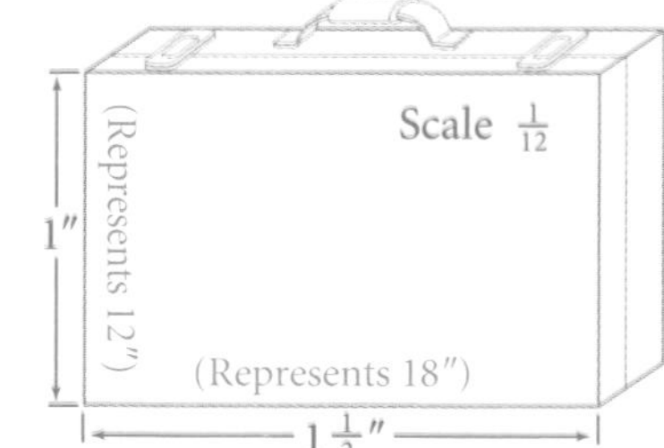

EXAMPLE Pamela makes a $\frac{2}{15}$ scale drawing. She shows a measurement of 30 inches. How long is her line on the drawing?

Step 1 Multiply the scale by the actual measurement.

$\frac{2}{15} \times 30''$

Step 2 Write both factors as fractions.

$\frac{2}{15} \times \frac{30}{1}$

Step 3 Look for common factors in the numerators and denominators. 15 and 30 have a common factor, 15. Divide 15 and 30 by 15.

$\frac{2}{\cancel{15}_{1}} \times \frac{\cancel{30}^{2}}{1}$

Step 4 Multiply the numerators. Multiply the denominators.

$\frac{2}{1} \times \frac{2}{1} = \frac{4}{1} = 4$

The line on the drawing is four inches long.

Exercise A Compute the scale length for each drawing.

	Scale	Actual Length	Scale Length		Scale	Actual Length	Scale Length
1)	$\frac{1}{8}$	32″	______	**6)**	$\frac{3}{16}$	64″	______
2)	$\frac{1}{4}$	48″	______	**7)**	$\frac{3}{16}$	32″	______
3)	$\frac{3}{8}$	24″	______	**8)**	$\frac{7}{8}$	56″	______
4)	$\frac{1}{4}$	20″	______	**9)**	$\frac{3}{8}$	40″	______
5)	$\frac{3}{32}$	96″	______	**10)**	$\frac{5}{8}$	64″	______

The actual measurement may be expressed as a mixed number.

EXAMPLE Raelene must compute the length of a $\frac{1}{2}$ scale line for a $3\frac{3}{8}''$ measurement.

Step 1 Multiply the scale by the measurement. $\frac{1}{2} \times 3\frac{3}{8}''$

Step 2 Write the mixed number as a fraction.

$3\frac{3}{8} = \frac{24}{8} + \frac{3}{8} = \frac{27}{8}$

Step 3 Multiply. $\frac{1}{2} \times \frac{27}{8} = \frac{27}{16}$

Step 4 Simplify. $\frac{27}{16} = 1\frac{11}{16}''$

Exercise B Compute the scale length for each drawing.

	Scale	Actual Length	Scale Length		Scale	Actual Length	Scale Length
1)	$\frac{1}{7}$	$3\frac{1}{16}''$	______	**6)**	$\frac{1}{5}$	$4\frac{3}{8}''$	______
2)	$\frac{1}{8}$	$5\frac{1}{8}''$	______	**7)**	$\frac{1}{3}$	$11\frac{1}{4}''$	______
3)	$\frac{3}{7}$	$5\frac{3}{8}''$	______	**8)**	$\frac{4}{11}$	$5\frac{1}{2}''$	______
4)	$\frac{7}{8}$	$6\frac{3}{8}''$	______	**9)**	$\frac{4}{5}$	$7\frac{1}{2}''$	______
5)	$\frac{5}{9}$	$12\frac{3}{4}''$	______	**10)**	$\frac{6}{7}$	$12\frac{1}{4}''$	______

Lesson 7 Machine Operators

> ***Driven gear***
> *A gear to which motion is transferred.*
>
> ***Driver gear***
> *A gear that transfers motion to another gear.*
>
> ***Revolutions per minute***
> *The rotations or turns per minute of a gear.*
>
> ***RPM or rpm***
> *The revolutions per minute of a driver gear or a driven gear.*

Many machines are driven by belts and gears. Operators change gears to speed up or to slow down an operation.

A gear is a wheel with teeth around the rim. It is used to drive machines and change speeds of operations. By interlocking its teeth with a second gear, a **driver gear** transfers motion to the second gear. The second gear is called the **driven gear**.

RPM is the **revolutions per minute** of the driver gear, and **rpm** is the revolutions per minute of the driven gear.

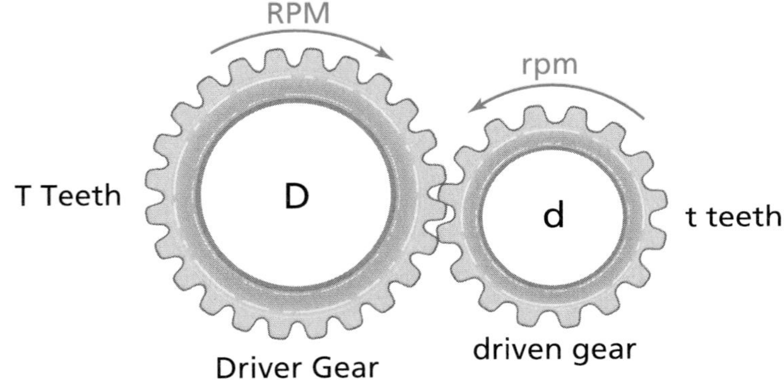

Rule For any two gears, a driver gear (D) and a driven gear (d), with speeds RPM and rpm, and numbers of teeth T and t, the following proportion is true:

$$\frac{\text{RPM}}{\text{rpm}} = \frac{\text{t}}{\text{T}}$$

EXAMPLE Richard needs to change a driver gear to increase the speed of the driven gear.
The speed of the driver gear (D) is 240 RPM.
The desired speed of the driven gear (d) is 360 rpm.
The number of teeth (t) in the driven gear is 40.
How many teeth (T) must be on the driver gear to achieve this speed?

EXAMPLE *(continued)*

Step 1 Write the proportion.

$$\frac{\text{RPM}}{\text{rpm}} = \frac{t}{T} \qquad \frac{240}{360} = \frac{40}{T}$$

Step 2 Solve the proportion.

a) Simplify the fraction by dividing both the numerator and denominator by 10 and then by 12.

$$\frac{\overset{2}{\cancel{240}}}{\underset{3}{\cancel{360}}} = \frac{40}{T}$$

b) Multiply across the equal sign.

$$\frac{2}{\boxed{3}} = \frac{\boxed{40}}{T} \qquad 3 \times 40 = 120$$

c) Divide the product by the third number. (In this case, divide 120 by 2)

$$2\overline{)120}\ \text{= }60 \qquad T = 60$$

Richard needs a gear with 60 teeth.

Exercise A Complete the chart by finding the missing items.

	Teeth	RPM	teeth	rpm
1)	4	50	____	20
2)	40	____	30	8
3)	____	60	28	15
4)	56	42	28	____
5)	____	250	25	100
6)	75	12	____	100
7)	70	____	56	100
8)	10	35	____	70
9)	____	20	12	50
10)	12	40	36	____

Chapter 12 Review

Solve these problems.

1) Find the 5% sales tax and compute the total bill for a purchase of \$10.95. Use the tax chart to help you.

5% State Sales Tax								
Amount of Sale		**Tax**	**Amount of Sale**		**Tax**	**Amount of Sale**		**Tax**
.01	– .20	.01	10.01	– 10.20	.51	20.01	– 20.20	1.01
.21	– .40	.02	10.21	– 10.40	.52	20.21	– 20.40	1.02
.41	– .60	.03	10.41	– 10.60	.53	20.41	– 20.60	1.03
.61	– .80	.04	10.61	– 10.80	.54	20.61	– 20.80	1.04
.81	– 1.00	.05	10.81	– 11.00	.55	20.81	– 21.00	1.05
1.01	– 1.20	.06	11.01	– 11.20	.56	21.01	– 21.20	1.06
1.21	– 1.40	.07	11.21	– 11.40	.57	21.21	– 21.40	1.07
1.41	– 1.60	.08	11.41	– 11.60	.58	21.41	– 21.60	1.08
1.61	– 1.80	.09	11.61	– 11.80	.59	21.61	– 21.80	1.09
1.81	– 2.00	.10	11.81	– 12.00	.60	21.81	– 22.00	1.10

2) A customer's change is \$7.68. List the smallest number of bills and coins a salesclerk might give as change.

3) Calculate the square root of 361.

Electrical Formulas			
Formulas for finding watts:	**Formulas for finding amps:**	**Formulas for finding ohms:**	**Formulas for finding volts:**
$W = EI$	$I = \frac{E}{R}$	$R = \frac{E}{I}$	$E = IR$
$W = I^2R$	$I = \sqrt{\frac{W}{R}}$	$R = \frac{W}{I^2}$	$E = \frac{W}{I}$
$W = \frac{E^2}{R}$	$I = \frac{W}{E}$	$R = \frac{E^2}{W}$	$E = \sqrt{WR}$

4) Compute the power produced by 110 volts over resistance of 36 ohms. Use one of the formulas to help you.

5) Compute the resistance of a current that produces 2,400 watts on a 20-amp line. Use one of the formulas to help you.

6) Sort these sizes from the smallest to the largest.

$10\frac{1}{8}$ $10\frac{3}{4}$ $10\frac{1}{16}$ $10\frac{3}{16}$ $10\frac{3}{8}$ $10\frac{1}{4}$

7) Measure this line segment to the nearest quarter inch.

8) Measure this line segment to the nearest eighth inch.

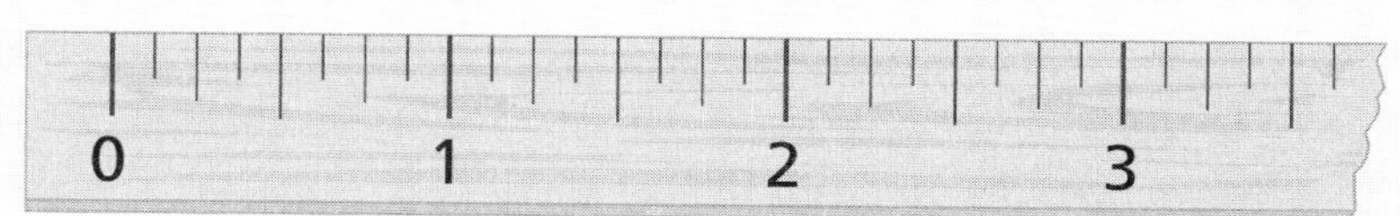

9) Find the length of a line segment that represents $3\frac{3}{4}''$ on a $\frac{2}{5}$ scale drawing.

10) How fast does a driver gear turn if it has 80 teeth (T) and drives a 35-tooth gear (t) at 400 rpm?

Test Taking Tip

Effective studying takes place over a period of time. Spend time studying new material for several days or weeks instead of trying to learn everything the night before a test.

Supplementary Problems

Review of Basic Skills 1

Identifying the Place Value of Whole Numbers

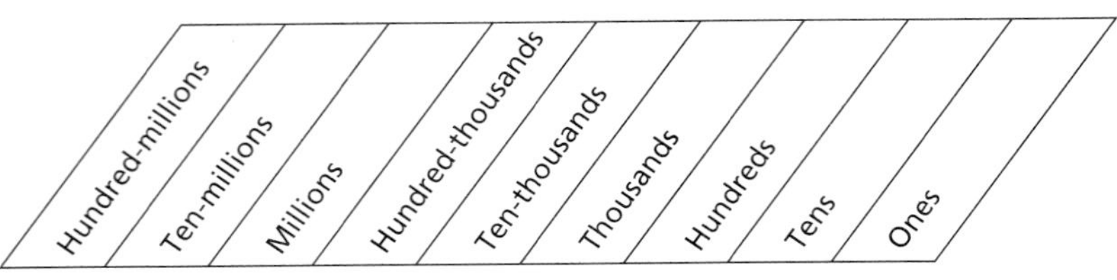

Example Write the name of the place of the underlined digit.

65,823	thousands
2,906	tens
4,790,098	millions

Exercise Write the name of the place for each underlined digit.

1) 23,456
2) 536
3) 5,126
4) 621
5) 150,341
6) 780,296
7) 3,103,615
8) 82,605
9) 26
10) 7,405
11) 41,811
12) 963
13) 31,005
14) 1,815
15) 1,007
16) 81,001
17) 567
18) 314,152
19) 72,855
20) 6,293,000

Review of Basic Skills 2

Rounding Whole Numbers

To the nearest ten		*To the nearest hundred*
582 ↑ tens	**Step 1** Find the place to be rounded.	68,154 ↑ hundreds
582 ↑	**Step 2** If the digit to the right is 5 or more, add 1 to the place to be rounded.	68,154 ↑
580	**Step 3** Change all digits to the right of the rounded place to zeros.	68,200

Exercise Round these numbers to the nearest:

		Ten	Hundred	Thousand
1)	26,311	______	______	______
2)	40,592	______	______	______
3)	7,098	______	______	______
4)	415	______	______	______
5)	89	______	______	______
6)	49	______	______	______
7)	2,900	______	______	______
8)	3,200	______	______	______
9)	4	______	______	______
10)	129	______	______	______

Adding Whole Numbers

Example 26 + 451 + 2 = ■

Solution

```
   26  }
  451  } Addends
+   2  }
  479 ←—Sum or total
```

Example 7 + 0 = ■

Solution

```
  7 ←— Addend
 +0 ←— Addend
  7 ←— Sum or total
```

Exercise Write these addends in vertical form. Then add.

1) 235 + 62

2) 503 + 263

3) 211 + 623

4) 26 + 78 + 9

5) 395 + 75 + 37

6) 314 + 625 + 893

7) 512 + 726 + 89

8) 1,033 + 78 + 201

9) 1,515 + 301 + 201

10) 51 + 8,992 + 7

11) 72 + 6,203 + 45

12) 10,638 + 2,957

13) 6,203 + 89 + 1,458

14) 1,502 + 84 + 201

15) 302 + 895 + 102

16) 4,403 + 789 + 62

17) 5,067 + 29,835

18) 26 + 2,419 + 231

19) 45 + 671

20) 215 + 823

21) 305 + 876

22) 516 + 23 + 8

23) 3,007 + 926 + 85

24) 27 + 851 + 623

25) 351 + 603 + 1,151

26) 403 + 1,151 + 69

27) 62 + 89 + 5 + 301

28) 702 + 98 + 304

29) 1,346 + 62 + 891

30) 29,063 + 29 + 305

31) 62,301 + 89 + 901

32) 375 + 1,002 + 962

33) 1,302 + 63 + 115

34) 463 + 891 + 200

35) 135 + 60,039 + 12

36) 48 + 121 + 2,635

Review of Basic Skills 4

Subtracting Whole Numbers

Example Subtract 26 from 235. The number following "from" is written first.

Solution

$$\begin{array}{r} 235 \\ -\ 26 \\ \hline 209 \end{array}$$

235 Minuend
26 Subtrahend
209 Difference

Check

$$\begin{array}{r} 26 \\ +209 \\ \hline 235 \end{array}$$

Exercise Write these problems vertically. Then subtract.

1) 208 − 45
2) 351 − 290
3) 265 − 28
4) 208 − 177
5) 1,066 − 815
6) 1,210 − 986
7) 6,213 − 866
8) 7,019 − 669
9) 5,287 − 2,008
10) 1,010 − 935
11) 37,115 − 235
12) 5,351 − 709
13) 17,315 − 9,115
14) 20,061 − 4,805
15) 30,155 − 7,132
16) 23,103 − 9,163
17) 50,167 − 12,735
18) 37,451 − 16,203
19) 81,131 − 17,788
20) 16,683 − 6,891
21) 55,103 − 2,317
22) 88,471 − 73,115
23) 400 − 28
24) 614 − 326
25) 3,105 − 106
26) 4,992 − 885
27) 3,001 − 223
28) 8,191 − 310
29) 3,355 − 2,665
30) 3,274 − 2,275
31) 8,101 − 4,283
32) 9,000 − 862
33) 2,113 − 421
34) 48,300 − 9,301
35) 41,041 − 8,597
36) 14,724 − 7,026
37) 65,913 − 27,261
38) 10,991 − 2,815
39) 41,568 − 29,321
40) 20,972 − 3,811
41) 10,014 − 2,560
42) 57,221 − 10,811
43) 51,371 − 5,119
44) 14,014 − 7,958

Review of Basic Skills 5 and 6

Multiplying Whole Numbers (5)

Example $23 \times 6 = ■$

Solution

$$\begin{array}{r} 23 \\ \times \quad 6 \\ \hline 138 \end{array}$$

23 and 6: Factors; 138: Product

Example $46 \times 35 = ■$

Solution

$$\begin{array}{r} 46 \\ \times \quad 35 \\ \hline 230 \\ +1\,38 \\ \hline 1{,}610 \end{array}$$

46 and 35: Factors; 1,610: Product

Multiplying Whole Numbers With Zeros (6)

Example $267 \times 10 = ■$

Solution

$$\begin{array}{r} 267 \\ \times \quad 10 \\ \hline 2{,}670 \end{array}$$

10: One zero; 2,670: One zero

Example $342 \times 100 = ■$

Solution

$$\begin{array}{r} 342 \\ \times \quad 100 \\ \hline 34{,}200 \end{array}$$

100: Two zeros; 34,200: Two zeros

Exercise Write these problems in vertical form. Then multiply.

1) 23×6

2) 403×5

3) 313×4

4) 26×45

5) 72×35

6) 567×10

7) 109×50

8) 815×400

9) 701×202

10) 511×120

11) $2{,}215 \times 63$

12) $6{,}057 \times 40$

13) $5{,}063 \times 41$

14) $2{,}267 \times 19$

15) $2{,}830 \times 110$

16) $5{,}011 \times 300$

17) 7,706 × 250

18) 1,127 × 277

19) 90,681 × 22

20) 15,012 × 50

21) 21,305 × 100

22) 89,000 × 62

23) 4,805 × 1,001

24) 57,119 × 1,010

25) 77,805 × 601

26) 38 × 9

27) 206 × 8

28) 231 × 11

29) 52 × 60

30) 391 × 20

31) 435 × 39

32) 623 × 67

33) 516 × 200

34) 870 × 270

35) 603 × 250

36) 4,120 × 10

37) 1,403 × 27

38) 8,010 × 50

39) 3,115 × 28

40) 4,100 × 310

41) 8,214 × 200

42) 5,066 × 305

43) 6,405 × 115

44) 40,363 × 100

45) 71,106 × 602

46) 28,015 × 101

47) 10,376 × 203

48) 72,011 × 78

49) 90,301 × 201

50) 53,103 × 111

Dividing Whole Numbers With Zeros (7)

Example 576 ÷ 12 = ■

Solution

$$\begin{array}{r} 48 \\ 12\overline{)576} \\ -48 \\ \hline 96 \\ -96 \\ \hline 0 \end{array}$$

Check

$$\begin{array}{r} 48 \\ \times\ 12 \\ \hline 96 \\ +48 \\ \hline 576 \end{array}$$

Dividing Whole Numbers With Fractional Remainders (8)

Example 3,191 ÷ 25 = ■

Solution

$$\begin{array}{r} 127\frac{16}{25} \\ 25\overline{)3{,}191} \\ -2\,5 \\ \hline 69 \\ -50 \\ \hline 191 \\ -175 \\ \hline 16 \end{array}$$

Write the remainder over the divisor

Check

$$\begin{array}{rl} 127 & \\ \times\ 25 & \\ \hline 635 & \\ +2\,54 & \\ \hline 3{,}175 & \\ +\ 16 & \text{Remainder} \\ \hline 3{,}191 & \end{array}$$

Dividing Whole Numbers With Zeros in the Quotient (9)

Example 2,380 ÷ 14 = ■

Solution

$$\begin{array}{r} 170 \\ 14\overline{)2{,}380} \\ -1\,4 \\ \hline 98 \\ -98 \\ \hline 00 \end{array}$$

Check

$$\begin{array}{r} 170 \\ \times\ 14 \\ \hline 680 \\ +1\,70 \\ \hline 2{,}380 \end{array}$$

Example 4,864 ÷ 16 = ■

Solution

$$\begin{array}{r} 304 \\ 16\overline{)4{,}864} \\ -4\,8 \\ \hline 064 \\ -64 \\ \hline 0 \end{array}$$

Check

$$\begin{array}{r} 304 \\ \times\ 16 \\ \hline 1{,}824 \\ +3\,04 \\ \hline 4{,}864 \end{array}$$

Review of Basic Skills 7–9

Exercise A Copy these problems and divide.

1) 138 ÷ 6

2) 882 ÷ 9

3) 1,030 ÷ 5

4) 1,806 ÷ 6

5) 1,631 ÷ 7

6) 3,060 ÷ 4

7) 1,404 ÷ 52

8) 4,980 ÷ 60

9) 5,040 ÷ 70

10) 5,700 ÷ 95

11) 6,510 ÷ 105

12) 9,108 ÷ 18

13) 30,954 ÷ 77

14) 15,257 ÷ 73

15) 9,646 ÷ 91

16) 19,520 ÷ 32

17) 30,310 ÷ 70

18) 32,040 ÷ 40

19) 45,150 ÷ 15

20) 56,221 ÷ 11

21) 44,520 ÷ 12

22) 65,160 ÷ 36

23) 51,090 ÷ 13

24) 80,080 ÷ 40

25) 12,524 ÷ 31

26) 371 ÷ 7

27) 3,159 ÷ 9

28) 1,744 ÷ 8

29) 3,018 ÷ 6

30) 2,564 ÷ 4

31) 6,033 ÷ 3

32) 1,539 ÷ 27

33) 4,100 ÷ 82

34) 8,820 ÷ 90

35) 3,375 ÷ 25

36) 3,450 ÷ 15

37) 19,418 ÷ 38

38) 31,626 ÷ 63

39) 19,530 ÷ 62

40) 10,160 ÷ 80

41) 34,310 ÷ 47

42) 52,920 ÷ 60

43) 8,866 ÷ 22

44) 138,253 ÷ 23

45) 738,500 ÷ 35

46) 50,300 ÷ 10

47) 103,200 ÷ 24

48) 82,212 ÷ 51

49) 90,900 ÷ 30

50) 57,414 ÷ 14

Review of Basic Skills 7–9

Exercise B Copy these problems and divide. Write any remainders as fractions.

1) 335 ÷ 6

2) 50 ÷ 8

3) 711 ÷ 9

4) 393 ÷ 6

5) 7,151 ÷ 8

6) 6,205 ÷ 15

7) 60,600 ÷ 15

8) 181,819 ÷ 18

9) 30,091 ÷ 25

10) 70,111 ÷ 80

11) 41,015 ÷ 32

12) 26,031 ÷ 26

13) 13,315 ÷ 25

14) 60,031 ÷ 81

15) 53,010 ÷ 52

16) 10,008 ÷ 50

17) 27,023 ÷ 62

18) 15,132 ÷ 25

19) 90,615 ÷ 23

20) 46,023 ÷ 23

21) 23,310 ÷ 70

22) 50,003 ÷ 85

23) 22,022 ÷ 60

24) 463,201 ÷ 71

25) 57,231 ÷ 500

26) 573 ÷ 6

27) 908 ÷ 9

28) 630 ÷ 9

29) 721 ÷ 8

30) 3,900 ÷ 9

31) 8,003 ÷ 15

32) 7,440 ÷ 22

33) 32,331 ÷ 16

34) 7,910 ÷ 19

35) 51,631 ÷ 25

36) 10,631 ÷ 81

37) 35,103 ÷ 34

38) 14,401 ÷ 72

39) 42,002 ÷ 60

40) 73,106 ÷ 73

41) 53,010 ÷ 38

42) 14,108 ÷ 80

43) 62,031 ÷ 20

44) 72,150 ÷ 80

45) 81,035 ÷ 90

46) 34,210 ÷ 81

47) 78,311 ÷ 30

48) 37,101 ÷ 51

49) 72,101 ÷ 82

50) 80,031 ÷ 198

Finding Values of Numbers With Exponents

Example Find 3^4.

Solution $3^4 = 3 \times 3 \times 3 \times 3$ (4 times)
$= 81$

Example Find 2^3.

Solution $2^3 = 2 \times 2 \times 2$ (3 times)
$= 8$

Exercise Write the value of each expression.

1) 3^2
2) 5^3
3) 9^2
4) 19^2
5) 3^5
6) 8^2
7) 9^4
8) 18^2
9) 6^3
10) 2^6
11) 25^2
12) 7^2
13) 2^7
14) 26^2
15) 7^4
16) 30^2
17) 200^3
18) 70^2
19) 100^3
20) 80^3
21) 30^4
22) $1{,}000^2$
23) 46^2
24) 5^6
25) 10^4
26) 4^3
27) 4^2
28) 2^5
29) 7^3
30) 2^4
31) 11^2
32) 16^3
33) 5^4
34) 10^4
35) 15^2
36) 5^5
37) 8^4
38) 50^3
39) 5^3
40) 40^3
41) 77^2
42) 60^3
43) 92^2
44) 30^3
45) 80^2
46) 32^2
47) 16^2
48) 10^2
49) 8^3
50) 23^2
51) 5^2
52) 8^2
53) 9^3
54) 4^5
55) 6^2
56) 13^3
57) 12^2
58) 18^2
59) 28^2
60) 17^2
61) 24^2
62) 150^2
63) 300^4
64) 70^3
65) 22^2
66) 500^3
67) 15^3
68) 13^2
69) 42^2
70) 90^3
71) 10^3
72) 30^4
73) 63^2
74) 10^5
75) 3^3

Using the Order of Operations (Fundamental)

Rules

1. Evaluate expressions with exponents first.
2. Multiply and divide from left to right in order.
3. Add and subtract from left to right in order.

Example $2 + 3 \times 4 - 8 \div 4 = ■$

Solution $2 + \underline{3 \times 4} - \underline{8 \div 4} =$

$2 + 12 - 2 = 12$

Example $2^3 + 3 \times 4 \div 2 - 48 \div 4^2 = ■$

$8 + \underline{3 \times 4 \div 2} - \underline{48 \div 16} =$

$\underline{12 \div 2} \quad \underline{3} =$

$8 + 6 - 3 = 11$

Exercise Use the rules for the order of operations. Find the answers.

1) $3 + 8 \times 2 \div 4$

2) $5 + 9 \times 4 \div 12 - 2$

3) $8 - 8 \div 4 + 3 \times 2$

4) $13 - 16 \times 3 \div 12 - 1$

5) $9 + 6 \times 3 - 8 \times 2 \div 4$

6) $1 + 16 \times 3 \div 12 - 4$

7) $14 + 32 \div 16 - 4 \times 2$

8) $32 \div 16 + 9 \div 3 \times 2$

9) $5 - 16 \div 4 + 1 + 3$

10) $35 - 25 \times 4 \div 20 + 5$

11) $2^3 + 8 \times 2^2 + 3$

12) $8 - 6^2 \div 12 + 2 \times 5$

13) $15 + 8^2 \div 4 - 6$

14) $26 + 13^2 \div 13 - 20$

15) $9^2 + 32 \div 8 \times 4 - 6$

16) $3 + 2^3 \div 2^2 - 4$

17) $5 + 8 \times 9 \div 6^2 - 4$

18) $25 + 11^2 + 8 \times 2 - 3$

19) $39 \div 13 + 12^2 \div 6 - 5$

20) $52 + 12 \div 2^2 - 82 \div 2 + 3^2$

21) $35 + 2^5 \div 2^4 \times 3^2 - 2^3$

22) $18 \div 3^2 + 6 \times 8 \div 4^2 - 5$

23) $4 \times 3 \times 5 \div 10 + 8 \times 2^3 \div 2^4$

24) $9 - 16 \times 3 \div 12 + 8 \div 2^2 - 2^2$

Finding an Average

Example Find the average for 98, 88, and 80.

Solution Add the numbers. Divide the sum by the number of addends.

$$\begin{array}{r} 98 \\ 88 \\ +80 \\ \hline 266 \end{array} \quad \text{3 addends}$$

$$\begin{array}{r} 88\frac{2}{3} \\ 3\,\overline{)\,266} \\ -24 \\ \hline 26 \\ -24 \\ \hline 2 \end{array}$$

Answer The average is $88\frac{2}{3}$.

Exercise Compute the averages for each set of numbers.

1) 25, 63, 48, 52, 49, 38, 42, 67, 38

2) 98, 53, 42, 56, 72, 36, 72

3) 39, 40, 39, 62, 53, 86, 29, 34

4) 95, 83, 39, 42, 88, 77, 75, 42, 67

5) 88, 62, 42, 53, 96, 35, 35

6) 53, 60, 72, 43, 35, 39, 53

7) 52, 65, 83, 96, 35, 100, 92, 53

8) 91, 62, 39, 50, 42, 88, 53, 60, 83, 72

9) 36, 50, 42, 53, 46, 82, 80, 50, 52, 39

10) 81, 90, 92, 90, 83, 43, 46, 72, 53

11) 100, 103, 96, 105, 105, 97, 102, 120

12) 36, 42, 85, 92, 30, 33, 88, 29, 62, 50

13) 109, 156, 95, 108, 90, 83, 45, 80, 90, 98, 93, 96

14) 40, 42, 43, 40, 41, 42, 43, 48, 44, 42, 45, 42

15) 40, 38, 37, 35, 42, 43, 36, 49, 48, 53, 42, 39, 34

16) 21, 20, 23, 28, 25, 23, 20, 25, 24, 29, 28, 24, 22, 20

17) 52, 50, 59, 62, 63, 55, 54, 58, 60, 50, 52, 53, 57, 52, 51

18) 56, 50, 53, 65, 73, 72, 80, 95, 81, 87, 70, 82, 96, 68

19) 23, 12, 94, 71, 44, 39, 62, 57, 68, 25, 53, 22, 19, 80

Comparing Fractions (13)

Example Compare $\frac{3}{4}$ and $\frac{5}{8}$.

Solution

$$\overset{24}{\frac{3}{4}} \times \overset{20}{\frac{5}{8}}$$

Because $4 \times 5 = 20$ Because $3 \times 8 = 24$

24 is greater than 20; therefore, $\frac{3}{4}$ is greater than $\frac{5}{8}$.

Changing Fractions to Higher Terms (14)

Example Write $\frac{5}{6}$ as a fraction with 30 as the new denominator.

Solution

Step 1 $\frac{5}{6} = \frac{■}{30}$

Step 2 Divide 30 by 6. ⟶ $6\overline{)30}$ = 5

Step 3 Multiply $\frac{5}{6}$ by $\frac{5}{5}$. ⟶ $\frac{5 \times 5}{6 \times 5} = \frac{25}{30}$

Answer $\frac{5}{6} = \frac{25}{30}$

Exercise Express these fractions in higher terms.

1) $\frac{3}{4} = \frac{■}{48}$

2) $\frac{1}{3} = \frac{■}{21}$

3) $\frac{2}{3} = \frac{■}{15}$

4) $\frac{5}{6} = \frac{■}{18}$

5) $\frac{7}{8} = \frac{■}{56}$

6) $\frac{3}{5} = \frac{■}{20}$

7) $\frac{1}{7} = \frac{■}{49}$

8) $\frac{5}{12} = \frac{■}{24}$

9) $\frac{3}{7} = \frac{■}{21}$

10) $\frac{4}{12} = \frac{■}{36}$

11) $\frac{4}{9} = \frac{■}{45}$

12) $\frac{3}{3} = \frac{■}{18}$

13) $\frac{2}{11} = \frac{■}{121}$

14) $\frac{15}{16} = \frac{■}{48}$

15) $\frac{3}{10} = \frac{■}{30}$

16) $\frac{12}{14} = \frac{■}{70}$

17) $\frac{9}{12} = \frac{■}{144}$

18) $\frac{5}{15} = \frac{■}{45}$

19) $\frac{2}{8} = \frac{■}{96}$

20) $\frac{1}{6} = \frac{■}{72}$

21) $\frac{17}{24} = \frac{■}{120}$

Renaming Fractions to Simplest Terms

Example Rename $\frac{14}{16}$ to simplest terms.

Solution $\frac{14 \div 2}{16 \div 2} = \frac{7}{8}$

Choose a number that can be divided into the denominator and the numerator.

Answer $\frac{14}{16} = \frac{7}{8}$

Example Rename $\frac{24}{30}$ to simplest terms.

Solution $\frac{24 \div 3}{30 \div 3} = \frac{8}{10}$

The division process may occur more than once if the divisor is not large enough in the first step.

$\frac{8 \div 2}{10 \div 2} = \frac{4}{5}$

Answer $\frac{24}{30} = \frac{4}{5}$

Exercise Rename these fractions in simplest terms.

1) $\frac{24}{48}$

2) $\frac{10}{230}$

3) $\frac{45}{99}$

4) $\frac{5}{25}$

5) $\frac{13}{39}$

6) $\frac{56}{58}$

7) $\frac{63}{81}$

8) $\frac{6}{54}$

9) $\frac{16}{112}$

10) $\frac{39}{52}$

11) $\frac{12}{60}$

12) $\frac{16}{64}$

13) $\frac{18}{36}$

14) $\frac{22}{121}$

15) $\frac{53}{106}$

16) $\frac{18}{72}$

17) $\frac{5}{15}$

18) $\frac{55}{242}$

19) $\frac{10}{52}$

20) $\frac{48}{96}$

21) $\frac{28}{56}$

Renaming Improper Fractions as Mixed Numbers or Whole Numbers (16)

Example Rename $\frac{13}{5}$.

Solution Divide the numerator by the denominator.

$$\begin{array}{r} 2 \\ 5\overline{)13} \\ -10 \\ \hline 3 \end{array} \longleftarrow \text{Remainder}$$

Answer $\frac{13}{5} = 2\frac{3}{5}$ ⟵ Write the remainder over the divisor.

Example Rename $\frac{42}{16}$.

Solution

$$\begin{array}{r} 2 \\ 16\overline{)42} \\ 32 \\ \hline 10 \end{array}$$

$2\frac{10}{16} = 2\frac{5}{8}$

Answer $\frac{42}{16} = 2\frac{5}{8}$

Writing Mixed Numbers in Simplest Terms (17)

Example Write $12\frac{4}{6}$ in simplest terms.

Solution $12\frac{4}{6} = 12 + \frac{4}{6} = 12 + \frac{2}{3} = 12\frac{2}{3}$

Answer $12\frac{4}{6} = 12\frac{2}{3}$

Review of Basic Skills 16 and 17

Exercise Rename these improper fractions as either mixed numbers or whole numbers.

1) $\frac{13}{5}$

2) $\frac{18}{3}$

3) $\frac{19}{6}$

4) $\frac{14}{3}$

5) $\frac{23}{4}$

6) $\frac{12}{2}$

7) $\frac{38}{5}$

8) $\frac{66}{11}$

9) $\frac{56}{11}$

10) $\frac{19}{5}$

11) $\frac{52}{32}$

12) $\frac{55}{8}$

13) $\frac{28}{6}$

14) $\frac{32}{4}$

15) $\frac{90}{3}$

16) $\frac{63}{8}$

17) $\frac{50}{6}$

18) $\frac{58}{7}$

19) $\frac{52}{10}$

20) $\frac{37}{3}$

21) $\frac{120}{10}$

22) $\frac{73}{8}$

23) $\frac{13}{2}$

24) $\frac{51}{4}$

25) $\frac{82}{9}$

26) $\frac{23}{5}$

27) $\frac{52}{8}$

28) $\frac{32}{15}$

Review of Basic Skills 18

Renaming Mixed Numbers as Improper Fractions

Example Write $2\frac{3}{4}$ as an improper fraction.

Solution **Step 1** Multiply the whole number by the denominator.

$2 \times 4 = 8$

Step 2 Add the numerator to the product from Step 1.

$3 + 8 = 11$

Step 3 Write the sum over the old denominator.

$\frac{11}{4}$

Answer $2\frac{3}{4} = \frac{11}{4}$

Exercise Rename these mixed numbers as improper fractions.

1) $3\frac{2}{5}$

2) $6\frac{2}{5}$

3) $5\frac{1}{6}$

4) $7\frac{2}{12}$

5) $2\frac{1}{6}$

6) $9\frac{1}{2}$

7) $4\frac{1}{9}$

8) $8\frac{2}{11}$

9) $5\frac{2}{3}$

10) $8\frac{1}{3}$

11) $6\frac{10}{13}$

12) $16\frac{2}{3}$

13) $7\frac{3}{8}$

14) $15\frac{2}{3}$

15) $13\frac{9}{14}$

16) $9\frac{2}{3}$

17) $5\frac{11}{10}$

18) $20\frac{2}{3}$

19) $16\frac{5}{21}$

20) $11\frac{1}{8}$

Multiplying Fractions

Example $\frac{5}{6} \times \frac{3}{4} = \blacksquare$

Solution $\frac{5 \times 3}{6 \times 4} = \frac{15}{24}$

$\frac{15}{24} = \frac{5}{8}$

Answer $\frac{5}{8}$

Example $7 \times \frac{4}{5} = \blacksquare$

Solution $\frac{7 \times 4}{1 \times 5} = \frac{28}{5}$

$\frac{28}{5} = 5\frac{3}{5}$

Answer $5\frac{3}{5}$

Exercise Multiply. Write your answers in simplest terms.

1) $\frac{1}{2} \times \frac{2}{3}$

2) $\frac{3}{5} \times \frac{5}{6}$

3) $\frac{7}{8} \times \frac{6}{13}$

4) $\frac{2}{9} \times \frac{3}{5}$

5) $\frac{6}{7} \times \frac{1}{2}$

6) $\frac{3}{11} \times \frac{2}{5}$

7) $\frac{2}{7} \times \frac{2}{9}$

8) $\frac{1}{6} \times \frac{1}{5}$

9) $\frac{5}{11} \times \frac{1}{4}$

10) $\frac{1}{6} \times \frac{2}{9}$

11) $\frac{5}{6} \times \frac{1}{4}$

12) $\frac{3}{11} \times \frac{2}{12}$

13) $\frac{4}{5} \times \frac{2}{9}$

14) $\frac{4}{7} \times \frac{1}{8}$

15) $\frac{3}{16} \times \frac{13}{21}$

16) $\frac{5}{21} \times \frac{7}{10}$

17) $\frac{5}{24} \times \frac{3}{13}$

18) $\frac{6}{28} \times \frac{7}{12}$

19) $\frac{2}{3} \times \frac{5}{6}$

20) $\frac{12}{21} \times \frac{7}{8}$

21) $\frac{13}{32} \times \frac{8}{26}$

22) $\frac{24}{25} \times \frac{5}{16}$

23) $\frac{1}{12} \times \frac{2}{7}$

24) $\frac{2}{17} \times \frac{3}{4}$

25) $\frac{10}{13} \times \frac{39}{100}$

26) $\frac{12}{18} \times \frac{9}{32}$

27) $\frac{2}{15} \times \frac{45}{50}$

28) $\frac{5}{11} \times \frac{55}{75}$

29) $\frac{4}{5} \times \frac{2}{13}$

30) $\frac{2}{11} \times \frac{3}{10}$

31) $\frac{3}{14} \times \frac{28}{30}$

32) $\frac{7}{13} \times \frac{39}{63}$

33) $\frac{24}{36} \times \frac{1}{3}$

Review of Basic Skills 20

Multiplying Mixed Numbers

Example $3\frac{2}{3} \times 1\frac{1}{2} = \blacksquare$

Solution $3\frac{2}{3} \times 1\frac{1}{2} = \blacksquare$ ← Change to improper fractions.

$$\frac{11}{\cancel{3}_1} \times \frac{\cancel{3}^1}{2} = \frac{11}{2}$$

$$\frac{11}{2} = 5\frac{1}{2}$$

Answer $5\frac{1}{2}$

Exercise Multiply these mixed numbers. Write your answers in simplest terms.

1) $2\frac{1}{2} \times \frac{1}{3}$

2) $\frac{1}{2} \times 1\frac{1}{5}$

3) $\frac{2}{7} \times 1\frac{1}{3}$

4) $\frac{1}{5} \times 1\frac{1}{7}$

5) $3\frac{1}{5} \times \frac{3}{4}$

6) $5\frac{2}{3} \times \frac{1}{5}$

7) $\frac{5}{7} \times 2\frac{3}{8}$

8) $1\frac{1}{2} \times \frac{15}{18}$

9) $4\frac{5}{7} \times \frac{7}{11}$

10) $2\frac{3}{5} \times 1\frac{1}{5}$

11) $2\frac{3}{7} \times 2\frac{1}{2}$

12) $5\frac{1}{7} \times 2\frac{1}{5}$

13) $5\frac{1}{6} \times 1\frac{1}{5}$

14) $1\frac{5}{6} \times 1\frac{1}{3}$

15) $1\frac{2}{7} \times 2\frac{1}{8}$

16) $6\frac{1}{2} \times 2\frac{3}{4}$

17) $2\frac{2}{5} \times 1\frac{3}{4}$

18) $4\frac{1}{2} \times 1\frac{1}{4}$

19) $3\frac{3}{7} \times 2\frac{1}{3}$

20) $5\frac{2}{9} \times 1\frac{1}{8}$

21) $5\frac{1}{4} \times 2\frac{1}{7}$

22) $6\frac{2}{5} \times 1\frac{1}{7}$

23) $13\frac{1}{3} \times 2\frac{1}{4}$

24) $1\frac{5}{9} \times 1\frac{3}{4}$

25) $3\frac{2}{5} \times 2\frac{2}{4}$

26) $5\frac{2}{5} \times 1\frac{1}{9}$

27) $5\frac{1}{3} \times 1\frac{1}{8}$

28) $5\frac{3}{9} \times 1\frac{1}{6}$

29) $1\frac{2}{8} \times 3\frac{1}{2}$

30) $3\frac{1}{2} \times 5\frac{1}{6}$

31) $2\frac{4}{5} \times 2\frac{1}{7}$

32) $4\frac{1}{5} \times 1\frac{5}{7}$

33) $3\frac{7}{8} \times 1\frac{1}{2}$

Dividing Fractions

Example $\frac{4}{7} \div \frac{1}{2} = ■$

Solution $\frac{4}{7} \div \frac{1}{2} = ■$ ← Invert the divisor. Then multiply.

$\frac{4}{7} \times \frac{2}{1} = \frac{8}{7}$

$\frac{8}{7} = 1\frac{1}{7}$

Answer $1\frac{1}{7}$

Exercise Divide. Write your answers in simplest terms.

1) $\frac{2}{5} \div \frac{2}{7}$

2) $\frac{5}{6} \div \frac{1}{3}$

3) $\frac{2}{7} \div \frac{1}{8}$

4) $\frac{4}{5} \div \frac{1}{6}$

5) $\frac{2}{7} \div \frac{5}{6}$

6) $\frac{3}{8} \div \frac{1}{2}$

7) $\frac{4}{5} \div \frac{5}{6}$

8) $\frac{8}{9} \div \frac{4}{5}$

9) $\frac{5}{6} \div \frac{2}{5}$

10) $\frac{5}{11} \div \frac{2}{22}$

11) $\frac{8}{11} \div \frac{5}{11}$

12) $\frac{5}{12} \div \frac{5}{6}$

13) $\frac{3}{8} \div \frac{5}{12}$

14) $\frac{2}{11} \div \frac{3}{22}$

15) $\frac{8}{13} \div \frac{24}{26}$

16) $\frac{3}{9} \div \frac{1}{5}$

17) $\frac{11}{12} \div \frac{24}{30}$

18) $\frac{5}{7} \div \frac{48}{49}$

19) $\frac{1}{2} \div \frac{5}{7}$

20) $\frac{5}{7} \div \frac{5}{14}$

21) $\frac{8}{9} \div \frac{3}{6}$

22) $\frac{3}{4} \div \frac{6}{7}$

23) $\frac{13}{14} \div \frac{3}{7}$

24) $\frac{8}{15} \div \frac{2}{5}$

25) $\frac{1}{2} \div \frac{1}{2}$

26) $\frac{2}{3} \div \frac{1}{7}$

27) $\frac{3}{7} \div \frac{15}{21}$

28) $\frac{5}{10} \div \frac{2}{6}$

29) $\frac{4}{7} \div \frac{5}{14}$

30) $\frac{2}{3} \div \frac{14}{21}$

31) $\frac{18}{20} \div \frac{15}{40}$

32) $\frac{22}{27} \div \frac{11}{18}$

33) $\frac{16}{30} \div \frac{8}{15}$

Dividing Mixed Numbers

Example $2\frac{3}{4} \div 3\frac{1}{3} = \blacksquare$

Solution $2\frac{3}{4} \div 3\frac{1}{3} = \blacksquare$ ← Rename mixed numbers as improper fractions.

$\frac{11}{4} \div \frac{10}{3} = \blacksquare$ ← Invert the divisor and multiply.

$\frac{11}{4} \times \frac{3}{10} = \frac{33}{40}$

Answer $\frac{33}{40}$

Exercise Divide. Write your answers in simplest terms.

1) $1\frac{1}{2} \div \frac{1}{2}$

2) $3\frac{2}{3} \div \frac{1}{9}$

3) $1\frac{1}{5} \div \frac{2}{5}$

4) $2\frac{1}{6} \div \frac{3}{12}$

5) $\frac{3}{12} \div 3\frac{1}{6}$

6) $\frac{13}{15} \div 1\frac{3}{5}$

7) $1\frac{2}{5} \div \frac{14}{15}$

8) $3\frac{1}{2} \div \frac{5}{6}$

9) $1\frac{1}{2} \div 1\frac{2}{5}$

10) $\frac{1}{2} \div 1\frac{1}{2}$

11) $1\frac{1}{12} \div 2\frac{1}{6}$

12) $2\frac{2}{3} \div 3\frac{5}{9}$

13) $2\frac{1}{2} \div 3\frac{1}{7}$

14) $1\frac{5}{7} \div \frac{6}{7}$

15) $2\frac{5}{8} \div \frac{21}{24}$

16) $3\frac{5}{7} \div \frac{13}{14}$

17) $5\frac{2}{5} \div \frac{3}{4}$

18) $4\frac{1}{3} \div \frac{26}{27}$

19) $5\frac{3}{7} \div \frac{1}{3}$

20) $3\frac{2}{9} \div \frac{1}{8}$

21) $5\frac{2}{5} \div \frac{9}{10}$

22) $8\frac{2}{3} \div \frac{1}{7}$

23) $6\frac{1}{7} \div \frac{7}{18}$

24) $5\frac{1}{5} \div 1\frac{1}{2}$

25) $2\frac{3}{4} \div 1\frac{1}{6}$

26) $1\frac{1}{7} \div 1\frac{1}{6}$

27) $1\frac{1}{8} \div 1\frac{1}{9}$

28) $13\frac{2}{3} \div \frac{1}{9}$

29) $3\frac{2}{3} \div \frac{22}{27}$

30) $3\frac{6}{7} \div 1\frac{1}{4}$

31) $5\frac{2}{7} \div 7\frac{2}{5}$

32) $2\frac{1}{6} \div 1\frac{1}{2}$

33) $1\frac{1}{12} \div 2\frac{1}{6}$

Adding Mixed Numbers With Like Denominators

Example $3\frac{2}{7} + 1\frac{3}{7} = ■$

Solution

$$\begin{array}{r} 3\frac{2}{7} \\ +1\frac{3}{7} \\ \hline 4\frac{5}{7} \end{array}$$

Step 1	Write in the vertical form.
Step 2	Add the numerators. 2 + 3 = 5
Step 3	Keep the denominator.
Step 4	Add the whole numbers.

Answer $4\frac{5}{7}$

Exercise Add. Write your answers in simplest terms.

1) $\frac{2}{5} + \frac{2}{5}$

2) $\frac{5}{7} + \frac{1}{7}$

3) $\frac{8}{12} + \frac{3}{12}$

4) $\frac{5}{8} + \frac{1}{8}$

5) $\frac{2}{7} + \frac{5}{7}$

6) $\frac{8}{11} + \frac{4}{11}$

7) $1\frac{1}{6} + 2\frac{3}{6}$

8) $2\frac{5}{8} + \frac{1}{8}$

9) $5\frac{3}{10} + \frac{2}{10}$

10) $5\frac{1}{6} + \frac{1}{6}$

11) $8\frac{1}{12} + \frac{3}{12}$

12) $5\frac{1}{6} + \frac{3}{6}$

13) $8\frac{5}{11} + 1\frac{2}{11}$

14) $9\frac{1}{10} + 3\frac{3}{10}$

15) $8\frac{2}{5} + 3\frac{4}{5}$

16) $6\frac{2}{9} + \frac{5}{9}$

17) $8\frac{2}{12} + 6$

18) $11\frac{12}{21} + 2\frac{3}{21}$

19) $5 + 2\frac{1}{7}$

20) $7\frac{1}{7} + 13\frac{1}{7}$

21) $13\frac{12}{21} + 1\frac{3}{21}$

22) $8\frac{6}{13} + \frac{6}{13}$

Adding Fractions With Unlike Denominators (24)

Example $\frac{7}{15} + \frac{2}{5} = \blacksquare$

Solution

$$\frac{7}{15} = \frac{7 \times 1}{15 \times 1} = \frac{7}{15}$$

$$+\frac{2}{5} = \frac{2 \times 3}{5 \times 3} = +\frac{6}{15}$$

$$\frac{13}{15}$$

Rename the fractions with like denominators.

Add the numerators.

Answer $\frac{13}{15}$

Adding Mixed Numbers With Unlike Denominators (25)

Example $5\frac{5}{8} + 2\frac{7}{12} = \blacksquare$

Solution

$$5\frac{5}{8} \qquad \frac{5}{8} = \frac{5 \times 3}{8 \times 3} = \frac{15}{24} \qquad 5\frac{5}{8} = 5\frac{15}{24}$$

$$+2\frac{7}{12} \qquad \frac{7}{12} = \frac{7 \times 2}{12 \times 2} = \frac{14}{24} \qquad +2\frac{7}{12} = 2\frac{14}{24}$$

$$7\frac{29}{24} = 8\frac{5}{24}$$

Rename the fractional portion with like denominators.

Rename $7\frac{29}{24}$.

$$7 + \frac{29}{24} = 7 + 1\frac{5}{24} = 8\frac{5}{24}$$

Answer $8\frac{5}{24}$

Review of Basic Skills 24 and 25

Exercise Find common denominators and add. Write your answers in simplest terms.

1) $\frac{3}{7} + \frac{1}{3}$

2) $\frac{5}{6} + \frac{1}{3}$

3) $\frac{8}{12} + \frac{1}{8}$

4) $\frac{4}{17} + \frac{3}{34}$

5) $\frac{6}{11} + \frac{3}{4}$

6) $\frac{8}{15} + \frac{1}{6}$

7) $\frac{2}{15} + \frac{3}{45}$

8) $\frac{5}{8} + \frac{5}{6}$

9) $\frac{7}{9} + \frac{5}{27}$

10) $2\frac{1}{6} + \frac{2}{9}$

11) $12\frac{3}{10} + \frac{1}{15}$

12) $5\frac{6}{72} + \frac{1}{8}$

13) $8\frac{5}{16} + 2\frac{1}{8}$

14) $15\frac{2}{17} + 1\frac{1}{3}$

15) $26\frac{5}{7} + 2\frac{4}{21}$

16) $10\frac{6}{11} + 2\frac{5}{121}$

17) $8\frac{3}{36} + 2\frac{1}{12}$

18) $9\frac{5}{18} + 2\frac{5}{54}$

19) $5\frac{1}{2} + 2\frac{1}{17}$

20) $7\frac{3}{36} + 2\frac{1}{12}$

21) $3\frac{5}{18} + 1\frac{5}{54}$

22) $10\frac{1}{2} + 12\frac{1}{17}$

Subtracting Mixed Numbers With Like Denominators

Example

$$\begin{array}{r} 14\frac{5}{11} \\ -6\frac{2}{11} \\ \hline 8\frac{3}{11} \end{array}$$

Step 1 Subtract 2 from 5.
5 − 2 = 3

Step 2 Keep the denominator.

Step 3 Subtract the whole number portions.
14 − 6 = 8

Answer $8\frac{3}{11}$

Exercise Subtract. Write your answers in simplest terms.

1) $\frac{5}{8} - \frac{2}{8}$

2) $\frac{6}{13} - \frac{2}{13}$

3) $\frac{4}{15} - \frac{1}{15}$

4) $\frac{12}{17} - \frac{2}{17}$

5) $\frac{8}{9} - \frac{5}{9}$

6) $\frac{6}{7} - \frac{3}{7}$

7) $\frac{8}{19} - \frac{2}{19}$

8) $2\frac{3}{5} - \frac{2}{5}$

9) $8\frac{7}{8} - \frac{3}{8}$

10) $5\frac{6}{10} - 4\frac{1}{10}$

11) $15\frac{12}{13} - 4\frac{1}{13}$

12) $7\frac{7}{10} - 5\frac{2}{10}$

13) $18\frac{15}{16} - 5\frac{7}{16}$

14) $12\frac{5}{8} - 2\frac{2}{8}$

15) $17\frac{3}{4} - 5\frac{2}{4}$

16) $31\frac{5}{18} - 2$

17) $39\frac{16}{21} - 5\frac{6}{21}$

18) $14\frac{5}{6} - 2\frac{2}{6}$

19) $22\frac{3}{10} - 5\frac{3}{10}$

20) $9\frac{35}{40} - 6\frac{10}{40}$

21) $3\frac{1}{7} - \frac{1}{7}$

22) $16\frac{3}{8} - 12\frac{1}{8}$

Subtracting With Unlike Denominators

Example

$$18\frac{2}{3}$$
$$-5\frac{1}{7}$$

$$\frac{2}{3} = \frac{2 \times 7}{3 \times 7} = \frac{14}{21}$$
$$\frac{1}{7} = \frac{1 \times 3}{7 \times 3} = \frac{3}{21}$$

Rename the fractional portions with like denominators.

$$18\frac{2}{3} = 18\frac{14}{21}$$
$$-5\frac{1}{7} = 5\frac{3}{21}$$
$$13\frac{11}{21}$$

Subtract the numerators and the whole numbers.

Answer $13\frac{11}{21}$

Exercise Find common denominators and subtract. Write your answers in simplest terms.

1) $13\frac{4}{5} - 5\frac{2}{3}$

2) $9\frac{7}{8} - 3\frac{1}{3}$

3) $5\frac{5}{6} - 2\frac{1}{3}$

4) $18\frac{4}{8} - 5\frac{2}{24}$

5) $15\frac{10}{24} - 5\frac{1}{6}$

6) $3\frac{5}{8} - 1\frac{2}{6}$

7) $10\frac{13}{14} - 3\frac{1}{2}$

8) $36\frac{2}{5} - 5\frac{1}{6}$

9) $11\frac{8}{9} - 5\frac{2}{8}$

10) $16\frac{9}{13} - 2\frac{2}{3}$

11) $8\frac{15}{17} - 2\frac{2}{3}$

12) $28\frac{10}{32} - 5\frac{1}{8}$

13) $18\frac{2}{7} - 16\frac{1}{28}$

14) $31\frac{5}{12} - 4\frac{3}{48}$

15) $16\frac{7}{13} - 5\frac{2}{39}$

16) $32\frac{5}{12} - 8\frac{2}{24}$

17) $28\frac{1}{6} - 3\frac{1}{9}$

18) $3\frac{1}{3} - 1\frac{1}{7}$

19) $56\frac{3}{11} - 5\frac{1}{9}$

20) $15\frac{32}{33} - 8$

21) $8\frac{15}{16} - 2\frac{3}{24}$

22) $23\frac{8}{15} - 6\frac{9}{20}$

Subtracting With Renaming

Example

$$\begin{array}{r} 12 \\ -\ 3\frac{1}{7} \\ \hline \end{array}$$

Solution

Step 1 Rename.

$12 = 11 + 1$

$12 = 11 + \frac{7}{7}$

$12 = 11\frac{7}{7}$

Step 2 Subtract.

$$\begin{array}{rcr} 12 & = & 11\frac{7}{7} \\ -\ 3\frac{1}{7} & = & 3\frac{1}{7} \\ \hline & & 8\frac{6}{7} \end{array}$$

Answer $8\frac{6}{7}$

Example

$$\begin{array}{r} 21\frac{1}{5} \\ -\ 4\frac{3}{5} \\ \hline \end{array}$$

Solution

Step 1 Rename.

$$\begin{aligned} 21\frac{1}{5} &= 21 + \frac{1}{5} \\ &= 20 + 1 + \frac{1}{5} \\ &= 20 + \frac{5}{5} + \frac{1}{5} \\ &= 20\frac{6}{5} \end{aligned}$$

Step 2 Subtract.

$$\begin{array}{rcr} 21\frac{1}{5} & = & 20\frac{6}{5} \\ -\ 4\frac{3}{5} & = & 4\frac{3}{5} \\ \hline & & 16\frac{3}{5} \end{array}$$

Answer $16\frac{3}{5}$

Review of Basic Skills 28

Exercise Find common denominators and subtract. Write your answers in simplest terms.

1) $13\frac{2}{5} - 5\frac{6}{7}$

2) $18\frac{1}{5} - 2\frac{3}{5}$

3) $14\frac{3}{10} - 2\frac{1}{2}$

4) $26\frac{5}{7} - 5\frac{13}{14}$

5) $10\frac{5}{12} - 6\frac{3}{4}$

6) $24\frac{1}{11} - 5\frac{6}{22}$

7) $8\frac{2}{9} - 3\frac{4}{5}$

8) $6\frac{1}{12} - 3\frac{1}{2}$

9) $13\frac{1}{7} - 6\frac{3}{8}$

10) $14 - 2\frac{5}{11}$

11) $28\frac{2}{13} - 6\frac{7}{8}$

12) $12 - 8\frac{3}{7}$

13) $25\frac{5}{6} - 1\frac{9}{10}$

14) $9\frac{2}{15} - 4\frac{4}{5}$

15) $42\frac{1}{5} - 3\frac{3}{8}$

16) $53\frac{6}{9} - 4\frac{17}{18}$

17) $13\frac{5}{11} - 1\frac{21}{22}$

18) $30 - 6\frac{15}{19}$

19) $18\frac{1}{9} - 3\frac{2}{3}$

20) $33\frac{12}{40} - 8\frac{9}{10}$

21) $5\frac{5}{13} - 2\frac{30}{39}$

22) $16\frac{7}{10} - 4\frac{49}{50}$

23) $7\frac{1}{18} - 2\frac{2}{3}$

24) $13\frac{1}{11} - 3\frac{4}{22}$

25) $36 - 8\frac{3}{7}$

26) $13\frac{1}{4} - 5\frac{3}{5}$

27) $27\frac{5}{13} - 6\frac{25}{26}$

28) $14\frac{1}{6} - 3\frac{5}{8}$

29) $18\frac{2}{9} - 6\frac{3}{4}$

30) $6\frac{27}{30} - 5\frac{13}{15}$

31) $7\frac{8}{11} - 1\frac{21}{34}$

32) $6\frac{1}{5} - 4\frac{7}{8}$

33) $4\frac{1}{2} - 2\frac{7}{12}$

34) $16\frac{5}{9} - 3\frac{17}{18}$

35) $14\frac{3}{17} - 2\frac{5}{34}$

36) $2 - 1\frac{5}{11}$

37) $45\frac{4}{9} - 5\frac{4}{5}$

38) $32\frac{5}{16} - 5\frac{15}{32}$

39) $8\frac{3}{14} - 2\frac{6}{7}$

40) $29\frac{1}{10} - 3\frac{10}{15}$

41) $13\frac{5}{16} - 8\frac{23}{24}$

42) $4\frac{2}{7} - 2\frac{4}{5}$

43) $13\frac{15}{35} - 1\frac{6}{7}$

44) $10\frac{2}{3} - 8\frac{8}{9}$

45) $15\frac{11}{20} - 4\frac{4}{5}$

Review of Basic Skills 29 and 30

Identifying Place Value With Decimals (29)

Example Write the place value of the underlined digits.

1) 23.0$\underline{6}$71 Hundredths

2) 105.106$\underline{2}$ Ten-Thousandths

Ten Thousands	Thousands	Hundreds	Tens	Ones		Tenths	Hundredths	Thousandths	Ten-Thousandths
			2	3	.	0	6	7	1
		1	0	5	.	1	0	6	2

Comparing Decimals (30)

Example Compare 2.38 and 2.4. Use the symbols < or >.

Solution Insert zeros to give each decimal the same number of places.

1) 2.38 and 2.4

2) 2.38 and 2.40 (After inserting a zero.)

Since 38 is less than 40, then 2.38 < 2.40.

Example Compare 19.2 and 8.8943.

Solution Since the whole number 19 is greater than 8, then 19.2 > 8.8943.

Exercise Write the place name for each underlined digit.

1) 35.$\underline{0}$6
2) .52$\underline{6}$03
3) 5.681$\underline{1}$
4) 1.06$\underline{1}$1
5) .5811$\underline{1}$
6) .40101$\underline{5}$
7) .00$\underline{2}$731
8) $\underline{2}$76.03
9) 2.0$\underline{8}$35
10) .2850$\underline{1}$
11) 12.3005$\underline{2}$
12) 52.083$\underline{1}$
13) .306$\underline{1}$11
14) .56$\underline{0}$891
15) 1.0065$\underline{1}$
16) 60.0$\underline{0}$79
17) 14.000$\underline{8}$1
18) 156.0$\underline{1}$23
19) 133.$\underline{0}$1
20) 15.0$\underline{1}$911
21) 1.9$\underline{9}$115
22) 8.567$\underline{2}$3
23) 12.03587$\underline{6}$
24) $\underline{8}$,315.67

Rounding Decimals

Example Round 2.7017 to the nearest thousandth.

Solution 2.7017 ← Number (7) to the right of the thousandth place is 5 or more, so add 1 to the thousandths place and drop all digits to the right.

Answer 2.7017 ≈ 2.702 (≈ means "about equal to.")

Example Round 8.1649 to the nearest hundredth.

Solution 8.1649 ← Number (4) to the right of the hundredth place is less than 5, so drop the 4 and 9.

Answer 8.1649 ≈ 8.16

Exercise Round each decimal to the places named.

		Tenths	Hundredths	Thousandths
1)	2.063	______	______	______
2)	.0891	______	______	______
3)	1.0354	______	______	______
4)	.15454	______	______	______
5)	32.70391	______	______	______
6)	7.63	______	______	______
7)	19.808964	______	______	______
8)	34.00354	______	______	______
9)	2.061155	______	______	______
10)	139.4181891	______	______	______

Adding Decimals

Example $23 + .62 + 1.9 = \blacksquare$

Solution

$$\begin{array}{r} 23. \\ .62 \\ +\ 1.9 \\ \hline 25.52 \end{array}$$

← Line up all the decimal points.

$$\begin{array}{r} 23.00 \\ .62 \\ +\ 1.90 \\ \hline 25.52 \end{array}$$

← Inserting zeros may help.

Answer 25.52

Exercise Write these problems in vertical form. Then add.

1) 2.3 + 6 + 8.41
2) .413 + 9.6 + .2
3) 17 + .205 + 1.6
4) 2 + .63 + .5 + 1.1
5) 3.5 + 8.21 + .006
6) 8 + .15 + 1.61 + 2
7) 81.7 + 10.73 + 1.673
8) .02 + .603 + 8 + .11
9) 13.06 + 1.5 + 9 + .41
10) 2.71 + .031 + 8 + 9.9
11) 39.4 + 3 + 8.27 + .1
12) 5 + 8.4 + .07 + 6
13) 42 + .126 + .1 + .23
14) 6.28 + .28 + 5.4
15) 7.6 + 1 + .212
16) .561 + 4.7 + 215
17) 81.4 + 6.7 + 8.41
18) 50.51 + 2.6 + 9.15
19) 42.6 + .57 + 23.5
20) 39.6 + .003 + 1.81
21) 95.1 + 1.63 + 101.1
22) 8 + 1.53 + .007
23) .203 + .72 + .025
24) 1.56 + 1.231 + .07
25) 13 + .92 + 6.7
26) 83 + 9.6 + 1.305
27) 5.03 + .607 + .19
28) 18.95 + 1.4 + .071
29) 39.9 + 14.62 + 2.3
30) 2.3 + 1.78 + .663
31) 8.702 + 3.7 + .63
32) 3.0101 + .62 + 4
33) 2.7 + .063 + 1.77
34) 12.8 + .14 + .03 + 3
35) 1.9 + 5.621 + .03
36) 4.7 + .726 + 89.1
37) 1.7 + 2.31 + .631
38) 6.7 + .815 + 2
39) .37 + 2.9 + 8
40) 6.09 + .261 + 9.2
41) 23 + 1.003 + 5.4
42) 5.21 + .53 + 15.6
43) 63 + 1.92 + 88.8
44) .38 + 7.02 + .115
45) 5 + .27 + 1.919
46) 1 + .006 + .0071 + 1.8
47) 11.001 + 1.1 + 6.27
48) 3.9 + 1.06 + .081

Subtracting Decimals

Example $12 - 1.68 = \blacksquare$

Solution

$$\begin{array}{r} 12.00 \\ -\ 1.68 \\ \hline 10.32 \end{array}$$

← Line up the decimal points and insert zeros.

Answer 10.32

Exercise Write these problems in vertical form. Then subtract.

1) 6.59 − .48
2) 36 − 2.3
3) 19.83 − 2.3
4) 33.89 − .32
5) 5.2 − .156
6) 31.4 − 8
7) 38.5 − 1.67
8) 7.6 − .67
9) .091 − .0197
10) 1.1 − .99
11) 7.7 − 2.63
12) 36.5 − 1.83
13) 6.7 − 2.34
14) 1.6 − 1.08
15) .89 − .098
16) 2.31 − .9
17) .011 − .00201
18) .3 − .234
19) 1.03 − .89
20) 75 − .108
21) 8.7 − 2.31
22) 1 − .9
23) 8.3 − .99
24) 45.1 − .06
25) .101 − .0982
26) 53.72 − 1.8
27) 9.01 − .6
28) 2.171 − .18
29) 5.6 − .42
30) 2.1 − .8
31) 9 − .62
32) 12 − 4.35
33) 1 − .08
34) .1 − .0356
35) .35 − .19
36) 5.51 − .6
37) 19.5 − .34
38) 2.81 − .931
39) 11.23 − 9.9
40) 31.3 − .61
41) 4.35 − .6
42) .68 − .086
43) .1 − .06
44) 1.63 − .89
45) 7.5 − 6
46) 3 − .4
47) 5.52 − .66
48) 6 − .9
49) .32 − .0832
50) 1 − .662

Multiplying Decimals

Example $.26 \times 1.3 = \blacksquare$

Solution

$$\begin{array}{r l} .26 & \leftarrow \text{2 places plus} \\ \times\ 1.3 & \leftarrow \text{1 place equals} \\ \hline 78 & \\ +26 & \\ \hline .338 & \leftarrow \text{3 places} \end{array}$$

Example $.321 \times .002 = \blacksquare$

Solution

$$\begin{array}{r l} .321 & \leftarrow \text{3 places plus} \\ \times\quad .002 & \leftarrow \text{3 places equals} \\ \hline .000642 & \leftarrow \text{6 places} \end{array}$$

Exercise Write these problems in vertical form. Then multiply.

1) $.2 \times .3$
2) $.7 \times 1.2$
3) $1.9 \times .3$
4) 2.6×8
5) $.26 \times .2$
6) $.62 \times .3$
7) $.81 \times 1.2$
8) $.42 \times 6.3$
9) $.92 \times .21$
10) $.65 \times .07$
11) 1.23×1.2
12) $.128 \times .52$
13) $5.8 \times .006$
14) $.081 \times .02$
15) $.96 \times .73$
16) $8.03 \times .67$
17) $.126 \times .73$
18) $25.3 \times .62$
19) $.5 \times 6$
20) $1.3 \times .8$
21) $2.3 \times .5$
22) $4.3 \times .8$
23) $3.5 \times .7$
24) $.85 \times 3$
25) $.26 \times 1.5$
26) $1.8 \times .18$
27) $4.8 \times .06$
28) $.31 \times .09$
29) $3.62 \times .05$
30) $.402 \times .11$
31) $.71 \times .62$
32) $1.62 \times .71$
33) $52.6 \times .36$
34) $4.2 \times .008$
35) $703 \times .02$
36) $.91 \times .083$

Scientific Notation

Example Express 2,800 in scientific notation.

Solution $2{,}800 = 2.800 \times 10^3$ ← 3 places

or

2.8×10^3

Example Express 0.00039 in scientific notation.

Solution $0.00039 = 3.9 \times 10^{-4}$ ← 4 places

(Use the negative sign ($^{-4}$) when the decimal point is moved to the right.)

Exercise Write these numbers in scientific notation.

1) 3,600
2) 35,100
3) 46,000
4) 75,100
5) 6,530
6) 391,000
7) 1,725,000
8) 5,301,000
9) 87,100,000
10) 267,000,000
11) 100,000
12) 1,700,000,000
13) 34,000,000
14) 306.2
15) 12.721
16) .0000623
17) .00002
18) .1602
19) 623.05
20) .000000005
21) .00000101
22) .00663
23) 510
24) 8,702
25) 92,300
26) 18,000
27) 980,000
28) 5,600,000
29) 7,810,000
30) 1,000,000
31) 45,000,000
32) 9,720,000
33) 5,300,000,000
34) 961,000,000
35) 171,800,000
36) 48.39
37) 150.82
38) .0000031
39) .000175
40) .003
41) .00231
42) .000000453
43) .000119
44) .0024

Review of Basic Skills 36–39

Dividing Decimals by Whole Numbers (36)

Example $.168 \div 14 = \blacksquare$

Solution

$$\begin{array}{r} .012 \\ 14 \overline{).168} \\ -14 \\ \hline 28 \\ -28 \\ \hline 0 \end{array}$$

Place the decimal point in the quotient directly above the one in the dividend.

Example $68.6 \div 28 = \blacksquare$

Solution

$$\begin{array}{r} 2.45 \\ 28 \overline{)68.60} \\ -56 \\ \hline 12\,6 \\ -11\,2 \\ \hline 1\,40 \\ -1\,40 \\ \hline 0 \end{array}$$

Adding a zero may terminate the answer.

Dividing Decimals by Decimals (37)

Example $8.04 \div .6 = \blacksquare$

Solution

$$\begin{array}{r} 13.4 \\ .6 \overline{)8.0\,4} \\ -6 \\ \hline 2\,0 \\ -1\,8 \\ \hline 2\,4 \\ -2\,4 \\ \hline 0 \end{array}$$

Step 1 Move the decimal point in the divisor to the right.

Step 2 Move the decimal point in the dividend the same number of places to the right.

Step 3 Divide and bring the decimal point straight up into the quotient.

Renaming Decimals as Fractions (38)

Example Rename .13 as a fraction.

Solution $.13 = \frac{13}{100}$

Example $.026 = \blacksquare$

Solution $.026 = \frac{26}{1{,}000}$ or $\frac{13}{500}$

Renaming Fractions as Decimals (39)

Example Rename $\frac{13}{25}$ as a decimal.

Solution $\frac{13}{25} = \frac{13 \times 4}{25 \times 4} = \frac{52}{100}$

$= .52$ OR

$$\begin{array}{r} .52 \\ 25\overline{)13.00} \\ -12\,5 \\ \hline 50 \\ -50 \\ \hline 0 \end{array}$$

Choose a multiplier that will give you a denominator that is a power of 10. (10, 100, 1,000, 10,000...)

Dividing the numerator by the denominator will also give the decimal equivalent.

Exercise Copy these problems and divide. Rename decimals as fractions.

1) $4.7 \div 2$

2) $.78 \div 3$

3) $1.448 \div .8$

4) $2.88 \div .9$

5) $10.2 \div 1.2$

6) $11.55 \div 2.1$

7) $4.545 \div .9$

8) $2.807 \div .7$

9) $.351 \div .09$

10) $4.004 \div .22$

11) $.777 \div .15$

12) $13.7046 \div .91$

13) $.0615 \div 1.5$

14) $.00902 \div .41$

15) $.01952 \div 3.2$

16) $.00206 \div .002$

17) $32.92 \div .4$

18) $.12741 \div .31$

19) $.08833 \div .11$

20) $.0084 \div .007$

21) $6.2432 \div 1.6$

22) $36.8 \div 8$

23) $3.51 \div 9$

24) $7.23 \div 3$

25) $2.412 \div .6$

26) $8.32 \div 3.2$

27) $10.44 \div 2.9$

28) $.159 \div .15$

29) $.266 \div .07$

30) $2.173 \div 4.1$

Calculator Handbook

There are many kinds of electronic calculators. Each calculator is a little different from others. Some have more keys than others. The keys may be placed differently. You may have to press the keys in a certain order. Most calculators, however, are very similar.

Here is a calculator that has the basic functions you find on most calculators.

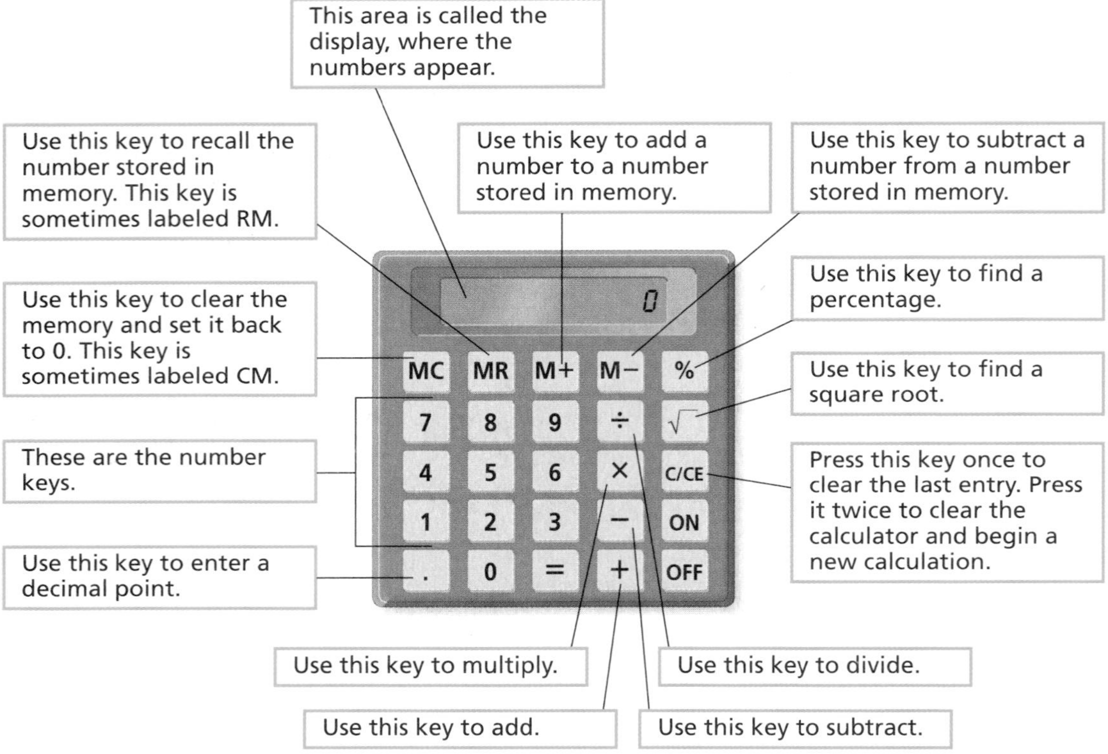

You can use a calculator to help you do arithmetic quickly and accurately. In many cases, you key the calculation the same way you would write it on paper.

Press 23 [+] 61 [=]
The display will read 84.
$23 + 61 = 84$

Press 98 [−] 18 [=]
The display will read 80.
$98 - 18 = 80$

Press 12 [×] 12 [=]
The display will read 144.
$12 \times 12 = 144$

Press 63 [÷] 9 [=]
The display will read 7.
$63 \div 9 = 7$

It's a good idea to look at the display after you key in each number. It helps to check that you haven't pressed a wrong key by mistake.

The √ key will give you the square root of a number.

Example What is the square root of 81?
Press 8 1 √
The display will read 9.

The % key will help you find a percentage. The % key works differently on different kinds of calculators. You may need to press = after % on some calculators. The examples show how the key works on most calculators.

Examples What is 25 percent of 44?
Press 4 4 × 2 5 %
The display will read 11.

What is 10 percent more than 50?
Press 5 0 + 1 0 %
The display will read 55.

What is 20 percent less than 65?
Press 6 5 − 2 0 %
The display will read 52.

If you are going to use the same number, or constant, in a series of calculations, you can store it in memory. Remember to clear the memory by pressing MC before you begin.

Examples What is 18 times 4? 18 times 12? 18 times 31?

Press 1 8 M+ C/CE
The display reads 0. The number 18 is stored in memory.

Press MR × 4 = The display reads 72.

Press MR × 1 2 = The display reads 216.

Press MR × 3 1 = The display reads 558.

You can add to or subtract from the number in memory by using the M+ and M− keys. Remember to clear the memory by pressing MC before you begin.

Press	Display	Number in Memory
2 2	22	0
M+	22	22
6	6	22
M+	6	28
2 0	20	28
M−	20	8

Glossary

A

A.M. (ā em) an abbreviation for *ante meridiem;* the hours before noon (p. 4)

Amps (amps) a measure of the intensity of electrical current (p. 310)

Annual (an´ yü əl) yearly; relating to a period of 12 months (p. 73)

Annual wages (an´ yü əl wājz) the amount of money earned during a full year (p. 3)

Area (âr´ ē ə) the number of squares of a given size that cover a surface; the surface included within a set of lines (p. 160)

Assessed value (ə sest´ val´ yü) a figure based on a percent of the market value of property; the rate is determined by the local government and is used for tax purposes (p. 295)

At (@) (at) a term and symbol used to indicate unit price; for example, 3 pairs of socks @ $2.59 per pair or 6 cans of oil @ $1.95 per can (p. 50)

Automated Teller Machine (ATM) (ȯ´ tə māt əd tel´ ər mə shēn´) (ā tē em) a computer terminal that allows 24-hour access to bank accounts (p. 257)

Average (av´ ər ij) the middle point in a group of numbers; the average is found by dividing the total of a set of figures by the number of items (p. 88)

B

Balance due (bal´ əns dü) a payment owed by the taxpayer when too little taxes have been withheld by the end of the year (p. 292)

Balancing a budget (bal´ əns ing ə bud´ jit) determining the state of finances after a given budget period, whether there is money remaining or a debt (p. 239)

Base price (bās prīs) the first amount listed on the sticker price of a car; the price includes standard equipment but not options or transportation and handling charges (p. 100)

Bimonthly (bī munth´ lē) every two months, or 6 times a year (p. 17)

Biweekly (bī wēk´ lē) every two weeks; or 26 times a year (p. 17)

Blueprints (blü´ prints) maps, mechanical drawings, or architectural plans (p. 318)

Brand name (brand nām) goods identified by name as the product of a single firm or manufacturer; a characteristic or distinctive kind (p. 44)

Budget (bud´ jit) a plan for managing income and expenses, usually for a set period of time (month, year, etc.) (p. 230)

Budget guidelines (bud´ jit gīd´ linz) an outline of suggested budget policies or plans (p. 232)

Bus schedule (bus skej´ül) a chart or table indicating arrival and departure times of buses at all the stops on a given route (p. 200)

C

Calorie (kal´ ər ē) a measurement of heat energy; the amount of energy needed to raise the temperature of one gram of water one degree Celsius (p. 126)

Catalog (kat´ l ȯg) a listing of items for purchase arranged in an organized way; descriptions are often included (p. 55)

Celsius (sel´ sē əs) relating to a temperature scale on which 0° represents the freezing point of water and 100° represents the boiling point of water (p. 126)

Charge account(chärj ə kount´) an account with a store or company to which the purchase of goods is charged and paid for at a later date (p. 65)

Check (chek) a written order that is considered the same as cash (p. 257)

Checking account (chek´ ing ə kount´) a bank account against which a depositor can draw checks (p. 257)

Circle graph (sėr´ kəl graf) a circular chart divided into sections to show relative sizes or amounts; also called pie chart (p. 232)

Commission (kə mish´ ən) payment based on a percentage of total sales; salespeople generally earn commissions (p. 20)

Compound interest (kom´ pound in´ tər ist) interest paid on both the original principal plus any interest added to date; compound interest is usually computed on deposits placed into savings accounts (p. 250)

Contractors (kon´ trak tərz) people that agree to erect buildings, to perform work, or to provide supplies on a large scale (p. 178)

Coverage (kuv´ ər ij) the area of wall that a can of paint is supposed to cover, usually measured in square feet; for example, 100 square feet per quart (p. 164)

Coverage rate (kuv´ ər ij rāt) the percent paid for homeowners insurance protection (p. 94)

Cross products (krȯs prod´ əkts) the answer obtained by multiplying the denominator of one fraction with the numerator of another (p. 129)

Cubic feet (kyü´ bic fēt) units used to measure volume; on a water meter, one unit of water equals 100 cubic feet (p. 86)

D

Daily Value (dā´ lē val´yü) nutrient levels listed on a food label (p. 133)

Deductions (di duk´ shənz) money withheld from gross pay; for example, federal income taxes, social security payments, union dues, or health insurance (p. 22)

Deductions and exemptions (di duk´ shənz and eg zemp´ shənz) amounts of money you may subtract from your income before you figure your taxes (p. 286)

Deferred price (di fėrt´ prīs) the total amount paid in down payment plus monthly payments (p. 104)

Denominator (di nom´ ə nā tər) the part of a fraction that is below the line and that tells the number of parts in the whole; in the fraction $\frac{1}{2}$, the denominator 2 shows that something has been divided into two halves (p. 58)

Dependent (di pen´ dənt) a person who depends on another person for support (p. 286)

Depreciate (di prē´ shē āt) to lose value (p. 102)

Dials (dī´ əlz) the part of a meter that shows how many units of the product have been consumed since the meter was installed (p. 84)

Discount (dis´ kount) an amount subtracted from the regular price, often given for cash or prompt payment or to reduce prices for a sale (p. 54)

Dividend (div´ ə dend) the amount of profit that a shareholder earns for each share of stock; the term comes from the idea of *divid*ing profits at the *end* of an earning period (p. 274)

Double occupancy (dub´ əl ok´ yə pən sē) a hotel room designed to be used by two people (p. 204)

Double time (dub´ əl tīm) payment of two times the regular hourly rate; often used to compute pay for work done on Sundays or holidays (p. 8)

Down payment (doun pā´ mənt) part of the full price paid at the time of purchase with the balance to be paid later (p. 74)

doz. (duz´ n) an abbreviation for dozen, a group of 12 (p. 33)

Dozen (doz.) (duz´ n) a group of 12 (p. 33)

Drafters (draft´ ərz) people who draw blueprints, plans, and sketches for construction and manufacturing projects (p. 318)

Driven gear (driv´ ən gir) a gear to which motion is transferred from a driver gear (p. 320)

Driver gear (drīv´ ər gir) a gear that transfers motion to a second gear, called a driven gear (p. 320)

E

Effective tax rate (ə fek´ tiv tax rāt) the product of the assessment rate and the property tax rate (p. 298)

EPA rating (ē pē ā rāt´ ing) Environmental Protection Agency estimate of how far a car can travel on one gallon of gas; figures are given for both city and highway driving in terms of miles per gallon (p. 114)

Estimate (es´ tə mit) to judge the value or worth of something; to determine roughly (p. 3)

a	hat	e	let	ī	ice	ô	order	ů	put	sh	she	ə	a in about
ā	age	ē	equal	o	hot	oi	oil	ü	rule	th	thin		e in taken
ä	far	ėr	term	ō	open	ou	out	ch	child	ŧh	then		i in pencil
â	care	i	it	ȯ	saw	u	cup	ng	long	zh	measure		o in lemon
													u in circus

Exchange rate (eks chānj rāt) the ratio at which the principal unit of money of two countries may be exchanged; such ratios change frequently and up-to-date tables must be used (p. 209)

Expenses (ek spen´ sis) money spent to pay for specific costs; typical expenses include housing, clothing, transportation, insurance payments, etc. (p. 232)

Expiration date (ek spə rā shən dāt) the point at which something comes to an end; for example, the time after which a cents-off store coupon can no longer be used (p. 37)

Expires (ek spīrz´) comes to an end (p. 37)

F

Factor (fak´ tər) the number being multiplied (p. 59)

Fertilizer (fėr´ tl ī zər) natural or chemical mixture applied to soil to help grass grow (p. 182)

Financed (fī´ nanst) borrowed; provided funds on credit under specified terms (p. 74)

Fixed-rate mortgage (fikst rāt môr´ gij) a financed loan on property in which the interest rate and the monthly payments on principal and interest remain the same until the loan is paid off (p. 78)

Flat rate (flat rāt) the base amount charged for monthly telephone service (p. 89)

G

gal. (gal´ ən) an abbreviation for gallon, a unit of capacity equal to four quarts (p. 33)

Gallon (gal.) (gal´ ən) a unit of capacity equal to four quarts (p. 33)

Gas mileage (gas mī´ lij) the average number of miles a car will travel on a gallon of gas (p. 113)

Greatest common factor (grāt´ əst kom´ ən fak´ tər) the largest factor of two numbers (p. 58)

Gross pay (grōs pā) the amount of full earnings before deductions (p. 22)

H

Homeowners insurance (hōm´ ō nərz in shůr´ əns) a policy covering both the home and its contents for damage or loss caused by fire, smoke, theft, severe weather, or collision by a vehicle; some policies cover injuries incurred by people on the property (p. 94)

Hour (hr.) (our) a measure of time equal to 60 minutes (p. 5)

Hourly rate (our´ lē rāt) the amount of money paid for each hour of work (p. 2)

hr. (our) an abbreviation for hour, a measure of time equal to 60 minutes (p. 5)

I

Income (in´ kum) the total money you earn (p. 286)

Income stock (in´ kum stok) stock that pays dividends (p. 274)

Insulation (in sə lā´ shən) materials used to prevent transfer of electricity, heat, or sound (p. 180)

Interest (in´ tər ist) a fee charged on the unpaid balance of a charge account; a payment or fee charged to the borrower for the use of money loaned; also the amount paid to a depositor for money kept in a savings account (pp. 65, 74)

International units (I.U.) (in tər nash´ ə nəl yü´ nits) the amount of a nutrient or vitamin that produces a particular biological effect agreed upon as an international standard (p. 133)

K

Key digit (kē di´ jit) the digit to which a number is to be rounded (p. 15)

Kilowatt (kil´ ə wot) a unit of electricity equal to 1000 watts (p. 88)

Kilowatt hour (kwh) (kil´ ə wot our) a unit of electricity equal to the energy used by one kilowatt in one hour (p. 88)

L

Landlord (land´ lôrd) the owner of property leased or rented to another (p. 72)

Layaway (lā´ ə wā) a plan under which customers can buy something, pay part of the price as a deposit, and receive the items when the remainder of the price is paid (p. 67)

lb. (pound) an abbreviation for pound, a unit of weight equal to 16 ounces (p. 30)

Lease (lēs) a contract to rent property for a particular amount of money and for a specified period of time (p. 72)

Legend (lej´ ənd) a chart that explains the symbols used on a map (p. 190)

Liability insurance (lī ə bil´ ə tē in shůr´ əns) insurance that protects the owner against claims resulting from an accident that is his or her fault; it covers personal injuries and property damage (p. 108)

Liable (lī´ ə bəl) legally responsible for damage done (p. 108)

Loss (lȯs) a decrease in value; the amount by which the purchase price of an item is more than the selling price. (p. 268)

M

m² (em skwârd) an abbreviation for square meters, a unit used for measuring area (p. 182)

Market value (mär´ kit val´ yü) the selling price of the property on the open market (p. 295)

Materials (mə tir´ ē əlz) supplies needed for making or doing something (p. 178)

Meters (mē´ tərz) devices used to measure the amount of gas, electricity, or water used by a customer (p. 84)

Mileage map (mī´ lij map) a map or drawing that gives the driving distance in miles between major cities (p. 196)

Miles per hour (mph) (mīlz pər our) a customary measurement of speed (p. 116)

min. (min´ it) an abbreviation for minute, a measure of time equal to 60 seconds (p. 5)

Minimum payment (min´ ə məm pā´ mənt) the smallest amount due to be paid on a charge account (p. 65)

Minute (min.) (min´ it) a measure of time equal to 60 seconds (p. 5)

Molding (mōl´ ding) a decorative strip used to finish a room; for example, at the base of the walls or around windows (p. 175)

Monthly payment (munth´ lē pā´ mənt) the amount of money paid every month in repayment of a loan (p. 78)

Monthly statement (munth´ lē stāt´ mənt) a summary sent out by the bank and showing recent transactions plus the current bank balance of an account (p. 262)

Mortgage (môr´ gij) a financed loan on property (p. 74)

Mortgage insurance (môr´ gij in shůr´ əns) a policy purchased by the owners of mortgaged property; if an insured owner dies, the insurance company pays the balance owed on the house to the beneficiary (p. 92)

mph (mīlz pər our) an abbreviation for miles per hour, a customary measurement for speed (p. 116)

N

Net pay (net pā) the amount a worker receives after deductions are subtracted from gross pay; also known as take-home pay (p. 22)

Ninety Days Same As Cash (nīn´ tē dāz sām az kash) a plan by which the purchase price must be paid off in full within 90 days after the date of purchase; no interest is charged for the use of this plan (p. 158)

Notions (nō´ shənz) small items needed to complete a sewing project; for example, thread, snaps, or zippers (p. 61)

Numerator (nü´ mə rā tər) the part of a fraction that is above the line and that tells how many parts are used; in the fraction $\frac{1}{2}$, the numerator 1 indicates one of two parts (p. 58)

Nutrient (nü´ trē ənt) a substance or ingredient that furnishes nourishment (p. 133)

O

Odometer (ō dom´ ə tər) a device that counts the miles a car has traveled; located on a car's dashboard (p. 110)

Off–peak hours (ȯf pēk ourz) a time period in which a minimum number of people travel (p. 202)

a	hat	e	let	ī	ice	ô	order	ů	put	sh	she	ə	a in about
ā	age	ē	equal	o	hot	oi	oil	ü	rule	th	thin		e in taken
ä	far	ėr	term	ō	open	ou	out	ch	child	ᴛʜ	then		i in pencil
â	care	i	it	ȯ	saw	u	cup	ng	long	zh	measure		o in lemon
													u in circus

Ohms (ōmz) a measure of electrical resistance (p. 310)

Optional (op′ shə nəl) involving a choice (p. 89)

Options (op′ shənz) extra items added to a car; for example, AM/FM stereo radio or air conditioning (p. 100)

Ounce (oz.) (ouns) a unit of weight equal to one-sixteenth of a pound (p. 30)

Overtime (ō′ vər tīm) working time beyond a standard day or week; the wage paid for overtime (p. 8)

oz. (ouns) an abbreviation for ounce, a unit of weight equal to one-sixteenth of a pound (p. 30)

P

Package plans (pak′ ij planz)low-priced trips planned for groups of people; these plans may include hotel rooms, transportation, some meals, tourist and side trips, and other special services (p. 208)

Parts and labor (pärts and lā′ bər) customers pay for new or rebuilt items plus an amount per hour for work done by mechanics (p. 120)

Pattern (pat′ ərn) a form or model used for making things; a sewer's pattern pieces and directions for making clothes (p. 60)

Peak hours (pēk ours) a time period in which the maximum number of people travel (p. 202)

Peak season (pēk sē′ zn) the time of year when business is at its best; for instance, at the beach in summer or in the mountains during ski season (p. 204)

Per (pər) for each or for one; for example, miles per gallon, miles per hour, or cost per gallon (p. 40)

Percent (%) (pər sent′) part per one hundred (p. 19)

Percentage (pər sen′ tij) an amount, not a percent; the amount is calculated by multiplying a percent times a number (p. 20)

Perimeter (pə rim′ ə tər) the distance around a figure (p. 160)

Piecework (pēs′ werk) work done by the unit and paid according to the number of units completed (p. 13)

Pkg. (pak′ ij) an abbreviation for package (p. 30)

P.M. (pē em) an abbreviation for *post meridiem;* the hours after noon (p. 4)

Pound (lb.) (pound) a unit of weight equal to 16 ounces (p. 30)

Premium (prē′ mē əm) the cost of an insurance policy (p. 108)

Principal (prin′ sə pəl) the amount of money loaned to a creditor; also the amount of money deposited into a savings account and earning interest (p. 74)

Processed (pros′ est) a term used to describe a check or a deposit that has been handled by the bank (p. 262)

Profit (pro′ fit) a gain or increase in value; the amount by which the selling price of an item is more than the purchase price; the amount that revenue exceeds expenses (p. 268)

Property tax (prop′ ər tē taks) a figure based on a percent of the assessed value; the rate is set by local governments (p. 295)

Proportion (prə pôr′ shən) two equal ratios; for example, $\frac{2}{4} = \frac{1}{2}$ (p. 129)

Q

Quarterly (kwôr′ tər lē) four times a year, or once every three months (p. 17)

R

Range (rānj) how far a car can travel on a given number of gallons of gas; the range is found by multiplying the EPA rating times the tank capacity (p. 114)

Rate (rāt) the percent of interest charged as a fee on a loan; also the percent of interest earned on a savings account (p. 248)

Rate of commission (rāt ov kə mish′ ən) the percent used to compute commissions; for example, 25% or 3% (p. 20)

Ratio (rā′ shē ō) number relationship between two or more things (p. 128)

RDA (är dē ā) an abbreviation for Recommended Dietary Allowance, the nutrient levels required to maintain energy and growth (p. 133)

Rebate (rē′ bāt) a return of part of a payment offered as a special deal to buyers (p. 103)

Rebuilt (rē bilt) describing items that have been reconstructed or extensively repaired (p. 120)

Receipts (ri sēts′) money received (p. 282)

Recommended Dietary Allowance (RDA) (rek ə mend′ əd dī′ ə ter ē ə lou′ əns) (är dē ā) the nutrient levels required to maintain energy and growth (p. 133)

Reconcile (rek′ ən sīl) to compare and check the accuracy of information recorded in the checkbook against bank statements (p. 262)

Refund (rē′ fund) a payment returned to the taxpayer when too much taxes have been withheld by the end of the year (p. 292)

Register (rej′ ə stər) a form on which bank account transactions and resulting new balances are recorded (p. 259)

Renaming hours (rē nām′ ing ours) to express time in a form that is equal to the original; for example, 1 hour = 60 minutes (p. 5)

Revenue (rev′ ə nü) the income (such as from taxes) that federal or state agencies collect and use for the common good; the amount of money a business takes in (p. 282)

Revolutions per minute (rev ō lü′ shənz per min′ it) the rotations or turns per minute of a driver gear (RPM) or a driven gear (rpm) (p. 320)

RPM (är pē em) the revolutions per minute of a driver gear (p. 320)

rpm (är pē em) the revolutions per minute of a driven gear (p. 320)

S

Salary (sal′ ər ē) payment of a fixed amount of money at regular intervals (weekly, biweekly, etc.) (p. 17)

Sales tax (sālz taks) a tax computed on the sale of goods and services; it is figured as a percentage of the purchase price and is collected by the seller (p. 50)

Savings accounts (sā′ vingz ə kounts′) bank accounts in which depositors can earn interest on money deposited (p. 250)

Scale (skāl) a ratio of the size on a drawing, map, or model to the original size ($\frac{1}{2}$ scale); an indication of the relationship between the distances on a map and the corresponding actual distances (1 inch = 6 miles) (p. 195)

Scale drawing (skāl drȯ′ ing) a picture that shows the relative sizes of actual objects (p. 318)

Sector (sek′ tər) a wedge-shaped section of a circle graph; the size is found by multiplying 360° times a percent or a fraction (p. 236)

Semiannually (sem ē an′ yü əl ē) every six months, or 2 times a year (p. 17)

Semimonthly (sem i munth′ lē) twice a month; or 24 times a year (p. 17)

Shareholders (shâr′ hōl dərz) the people who own the stock of a corporation (p. 274)

Shares (shârz) the equal parts into which the entire capital stock of a corporation is divided (p. 266)

Simple interest (sim′ pəl in′ tər ist) a one-time payment or fee charged for the use of money loaned; simple interest = principal × rate × time (p. 248)

Single occupancy (sing′ gel ok′ yə pən sē) a hotel room designed to be used by one person (p. 204)

Square (skwâr) the product of a number multiplied by itself; for example, the square of 5 is 25 (p. 161)

Square meters (m^2) (skwâr mē′ tərz) a metric unit used for measuring area (p. 182)

Square root (skwâr rüt) one of two equal factors of a number; for example, 5 is the square root of 25 because 5 × 5 = 25 (p. 308)

Statement (stāt′ mənt) a monthly record sent to charge account customers; it indicates all payments and charges to date (p. 65)

Stock (skok) the element in a corporation that is divided into shares; a buyer of shares of stock becomes part owner of the corporation issuing the stock (p. 266)

Straightline distance (strāt′ lin dis′ təns) a distance measured along a straight line; the shortest distance between two points on a map (p. 195)

Stub (stub) the part of a checkbook that remains after the check has been removed; it serves as a record for the information written on the check, for deposits made, and for resulting new balances (p. 259)

a	hat	e	let	ī	ice	ô	order	u̇	put	sh	she	ə	a	in about
ā	age	ē	equal	o	hot	oi	oil	ü	rule	th	thin		e	in taken
ä	far	ėr	term	ō	open	ou	out	ch	child	ᴛʜ	then		i	in pencil
â	care	i	it	ȯ	saw	u	cup	ng	long	zh	measure		o	in lemon
													u	in circus

Suite (swēt) a group of connected hotel rooms (p. 204)

T

Take-home pay (tāk hōm pā) the amount a worker receives after deductions are subtracted from gross pay; also known as net pay (p. 22)

Taxable income (tak′ sə bəl in′ kum) the total income (minus deductions and exemptions) on which taxes are paid (p. 286)

Term(tėrm) the period of time for which money is loaned (p. 80)

Time (tīm) the period of time for which money is loaned; also the period of time for which money is deposited into a savings account (time is usually measured in years or parts of years) (p. 248)

Time and a half (tīm and ə haf) payment of one and one-half, or 1.5, times the regular hourly rate; often used to compute overtime pay on regular workdays, Monday through Saturday (p. 8)

Time zone (tīm zōn) a geographical region within which the same standard time is used; the world is divided into 24 different time zones (p. 219)

Tip (tip) extra money given in appreciation of good service (p. 12)

Total interest (tō′ tl in′ tər ist) a total fee for borrowing money found by subtracting the amount borrowed (the principal) from the amount paid to the bank over the life of the loan (p. 79)

Tourist season (tür′ ist sē′ zn) a period of the year when many people visit a given area; the highest rates are in effect during this peak season (p. 204)

Trace (T) (trās) (tē) a very small and often barely detectable amount (p. 133)

Transaction (tran zak′ shən) the act of depositing to or withdrawing from a bank account (p. 259)

Transportation/handling (tran spər tā shən/han′ dling) a fee charged to the buyer of a car (p. 100)

U

Unit (yü′ nit) a single quantity; for example, a cubic foot of water or a kilowatt hour of electricity (p. 86)

Unit price (yü′ nit prīs) the cost of one unit of something; for example, the cost per pound or per gallon (p. 42)

Utilities (yü til′ ə tēz) services for the home, such as gas, electricity, water, and telephone (p. 84)

V

Variable-rate mortgage (vâr′ ē əbəl rāt môr′ gij) a financed loan on property in which the interest rate and the monthly payments may change periodically (p. 78)

Volts (vōlts) a measure of electromotive force (p. 310)

W

Wages (wā′ jiz) the money received on payday; the amount is found by multiplying the number of hours worked by the hourly rate (p. 2)

Wall area (wȯl âr′ ē ə) the perimeter of the floor times the height of the room (p. 170)

Watt (wät) a unit of electrical power; named after James Watt, a Scottish inventor (p. 88)

Y

Yard (yd.) (yärd) a measure of length equal to three feet (p. 60)

Yield (yēld) the number of servings provided by a given recipe (p. 144)

yd. (yärd) an abbreviation for yard, a measure of length equal to three feet (p. 60)

Index

D

S